NEWNES'
PICTORIAL KNOWLEDGE

VOLUME SIX

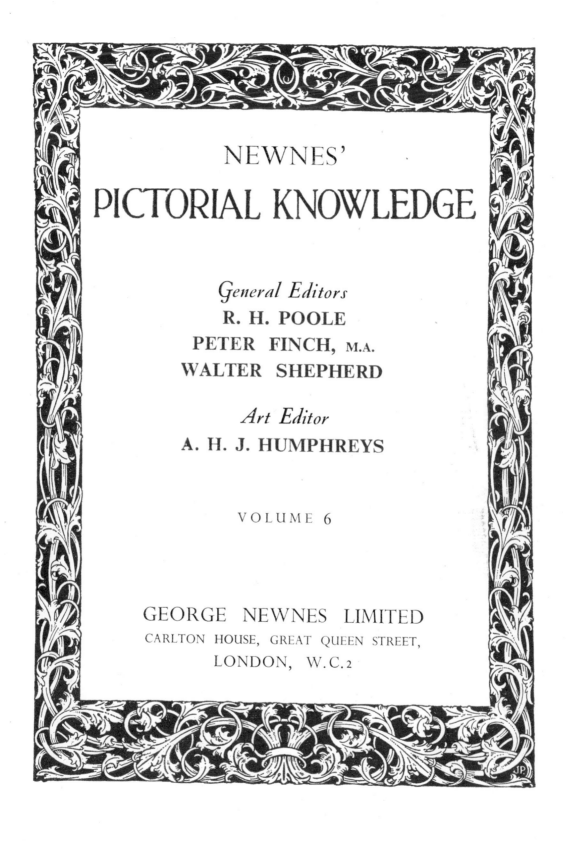

NEWNES'
PICTORIAL KNOWLEDGE

General Editors
R. H. POOLE
PETER FINCH, M.A.
WALTER SHEPHERD

Art Editor
A. H. J. HUMPHREYS

VOLUME 6

GEORGE NEWNES LIMITED
CARLTON HOUSE, GREAT QUEEN STREET,
LONDON, W.C.2

PRINTED IN GREAT BRITAIN
BY THE WHITEFRIARS PRESS LTD., LONDON AND TONBRIDGE, AND
BOUND BY HAZELL, WATSON & VINEY LTD., AYLESBURY AND LONDON
N.P.K. 7055.   W.P. 5316

CONTENTS OF VOLUME SIX

PAGE

TREASURES WON FROM THE EARTH'S CRUST—
THE ROMANCE OF COAL, IRON AND STEEL

The Story of a Lump of Coal	I
What We Owe to Coal	13
A Day in the Life of a Miner	23
All About Iron	41
The Story of Steel	55
Out of the Fiery Furnace	70

TREASURES WON FROM THE EARTH'S CRUST (Contd.)—
METALS THAT SERVE US IN A HUNDRED WAYS

That Precious Metal—Gold	85
Beating Out Gold Leaf	97
Silver, The Queen of Metals	101
Nickel, The Goblin Metal	107
Copper, The Red Metal	112
Zinc, The Galvanising Metal	121
Tin and Tin Plate	125
The Story of Aluminium	131
The Metal of Saturn—Lead	136
Uranium—Source of Atomic Energy	141

MAGNETISM AND ELECTRICITY—
A GREAT DISCOVERY AND ITS MANY DEVELOPMENTS

Electricity and Its Uses	151
The Romance of the Magnet	161
Heat and Light from Electricity	169

PAGE

FAMOUS INVENTIONS AND HOW THEY WERE EVOLVED— WHAT MASTER MINDS HAVE DONE FOR THE GOOD OF MAN

How Sounds are Written Down 179

Messages and Pictures by Wire 186

The Telephone and How it Works 201

Radio Telephony 211

The Marvel of Radio 219

Television—The Magic Mirror 235

The Wonders of X-Rays 243

Invisible Rays 249

SERVICES WE MAINTAIN FOR THE COMMON GOOD— THE WORK THEY DO AND HOW IT IS CARRIED OUT

The Water We Drink 252

With the Fire Fighters 269

How We Get Our Gas 277

The Business of the G.P.O. 293

How Electricity is Supplied 305

THE WORLD AND ITS WORK— THE STORY OF SOME GREAT INDUSTRIES

This Age of Oil 321

The Ever-Useful Rubber 337

How Paper is Made 347

Cotton Growing and Spinning 353

From Silk to Rayon and Nylon 363

The Romance of Wool 375

Plastics—A Modern Industry 385

Machines for the Farmer 397

THE WORLD AND ITS WORK (Contd.)— AGRICULTURE—PRODUCING FOOD FROM THE LAND

The Farmer's Busy Year 411

PAGE

THE SECRET OF MAN'S SUPREMACY—
ABOUT THE MENTAL EQUIPMENT OF THE HUMAN BEING

How the Brain and the Mind Work 433

Colour Plates

Above and Below Ground at a Colliery . . . . . *Facing* 48
A Blast Furnace in Action . . . . ,, 49
Casting Steel into Ingots . . . . ,, 64
An Ingot Charging Machine at Work . . . . . ,, 65
A Pioneer Gold Prospector in Australia . . . . ,, 112
How Scotland's Water Drives an Aluminium Works . . ,, 113
Boring for Oil by Turbine . . . . ,, 128
Costumes Through the Centuries . . . . . . ,, 129
Cotton Gathering in Egypt . . . . ,, 336
Tapping a Tree for Rubber in Malaya . . . . . ,, 337
A Paper-Making Machine in a Modern Mill . . . . ,, 352
Sheep-Shearing in Australia . . . . ,, 353
Animals that Give Us Wool and Hair . . . . . ,, 400
Weaving Figured Fabric on a Jacquard Loom . . . ,, 401
Harvesting in the Modern Manner . . . . . . ,, 416
Rick-Building on a Kentish Farm . . . . . . ,, 417

Photo=tone Supplements

How This Book Was Built . . . . . . *Between* 176–177
Transport in Many Lands . . . . . ,, 272–273

Treasures
Won from the
Earth's Crust

The Romance
of Coal,
Iron and Steel

Scotsman Publications Ltd.

A MODERN COLLIERY IN SCOTLAND

Coal is of vital importance to British industry and the prosperity of the country largely depends upon the output from our mines. In the past few years mechanisation in the collieries has been speeded up and many new types of machinery introduced. Even the outward appearance is changing to some extent, as shown in this photograph of the general surface layout of the Comrie Colliery in Fifeshire.

THE STORY OF A LUMP OF COAL

A VERY old proverb says that familiarity breeds contempt. One might widen the proverb by using the word " indifference " in place of " contempt." There are many very useful things which we take for granted because we have always been accustomed to seeing and having them.

Product of the Sun

Among these last is coal. Its great value to us has been fully recognised in the past few years ; yet we smash it up roughly and shovel it thoughtlessly, and often wastefully, into furnaces or on to the fire, and while enjoying the heat which it gives us, grumble at it for the dust, dirt, soot and smoke which it makes.

Coal deserves our greatest respect, if only on account of its age. That lump of coal now burning on the fire came into existence during the passage of perhaps many millions of years, and was what it is now untold centuries before man first began to people the earth. It is the product of ages of sunshine, moist atmosphere and rank growth, followed by burial and an enormously long period of steadily increasing pressure, resulting in the formation of a black rock—for coal must be regarded as a rock—which differs from other rocks in that it burns readily.

Now, suppose that you took a piece of wood, say a cricket stump, and the lump of coal, and handed them over to a chemist to be analysed—that is, broken up into their elements. The report that he would send you would show that both are made up of the

Fuel Research Board.

IN A SEAM OF COAL

A single seam or layer of coal may contain many grades, hard, soft, steam, and so on. Here a section of a seam has been cut and reassembled in a wooden box.

same main things—carbon, nitrogen, hydrogen and oxygen—though the coal would contain a much higher proportion of carbon than the wood. This similarity is not to be wondered at, since coal is nothing more than woody matter that has had a great part of the gases that once were in it squeezed out by a pressure which has altered its structure. It has also been changed by heat and fermentation.

Through a Coal Forest

In the times when the trees and other vegetation which formed our coal were growing, Britain did not exist in its present form. It was merely part of a vast swampy expanse covered with a very strange growth. We know what the trees and plants of the period were like from remains that have been found in coal itself, or in the layers of clay above and below the coal-seams.

We may picture vast, gloomy forests of monkey-puzzle trees, gigantic reeds, and plants which resembled our club-mosses, but grew to a height of 60 feet, and had trunks up to 5 feet in thickness. The scene could hardly have been picturesque, as most of the trees had tall, straight trunks, with very few branches at the top, and very few leaves on a branch. They lacked entirely the beauty of our own forest trees.

Among the trees was a luxuriant growth of many kinds of ferns, with large fronds curling like the end of a bishop's crozier ; and there may have been some plants bearing flowers, which began to appear at this period of the earth's history. In and out between the trees flitted insects of many kinds, but there were as yet no birds; and over the slime in which this vegetation was rooted crawled worms, snails, and various reptiles. The lagoons spreading here and there contained fish and molluscs. In many ways the coal forest, with its slime, decaying vegetation, and hot, moist atmosphere, must have been somewhat like a modern mangrove forest, and probably as unpleasant a place for men to live in—if there had been any men.

We may imagine many generations of trees and plants growing, and rotting into a carpet of stems, roots and leaves, similar to the pulpy mass of a peat bog, until it has a thickness of many feet. All the time the ground is sinking very, very slowly. Then there begins a quicker subsidence, and water from the sea or rivers begins to flow in, bringing with it sand and fine particles of rocks. These settle and form a layer of dense clay or sandstone over the vegetation. Presently the filling-up reaches a stage at which it becomes possible for vegetation to grow again, and what was once open water returns to forest. This in turn sinks, and is covered up; and the alternate processes of growth and burial may be repeated many times.

The " Coal Measures "

In the end, one gets a series of seams of coal, separated by layers of clay, shale, and sandstone. A " coal measure," as such a series is called, may be compared to streaky bacon. The lean is represented by coal and the fat by the other materials. The coal seams may vary in thickness from a few inches to many feet; and the same seam may contain coal of different qualities, produced, perhaps, from different kinds of vegetation.

Ages pass, and there is a further sinking of the ground. If the settlement is great, the ground may be covered deeply with sea-water. The lime-encrusted remains of myriads of tiny creatures living in this settle to the bottom, and in the course of a million years or so produce a thick layer of chalk, which itself may have strata of clay and sand spread over it.

One should notice that the layers found over the coal measures always come in the same order, though they are not all present in every case ; and that they are all deposited from water, unless it should so happen that some molten rock has been forced among them from the interior of the earth. It should be mentioned, too, that coal occurs not only in the true coal measures, but among the layers which cover them. For whenever the conditions were right for the growth of coal-jungle, it grew.

We have pictured the ground as always sinking, to get an orderly view of things. But the earth's crust has moved up as well as down, and upward movements have been responsible for many coal-seams by making it possible for vegetation to grow. It was upheaval of the layers that brought much of the world's coal within

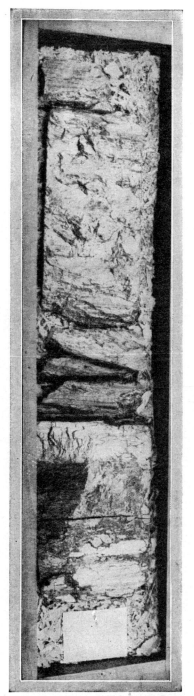

Fuel Research Board.

A LIGHTER FORMATION

The seam of coal here depicted is scarcely half the thickness of the layer shown on the previous page. Coal seams vary considerably.

our reach. In many cases the coal-seams have been pushed up above sea-level, at least along their edges, and so can be mined by tunnels driven into them. In some places seams of coal are visible in sea-cliffs and river banks; in others, in mountain sides. Most of the British coal deposits, however, lie along the bottom of great shallow basins of rock, filled in with more recent formations; and, fortunately for us, they are very level and unbroken, so that, once reached, they are easy to mine.

Varieties of Coal

There are different kinds of coal, and though they all burn, they behave in different ways.

What we may call the youngest kind of coal is named *lignite*, from the Latin word *lignum*, wood, because the shapes of tree-trunks are plainly to be seen in it. It is also called "brown coal," being in some cases of much the same colour as peat, though it is sometimes black. We may regard it as imperfectly formed coal, containing a great deal of water, and much less carbon than true coal. Very little of it is found in Britain, but it is plentiful in Germany, North America and Australia. It burns smokily, and is unsuitable for household use, though large quantities are consumed in power stations supplying electricity to big cities.

The next and largest class of coal is *bituminous* coal. This has been squeezed and heated more than lignite, and has got rid of much of its hydrogen. But a good deal of that gas still remains in it, and

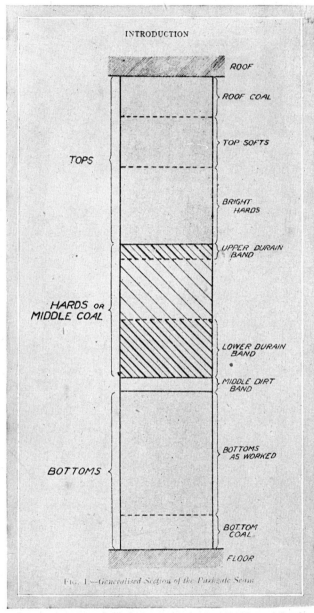

INTRODUCTION

ROOF

ROOF COAL

TOPS

TOP SOFTS

BRIGHT HARDS

UPPER DURAIN BAND

HARDS OR MIDDLE COAL

LOWER DURAIN BAND

MIDDLE DIRT BAND

BOTTOMS AS WORKED

BOTTOMS

BOTTOM COAL

FLOOR

Fig. 1.—*Generalised Section of the Parkgate Seam*

Fuel Research Board.

ALL FOUND IN ONE SEAM

To many of us all coal appears alike, but the expert divides it up into different classes and qualities, largely according to its non-carbon content, as is here illustrated. Coal in the seam varies according to the materials out of which the "measures" were formed in the earliest ages of the earth.

it burns with a bright flame, and some smoke. The harder and less gaseous varieties are used a great deal in steam boilers; while the softer kinds, which send out spurts of gas when burning and tend to cake together, are in great demand as household coals and for making gas.

Then we come to the purest coal of all, *anthracite*, mined chiefly in South Wales and Pennsylvania. Owing to its great hardness it is also called " stone coal." It is practically pure carbon, and so burns slowly and without flame or smoke, like charcoal or coke, and it leaves very little ash. It is used chiefly in enclosed stoves for heating houses or water, or for cooking.

For " Lead " Pencils

In graphite, or plumbago, used in making " lead " pencils, we have coal in a still purer state, every substance other than carbon having been driven out of it almost entirely by extreme pressure lasting for many more years; and in the diamond we have the final stage, in which intense heat has played a part, producing absolutely pure carbon in a crystallised form. So you see that there is some reason for calling coal " black diamonds," apart from the question of its value to us.

Why do some coals burn with little ash, while others leave a great deal ?

The chief reason, no doubt, is that, while the coal vegetation was being covered up, it got more or less intermingled with sand and clay brought in by water. In one place the water might

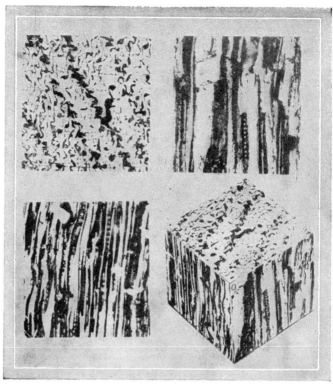

Fuel Research Board.

COAL OF VARYING STRUCTURE

From these micro-photographs we can see that coal is built up of many layers or structures. Polished coal surfaces show us a grain not unlike that of wood. Prints of this nature may be placed together to demonstrate the formation of a cube of coal, as shown in the lower right-hand corner.

have been strained by vegetation or been purified by depositing any solid matter in it before it reached the forests ; and in another it may have come in with more of a rush, and dumped tiny fragments of rock among the coal of the future.

Or, again, some trees and plants may have contained more unburnable matter than others.

The Early Use of Coal

The Romans first made use of coal in these islands. We know that they burned it, because coal ashes have been found among the ruins of old Roman military stations in Durham, Northumberland and Lancashire. After the Romans left Britain, the mineral seems not to have been employed for many

DRILLING RODS →

SUBSTITUTE for connecting tools of various sizes →

DRILLING JAR for breaking the solid blow of the rods →

SINKER BAR for adding weight to the blow. →

CHISEL or BIT →

OLD METHOD of BORING

In days gone by the earth was bored to make tests for coal by means of a string of tools, as illustrated. It was not a satisfactory method.

centuries. No mention is made of it in Domesday Book (1086), which gives a very complete record of all minerals known at the time.

By the thirteenth century people were beginning to collect lumps of coal found on the sea-shore along the north-eastern coast of England. It was called "sea-coal," to distinguish it from charcoal, the common fuel, and this name stuck to it for four centuries, long after inland coal-mines were working. Then the monks of Tynemouth began to mine it in a small way, sinking shallow pits into the coal where it came near the surface, and their example was copied in Derbyshire, Yorkshire, South Wales, Shropshire and Staffordshire.

As long ago as 1253 a street in London was called Secole Lane, and this shows that already coal was being shipped to the capital. But until the fourteenth century none but poor people used this kind of fuel, and it was only when buildings were provided with chimneys to carry away the smoke that it found its way into the houses of the great. Even then there was considerable prejudice against it as being injurious to health, and people generally had to be more or less driven to its use by the

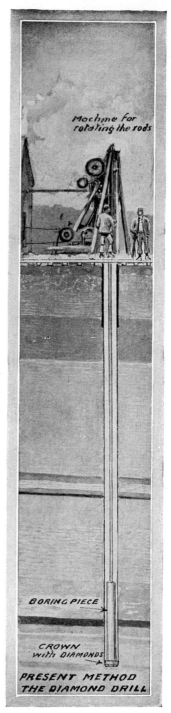

Machine for rotating the rods

BORING PIECE

CROWN with DIAMONDS →

PRESENT METHOD THE DIAMOND DRILL

Our mining engineers now depend upon the diamond drill, depicted above. By this means a core can be brought to the surface.

dwindling supply of charcoal.

Queen Elizabeth, though she levied taxes on mined coal, would have nothing to do with it; but her successor, James I., had been accustomed to burning coal at his seat in Fife, and introduced it to the palace of Westminster. As soon as the royal favour shone upon it, coal became fashionable, and we read that in James's reign " pitt-cole is become the general fewell of this Britaine Island, used in the houses of the nobilitie, cleargy and gentrie in Londone and in all other cities and shyres of the Kingdome."

It is an interesting fact that St. Paul's Cathedral and many parish churches destroyed in the Great Fire of 1666 were rebuilt largely with money got by taxing coal imported into London.

What established coal-mining as a great national industry was the adoption of coal, about the middle of the eighteenth century, for iron smelting, and the application of the steam-engine to keeping mines clear of water.

Boring and Shaft-sinking

British coal lies far below the surface, and must be raised through shafts—great wells sunk into the ground till they reach the seams. The shafts allow men to enter and leave the workings, give entrance to all articles, such as timber, rails and machinery, needed for getting coal; provide a way out for the mined coal, and for water pumped to the

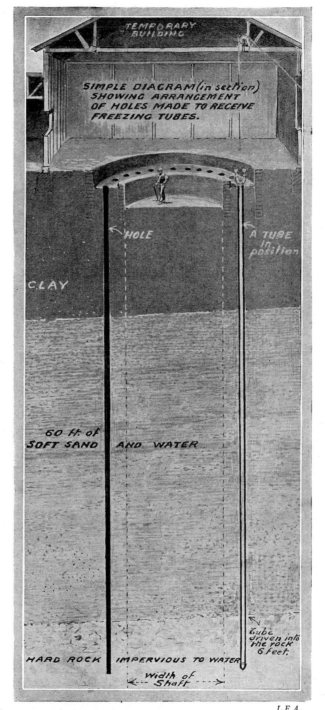

L.E.A.

SINKING THROUGH SOFT SAND AND WATER

This sectional drawing shows how a coal pit was sunk through soft sand and water. Tubes were driven 6 feet into hard rock below the sand. Through these tubes a freezing mixture was circulated.

surface ; and are the channels through which the mine is ventilated.

The sinking of a shaft may cost hundreds of thousands of pounds. So, before one is sunk the ground is explored thoroughly to find out whether the coal seams will justify the expense, how deep down they are, and where the shaft may best be placed. Test-holes are put down in selected places. An engine is erected over the spot chosen for a hole, to work a drilling apparatus. The tools used are in some cases heavy chisels, fixed to the ends of iron rods, lifted and dropped by the engine, and given part of a turn between blows.

But if complete samples, or " cores," of the strata passed through are wanted, the rotary drill is used. This is a short hollow cylinder with its bottom edge studded with diamonds, or having removable hard sharp spikes projecting from it. Or it may be grooved at the bottom, so that hard steel shot may be fed between it and the material it is boring, to wear the latter away.

The drill is on the end of a string of hollow rods, through which water is pumped to wash up the fine matter worn away by the drill as it turns round and round. When the drill has cut out a core of its own length, grit is poured down the tube to wedge the core, and the drill is lifted to the surface, bringing the core with it. The core is removed, examined, and numbered, and the drill lowered again. In this way ground has been explored completely to a depth of 7,000 feet.

If the bore-hole passes through a soft, water-bearing stratum, such as quicksand, it has to be lined with steel tubbing, driven down from the surface, until firm ground is again met with.

Lining the Shaft

We will assume that it has been decided to sink a shaft. In Britain, coal-mine shafts are usually circular, as this shape resists great pressure most easily; and square-cornered shafts are used only in firm, dry ground. In any case, the shaft will be lined from top to bottom with masonry, concrete or iron. Where the ground is loose or soft, it is removed with pick and shovel ; while rock has to be bored and blasted. Where a masonry lining is used, it is built in sections as the sinking proceeds. At intervals a deep groove is made in the side of the excavation, and in it a wooden ledge, or curb, is fixed. This curb acts as the

L.E.A.

DIGGING THE SHAFT OF A COAL-MINE

This picture shows a continuation of the engineering feat explained on the previous page. The soft, watery layer of sand has been frozen hard, and men called " sinkers " are now engaged in excavating for the shaft, which at the soft section will be lined with metal plates wedged in position with wood.

foundation for masonry, which is built up till it reaches the curb above.

Should a concrete lining be preferred, a steel lining is fixed round the shaft, and the space between it and the ground is filled in with concrete. When the concrete has hardened, the lining is removed, to be used again lower down.

Fighting Water

The shaft-sinker's great enemy is water. If it is known that the shaft will have to pass through water-bearing rock or quicksand, special measures are taken to keep the water at bay while the shaft is being sunk through the watery ground and lined.

When a quicksand has to be pierced, bore-holes are sunk through it in a ring, so as to enclose a cylinder of ground a few feet wider across than the shaft will be. Each hole is lined with a steel tube, closed at the bottom, which has inside it a smaller tube open at the bottom. Brine chilled far below the freezing-point of water is pumped down through the smaller tube and rises between it and the larger tube. This circulation of brine is kept up for months, until the ground all round the tubes is frozen solid. Then the miners get to work and dig out the frozen sand, and line the shaft with brickwork or iron rings like those used for the lining of a " tube " railway.

The same method may be used for dealing with rock with fissures in it which act as water-channels. But engineers employ also a quite different process, called cementation. In this case open-ended tubes are sunk into the rock, and liquid cement is forced in under enormous pressure until all the cracks in the rock near the path of the shaft have been filled in, and the rock becomes solid and water-tight. Sinking of the shaft can then proceed as if through dry ground.

At the bottom of a shaft is a large chamber, lined with strong arches of masonry to carry the weight of the

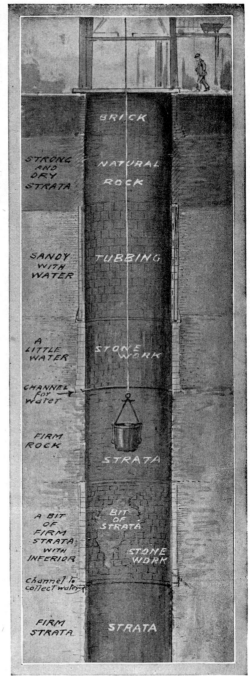

L.E.A.

LINING A MINE SHAFT

The shafts or wells of coal-mines are lined with different materials, according to the strata. In parts the natural rock suffices as a wall, and brickwork serves in places.

THE PRESENT SOURCES OF OUR COAL

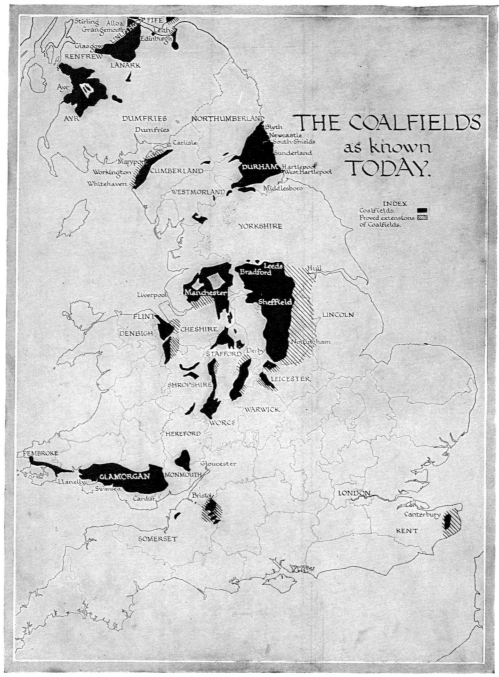

THE COALFIELDS
as known
TODAY.

INDEX
Coalfields.
Proved extensions
of Coalfields.

By courtesy of the B.B.C.

This map of part of Great Britain shows in black our coal-fields as they are to-day. Almost all our coal lies far below the surface and must be raised through shafts, which are like great wells sunk in the ground. People live together most thickly in those parts of the country where coal measures are found because the " black diamonds " feed busy factories. The development of the Kentish coal-field is of recent date.

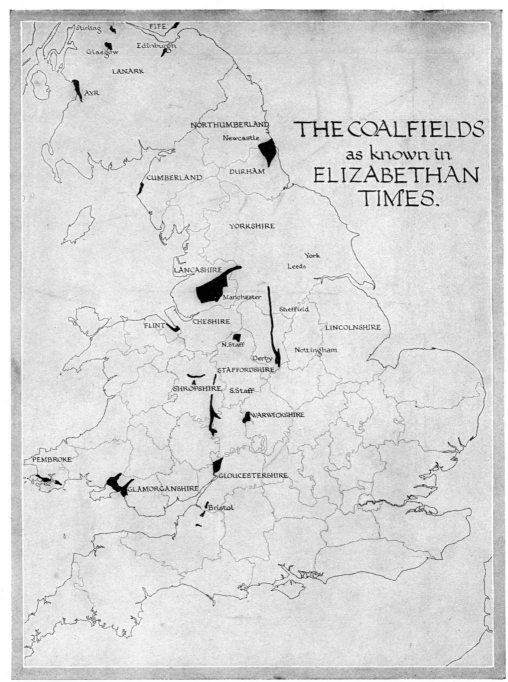

THE COALFIELDS
as known in
ELIZABETHAN
TIMES.

By courtesy of the B.B.C.

The first people to burn coal in this country were the Roman invaders, but not for centuries after their departure was the commodity used again. Folk then began to pick up lumps on the seashore near the mouth of the Tyne, calling the fuel " sea-coal " to distinguish it from charcoal, which was normally burned. In the days of Good Queen Bess a tax was levied on mined coal. The above map shows that many coal-fields were known even then.

shaft. It extends below the level of the seams, so that water may drain into it from the workings and be pumped up ; and it is provided with platforms at which the coal tubs are put on to or drawn off the lifting cages.

Ventilation of Mines

Every coal-mine must have at least two shafts equipped with winding gear, so that the miners may not be trapped if one should be blocked. Two shafts are needed also to give good ventilation underground.

Enormous quantities of air must be circulated through all parts of the workings to supply the miners with plenty of oxygen, as well as to carry away any dangerous gases leaking out of the coal. The deeper a mine is, the hotter it becomes, and the greater is the need for an abundance of fresh air to keep the heat within bounds. Usually the air-current is produced by a huge fan at the top of one shaft, called the " upcast " shaft. The foul air sucked up through this is replaced by fresh air rushing down another shaft, the " downcast," and led through all parts of the mines by light partitions, named brattices, placed in the workings, before it reaches the " upcast."

In many mines to-day about $8\frac{1}{2}$ tons of air are circulated every minute of the day. This means that 5 or 6 tons of air are often circulated for every ton of coal produced.

Getting water out of a mine is as important as getting air into it. Many mines would be flooded if the pumps ceased working for only twelve hours. In some mines more than 1,000 gallons of water per minute are pumped out, equal in many case to several times the weight of the coal raised in the same time.

Early pumping-engines were set at the top of a shaft and connected by rods with pumps at the bottom. Nowadays pumps are usually driven by electric motors placed in a chamber near the foot of the shaft and fed with current through cables running down to them from the surface. The pumps themselves may have plungers working in and out, or contain fan-like blades which fling the water from them against the casing with such pressure that it is forced to the surface.

Electricity is being more and more used in coal-mines for lighting the workings, hauling coal, and driving mechanical cutters, and we have now a number of " all-electric " collieries.

National Coal Board.

SCOTLAND'S NEWEST COAL MINE

In every branch of the coal industry new ideas and modern methods are being introduced, and the architect is called upon as well as the geologist and engineer. This photograph shows the model of the new Rothes Colliery in Fifeshire, and gives an excellent idea of what it will look like when completed.

WHAT WE OWE TO COAL

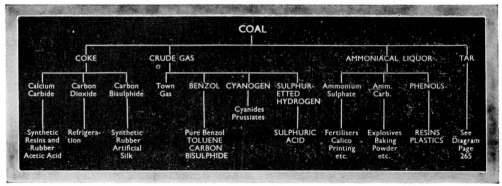

COAL AND ITS BY-PRODUCTS

Specially drawn for this work.

We are apt to think of coal mainly as a substance that produces heat by being burned. As a matter of fact, the by-products of this fuel are of almost incalculable importance, as can be seen from this diagram. From the chemist's point of view coal is a complex mixture of valuable chemicals and although the production of gas from coal is not a new story the record of the chemicals now obtained during the process of gas-making is a much newer and more fascinating story.

THE fire having burned rather low, you take a lump of coal from the scuttle and throw it on to the fire. Why do you do this? Because you know that the coal will burn and give out heat.

Yet you will be surprised to learn that from coal chemists can derive well over *two thousand* different substances, all of use to us! "Two thousand!" you may say; "surely that is impossible?" It is not impossible, because it is actually being done. Experiments carried out patiently over a long period of years have shown that coal is a real treasure-house. We do not yet know the total of the riches that a lump of coal may conceal under its dull, dirty exterior.

The Elements of Coal

If you were given, say, five little squares of cardboard, each bearing a different number, you could spend a long time arranging them in different orders, without repeating yourself. Every time you made a new arrangement they would give you a new value, though the figures themselves would remain individually the same.

Now, in coal we have five main elements ; Carbon, hydrogen, nitrogen, oxygen and sulphur. Like the figures, they can be combined together in a great number of different ways ; and the substances which result from the different combinations may be far more unlike each other in their qualities than 12345 is unlike 54321 in value.

We get these substances out of coal by breaking it up into its elements, which are made to unite again in various ways.

We can break up coal on a small scale in the following manner : We take a tin canister—a $\frac{1}{2}$-lb. coffee-tin does very well—fill it partly with small coal, replace the lid, and punch a small hole in the bottom. The tin is then placed bottom upwards in a clear fire.

Vapour soon begins to issue from the hole. This is at first mostly steam, from the little water in the coal. Presently the vapour will light if a match be applied to it. A mixture of carbon and hydrogen, called coal-gas, is now coming away. It burns for a long time, but with a smoky flame, because it contains impurities. One of these, tar, blackens the tin round the hole.

Ammonia gas and sulphur also pass out. When the flame dies down, the coal has parted with everything that can be driven out of it by heat. On the tin being opened, there falls out a mass of coke, which is carbon mixed with certain mineral impurities. When the coke is put into the fire it burns without smoke, and the impurities become ash.

How Coke is Used

You see, then, that we have with our canister broken coal up into several things, two of which, coke and gas, can both be burned to give heat, and the gas to give light as well. Coke is used in stoves and boiler furnaces, and for smelting iron.

In the early days of railways people thought that the smoke from the locomotives would ruin the crops and injure cattle near a track. So for a time the railway companies burned only coke in their engines because it gave out no smoke ; and you can still see in places the ruins of the old coke ovens used in those now distant days. But when it was found that, after all, coal smoke from engines did no harm in the country, and that what people took for smoke was mostly steam, coal filled the place of coke. It was less expensive, and a greater weight of it could be carried on the tender, as it took up less room.

Iron-smelters use coke for a different reason, which is that raw coal contains chemicals that would hinder the production of good iron.

Woodall Duckham Company.

A SCENE INSIDE THE GAS WORKS

Here we have a scene in an up-to-date gas works. In the foreground is the top of a producer with air blast equipment round it, while in the background is the waste heat boiler. The photograph was taken at the Poole and Pitwines works where 236 tons of coal are carbonised each day, making nearly four million cubic feet of gas, besides providing valuable by-products.

Gas Council.

AT THE WORLD'S LARGEST GAS WORKS

Coal is not a simple substance but a complex mixture of valuable chemicals. It is only in compara-tively recent times that the full possibilities of these chemicals have been realised, and new discoveries made concerning the by-products obtained from the carbonisation of coal at the gas works. The largest gas works in the world is at Beckton, North Woolwich, seen here.

William Murdoch's Lamp

In the early days of coke-making, no account was taken of the gas. This was allowed to escape into the air. In 1792 a Scottish engineer, William Mur-doch, baked coal in iron vessels and collected the gas that came from it in air-tight bags. He would take one of these bags, and fit its neck with a stop-cock and a metal tube having a small hole in the end of it. When he wanted a light to guide him through the dark-ness to or from his work, he turned on the cock and lit the gas coming from the bag carried under his arm.

Later on, Murdoch lit his house with gas, and presently some works at Birmingham. The idea of conveying gas through pipes for street lighting

was soon afterwards taken up. Like most great inventions, gas-lighting had its opponents. It would blow up towns and poison the air, said some. It will destroy our Navy, said others, who argued as follows : "We have used whale-oil for lamps in the past. If we use gas, whale-oil will not be wanted, and the whale fisheries will disappear. As our best sailors are those trained on whalers, our Navy will be ruined when the supply of such sailors ceases."

But arguments similar to these could not stop progress. In 1813 West-minster Bridge was lighted with gas, and people flocked to it to see the new lamps. "How wonderful! How brilliant!" they exclaimed. With the burners then used the brilliancy cannot have been very great, as compared with our modern street illumination. But it was doubtless an improvement on the murky light from the parish oil-lamps which the gas-jets replaced.

Gas-lighting soon spread all over the country. Every town got its gas-works, and gas pipes invaded one house after another. Explosions might occur, but they were few and far between. So people accepted gas as a good and convenient friend which dispelled darkness and was always at hand when wanted.

Heat Laid on Through Pipes

For many years gas ruled as the king of light in towns. Then a rival—electricity—put forward its claims. The electric lamp was more brilliant, and it did not soil ceilings and decorations. But presently Auer von Welsbach invented the incandescent gas mantle, which in turn beat electric light hollow for a time. Inventors replied

with greatly improved electric lamps, and now the victory, as far as lighting is concerned, rests with electricity.

If lighting had been the only use which could be made of coal-gas things might have gone badly with the gas companies. But gas has great advantages as a heat-giving factor ; it can be more easily regulated than any other form of fuel for general use, and its cleanliness, speed and flexibility give it great advantages in such industries as food manufacture, whether in baking bread and cakes, sweet-making, or in cooking a host of other articles of everyday consumption.

In millions of homes all the cooking is now done by gas, which, in effect, is heat laid on through pipes, like water. Hundreds of thousands of rooms and shops are heated by gas fires and gas radiators. And many thousands of factories use furnaces heated by coal-gas for industrial processes. So coal-gas,

Gas Council.

DYEING KNITTED FABRICS AT THE DYE WORKS

It was an Englishman, W. H. Perkin, who first obtained a dye from the substances derived from coal tar, and it was his dye which was first used to print the mauve penny postage stamps in the later years of Queen Victoria's reign. Yet the artificial dye industry was not developed in this country until after the 1914–18 war. To-day we are making 90 per cent. of our own dyes from coal tar.

Gas Council.

SHEEP TAKING THEIR ANNUAL DIP

Most of our well-known disinfectants come from one or other of the oils dissolved from the tar produced at the gas works when coal is carbonised to obtain gas. It is from these oils that such preparations as sheep dip are made, and by law all sheep in this country must be dipped once a year. In this photograph sheep are receiving their annual bath.

after being threatened with downfall, is consumed in larger and larger quantities as the years pass by, and more people realise how convenient and clean it is in comparison with the raw coal from which it comes.

The Four Useful Friends

We said a little way back that coal-gas contains impurities. But even these impurities have their uses. Into a gas works there goes coal. Out of a gas works there come, besides coke and gas, coal-tar and sulphate of ammonia.

The last of these is the sulphur and nitrogen in the gas, collected and combined together. It is a very valuable fertiliser. Many people scatter it thinly on their lawns to make the grass grow. British farmers use many tons of it each year to help their crops. Some crops must have nitrogen supplied to them in a suitable form, and the sulphate is just the thing for the purpose. A great deal of the food we eat has in it nitrogen derived from coal. Curious, is it not?

But it only goes to show that there is more in coal than one may suspect.

A Journey to the Seaside

It is really very difficult to get away from coal. We are off to the seaside for our holidays. How jolly it will be to exchange the smoke-laden air of the town for the fresh sea-breezes!

We hail a taxicab, and are driven to the station over roads made smooth and dustless with the help of coal-tar. The petrol used by the taxicab's engine which hustles us along very possibly contains some spirit — benzole — extracted from coal-tar. The locomotive which rushes us seaward is burning coal. The sleepers which support the rails flying away from under us are soaked with creosote, which is a product of coal-tar. Every one of them contains a large amount of this liquid. We flash past hundreds of telegraph poles, every one of which also has been steeped in the same liquid. And when we reach our destination and again take a cab, as likely as not we shall travel over wood blocks protected from the weather by the same substance.

If it were not for this very useful creosote, sleepers, poles and blocks would perish so quickly from decay that the expense of railway, telegraph and road repairs would increase enormously.

The creosoting has to be done in a very thorough way. Mere painting over with creosote is of little use if the protection it gives is to last for years. The method used is very interesting. Truck loads of sleepers are pushed into a long steel cylinder. The doors at the end of this are then closed and sealed, and all the air is sucked out. The pores of the wood are now quite empty,

even of air. Next, the cylinder is filled with hot creosote under great pressure. The creosote sinks deep into the wood, filling every crevice, and making it quite waterproof.

Wonders of Tar

Creosote is only one of very many things obtained from tar. Have you ever tasted saccharine? It is a white powder hundreds of times sweeter than sugar. People whom the doctors do not allow to eat sugar sweeten their food with it. It is extracted from tar; as, too, is the hard white substance with a rather pleasant smell, called naphthalene, which is put into drawers containing clothes and furs to keep away moths and other insects.

The Science Museum, London.

MINERS' LAMPS OF THE OPEN TYPE

Times have changed since these lamps were used by miners, and, just as there have been great advances made in coal-getting and in safer equipment for miners, so has tremendous progress been made in the utilisation of coal. All the lamps in the unique collection seen above had exposed flames; most of the lamps were made to hang up or to be supported by metal which could be driven into the coal face.

We clean our clothes with another tar product—benzene. Carbolic acid, which can burn the skin dreadfully, but is a very useful disinfectant, comes from tar. From tar also we get a great number of drugs. If you are a photographer and develop your own plates or films, you will use chemicals that once were locked up in coal.

The chemist has succeeded in winning from tar a whole host of perfumes imitating very closely the scents of thyme, hyacinth, mimosa, rose, lilac, musk, lilies, violets, heliotrope, jessamine and other flowers. And from evil-tasting tar he extracts also essences which deceive one into thinking that they came from cinnamon, almonds, peaches, cherries, vanilla, and so on.

The Romance of Tar Dyes

About the middle of the last century, a young English chemist, William Henry Perkin, carried out some experiments with coal-tar in his little private laboratory. One day he obtained a black powder that stained things a purplish colour, to which he gave the name of " mauve." He sent a sample of the powder to a great firm of dyers to test. They were so pleased with it that Perkin set to work on extracting other dyes from coal-tar and discovered several new ones.

Perkin thus became the founder of the great industry of making artificial dyes from coal-tar. Hundreds of different colours have been found, very many of them by German chemists. Artificial dyes have largely taken the place of natural dyes extracted from indigo, logwood, madder and other vegetable substances, being cheaper and in some ways better.

The industry had become German to such an extent that, when the War of

Gas Council.

PURIFICATION PLANT

Some idea of the complicated processes by which the many valuable products from coal are obtained during the manufacture of gas is given by this picture of the complete wet purification plant installed in recent years at a South London gas works.

1914–18 broke out, and we could no longer obtain dyes from Germany, a very difficult position was created. For without dyes the making of coloured woven fabrics of all kinds and printing in colours would be brought to a standstill. British chemists had to buckle to and find out how to produce dyes in British factories. They were soon turning them out in large quantities.

We have said that it is difficult to get away from coal. The truth of this becomes more evident when we reflect that the clothes we wear, the curtains of our rooms, our wall-papers, and a host of other coloured objects, are dyed with substances derived from coal.

Oil from Coal

When coal is heated in containers, called retorts, to drive the gas out of it,

2—2

the heating may be carried to a point at which the greatest possible amount of gas is obtained. This would yield about 15,000 cubic feet of gas from a ton of coal.

But if less heat be used and we are content with less gas, we can obtain from coal a very useful quantity of oils of different kinds, which are made up of the same elements as coal-gas, differently combined.

It has been calculated that it would be *possible* to obtain 560,000,000 gallons of motor spirit and 3,000,000,000 gallons of fuel oil from the 150,000,000 tons of coal which we burn in Britain every year. And we should still have for our fireplaces and boilers about 100,000,000 tons of a fuel rather more gassy than coke, but burning readily, without smoke. At present we import hun-

dreds of millions of gallons of petrol (motor spirit) and huge quantities of fuel oil, paying out millions of pounds of money in exchange.

Artificial Oil

Even yet we do not know the full value of coal. It may have possibilities of which we hardly dream. Chemists are greatly interested in a process for getting oil from coal, not by distilling the coal, but by forcing hydrogen to combine with raw coal.

The process brings powdered coal and hydrogen-gas together in a very strong chamber, into which the gas is pumped until it has a pressure of about 3,000 pounds to the square inch. The chamber is heated from outside, and the pressure and heat between them produce a tarry liquid, somewhat like

Gas Council.

FOR FERTILISING THE GROUND

Sulphate of ammonia is well-known to farmers and gardeners as an important artificial fertiliser, and in this picture is seen a centrifugal machine for the separation of sulphate of ammonia for this purpose. At the gas works nearly 75,000 tons of sulphate of ammonia are made available each year to meet the demand both by agriculturists and by the chemical industry.

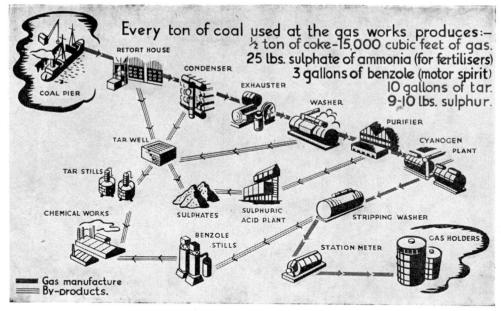

Every ton of coal used at the gas works produces:—
½ ton of coke—15,000 cubic feet of gas.
25 lbs. sulphate of ammonia (for fertilisers)
3 gallons of benzole (motor spirit)
10 gallons of tar.
9-10 lbs. sulphur.

Gas Council.

THE TREASURE IN COAL

In this diagram a general indication is given of what by-products are obtained from a ton of coal during its treatment at the gas works. Gas is the primary product, but the tar which is one of several by-products is also highly valuable since it provides the raw material for a large number of other industries. From it come disinfectants, preservatives, explosives, dyes, synthetic perfumes, food flavourings, and many other useful substances.

petroleum as it comes from the ground, and containing most of the coal in a new form. When distilled the liquid yields motor spirit, lubricating oil, fuel oil and pitch.

It is at present perhaps too early to say whether the hydrogenation of coal, as this process is named, will be an entire success. But if it turns out to be all that is hoped for, coal-fields will become a more valuable possession even than they are at present.

Paying with Coal

We have to import a great many things which we cannot produce at all ourselves, such as tea, coffee, cocoa, maize, tobacco, cotton, silk and zinc; or of which we do not produce enough to meet our needs, such as wheat, sugar and meat. These must be paid for largely in things exported. Chief among these are woven fabrics, steel, iron and coal. Coal was at one time sent abroad in very

large quantities, amounting in 1913, for instance, to 73,000,000 tons. Owing to the war, exports fell almost to zero, but great efforts are now being made to build up this important trade once again.

All the year round ships were loaded with coal in ports in South Wales, on the north-east coast of England, on the Humber, and on the Clyde. Many of the docks are equipped with special coal-loading machinery. A truck is lifted bodily with its contents, which are discharged through end doors into a chute. After the war the export of coal practically ceased as we needed every ton in our own country.

It is hoped that this great export trade will be restored in due time, but at present strict economy in the use of coal is essential. In the past we have treated it in rather the same fashion as the Chinese of Charles Lamb's famous story treated their huts when they burned them down to roast pigs shut up inside them. Coal is a great deal more than fuel. By burning it in its raw state to get heat, we waste an immense amount of valuable substances. This is being realised more fully every year. Many people are working out methods of distilling coal which will give us a smokeless fuel while saving the precious things which we allow to go up our chimneys.

The importance of this aspect was stressed in the Report on Coal Utilisation Research in Great Britain, issued by the Parliamentary and Scientific Committee: " Our very life as an industrial nation depends upon maintaining supplies of energy and raw materials for manufacturing processes. Our climate obliges us to use immense quantities of fuel to warm our homes and places of work. There is no possible means by which we can offset the falling productivity of our mines except by increasing the value and efficient use of the coal we are able to produce."

Nearly a Foot Deep

The gain will be twofold. We shall use our coal better, and at the same time get rid of a great deal of smoke which, while in the air, shuts out sunlight and is bad for our health, and, when it falls, fouls and damages everything upon which it settles.

We are told that the soot which falls in London alone during a year is enough to cover the 390 acres of Hyde Park nearly a foot deep. Experts also say that smoke costs the country over £40,000,000 a year in waste and damage to property. Things are not, however, as bad as they were, since more gas is used now than formerly for heating. But there is plainly plenty of room for improvement in this respect when you hear that in a test it was found that in one year dust, soot and other impurities equal to 563 tons to the square mile fell at Liverpool; 390 tons in London; and 237 tons at Edinburgh.

Woodall Duckham Company.

WHERE COAL IS CARBONISED

Here is another view taken in a large gas works. In the middle of the picture can be seen the chamber charging lids ; on the right are the gas offtake pipes. In the centre background is the coal charging car for the chambers. The coke charging skip for the producers is in the left background, while the charging lids for the producers are on the extreme left.

A DAY IN THE LIFE OF A MINER

National Coal Board.

WORKING AT THE COAL FACE

Crawling up to the coal face is hard on the knees and miners often wear protective pads. In this picture a miner is " filling " coal—clearing away the coal which has been cut by the machines on to the conveyor which carries it along to the loading point where the tubs, controlled by the loaderman, are marshalled and filled before being hauled away on the first stage of their journey to the surface.

WE have read in previous chapters the story of a lump of coal : how it was formed under pressure through untold centuries from the forests and vegetation that existed before man had appeared on the earth. We have learned, too, something of the many different substances which this black rock from beneath the surface yields us to-day apart from its use as a fuel.

Now we come to the mine itself and particularly to the men who go down the deep pits where this buried treasure lies. The most prominent object at a coal mine is the winding or head gear, those twin wheels at the top of a steel structure which are usually visible for miles around. Over these big wheels run the steel cables which raise or lower the cages to carry their loads of men or materials between the surface and the workings underground.

There are always two or more shafts to any colliery. One of these two shafts is called the upcast shaft because it has a power-driven fan which sucks the used air out of the mine. The vacuum thus caused automatically draws fresh air in down the other, which is the downcast shaft. Around the bottom of the shafts an area of coal is left unworked and this serves as a pillar of support to the shaft and to the winding gear and buildings on the surface.

In the Lamp Room

Before going down the pit, the miner first calls at the lamp room. To-day this is usually lined with racks fitted with electric lamp accumulators which are being charged. On his head he has a black, light-weight helmet, and to the front of this his electric cap-lamp is fitted. A belt round his waist takes the accumulator, connected to the lamp by a length of strongly-

THE DEPUTY GIVES FIRST AID

One of the important underground officials is the deputy who is in charge of a district, and is particularly responsible for safety precautions in the mines. In this picture the deputy is seen after collecting his lamps as he receives his First Aid box before going on duty.

Photos : National Coal Board.

Safety and health are two aspects of the miner's life which receive constant study. Many mines now have a medical centre under a medical officer and with a trained nurse in attendance. Training in First Aid is given in all Divisions, and there are First Aid rooms in every mine. Here we see a coal-getter who has received a minor injury having attention in an underground office.

IN CHARGE OF THE WINDING GEAR

Above the underground workings is the winding or head gear, and the operator in charge works to the signals from the pithead, and is also in constant touch with the onsetter at the bottom of the shaft. A cage carrying men makes its journey at a slower rate than one carrying a load of coal tubs.

Photos : National Coal Board.

Some idea of the winding gear itself is given in this picture. Apart from the men working down the mine there are highly responsible jobs for trained men on the surface, and not the least important are those of the operators in charge of the winding gear and the power-driven fans which give full and adequate ventilation to all parts of the workings underground.

insulated flex. Certain men may take an oil safety lamp as well. The deputy, for instance, who is particularly concerned with the safety of the mine, uses a safety lamp when making his regular tests for gas in the workings.

Then from the lamp room the miner walks across to the big shed from the top of which the winding gear is seen, and in this shed are the gates of the shafts. Both tubs and men are carried up and down the shaft by two cages, most of which have two decks. Tubs and men, of course, are never carried in the same cage, and there is a different speed, strictly kept, for lowering the tubs or lowering the men. The cage carrying the tubs travels at a much faster rate than that used by the men.

The bell signals are given to the engineman in control of the winding gear, and to the onsetter guarding the gates at the shaft bottom, perhaps 2,000 feet or even more below in the blackness. None of the men who enter the cage has either cigarettes or matches in his pockets.

There are of course many types of job in a modern colliery both above and below ground. Mechanisation has gone rapidly ahead and much of the hard work of cutting the solid coal seam is now done by machines. Plenty of hard work remains to be done, however, and coal-getting is still a " man's job " in every sense of the term.

Down the Mine

Inside the cage the men who are going down grasp the bar above their heads and the final bell signals are exchanged. Then the cage begins to sink, gathering speed as it descends, but gradually slowing down on the last stage till it lands gently at the bottom of the shaft. Here one steps out into a brick or concrete-lined hall, well-lighted, and from this runs the " main road," as the principal tunnel into the mine is called. At intervals along this main road are telegraph signal points to communicate with the engine man in control of the hauling of the tubs. There are telephones, too, in communication with every part of the mine through the central telephone exchange at the surface.

This main road is also a railway, and

National Coal Board.

A MODERN COAL-CUTTING MACHINE

Both above and below ground expert mechanics, fitters and electricians are employed in installing and servicing the coal-cutters, loaders, conveyors, ventilating fan motors, electric drills, etc. Here we see one of the coal-cutting machines being serviced in the workshop.

DRIVING A NEW ROADWAY

National Coal Board.

There are about 14,000 miles of underground roadways in the coal mines of Britain, and the work of driving new roadways or extending old roads is carried on steadily as the mine is developed. This photograph shows part of a modern drill rig, which is mounted on a truck. High-speed drills, carried on booms, bite into the solid rock which is later brought down by explosives.

SETTING SCREW JACK PROPS

Mechanisation in the mine has not robbed coal-getting of all its hard work, nor has it yet made it a clean job. Here we see miners at work setting screw jack props behind the cutter of a Meco-Moore Cutter-Loader.

work goes on throughout the 24 hours and is divided into three main shifts, each working $7\frac{1}{2}$ hours, though the men on the shift may be up to another half-hour below ground, according to the time it takes to raise them all in the cages.

Coal-getting depends on team work. As the coal face advances each day the rocks forming the roof subside towards the floor. Men on the afternoon shift build " packs " — piles of tightly-rammed débris encased in walls built of larger pieces of stone —at intervals. At the same time the roadways too are being

both full and empty tubs are on the move to and from the cages all the time. The noise can be imagined. Where there is a long journey from pit bottom to coal face the men may do the first part of their journey in one of these trains or tubs. They may have to go a couple of miles or more to the place where they are actually working.

At first the road may be ten feet high and steel girders support the roof and sides which are bricked or concreted. But gradually the tunnel narrows and the tidy sides give way to rougher planks.

In   most   collieries

Photos : National Coal Board.

IN THE PITHEAD BATHS

At the end of his shift the miner gets rid of his grime in the pithead shower baths before going home. Each man has an aluminium locker for his clothes to which hot air is supplied by a duct.

advanced, and girders are set to support the roof and the sides of the roadway. Probably the men on this shift dismantle the conveyor and reassemble it in a path closer to the face.

As the men on this shift complete their work their places are taken by the men on the night shift. On this shift the coal is cut, the rows of props and bars that supported the roof on the previous day are moved forward and the conveyor in the " main gate " is extended so that the coal from the face conveyors, which have now been moved possibly a yard and a

A PIT PONY AT WORK

Gradually the pit ponies are being replaced by electric traction or diesel locos. There were still some 17,000 ponies at work in the pits in 1951. They go down as four-year-olds, and often stay for between ten and twenty years.

Photos : National Coal Board.

REPLACING THE PONY

Other methods of transport have invaded the mines just as the horse-drawn 'buses in the streets have given way to motor transport. Here we see one of the diesel locos at Hatfield Main Colliery coming in to its underground garage.

half forward, will still pour on to it.

Two men normally work with the coal-cutting machine. One is in charge of the operation of the machine, a second clears up the small pieces of coal and dust made in cutting, and inserts wedges into the cut to keep the coal from falling too soon. Other men remove and re-set props as the machine moves along the face.

Other men bore holes, usually about 2 inches in diameter, into the coal. In these shot-holes explosives will be put to blast down the coal. One man will operate a compressed air or electric drilling machine, boring the shotholes along the face. One or two shotfirers will later insert a charge of explosive in the holes, fill up the rest of the hole with clay or " stemming " and blast down the coal. These " breaking in " shots enable the colliers who go to work on the next shift to get the coal.

Working at the Face

Usually the men on the morning shift " get " the coal at the face, while other men work the haulage to transport the coal from the face to the shafts. At the pit bottom are men who load the full tubs into the cages, as well as pushing out and sending back to the workings the empty tubs that return down the shaft.

There may be thirty, or even twice as many, employed on a longwall face " filling " coal, the number depending on its length. They set supports to secure the new roof as it is exposed.

National Coal Board.

The coal from the face conveyors is fed on to the " gate " conveyor which carries it along the " gate " to the loading point where the tubs, controlled by the loaderman, are marshalled and filled. The tubs pass along the roadways where the boys and men working on the haulage couple them up into trains and clip them to the haulage rope.

A haulage engine-man looks after the engine which keeps the haulage ropes moving, pulling the full tubs away from the face and drawing the empty tubs back towards it. At a junction of two or three roadways the haulage workers may have to detach the trains from one rope and attach them to another. At some junctions the work may be supervised by a " corporal " whose job it is to see that the track is properly laid, that supplies needed at the coal

PIT-HEAD GEAR AT A MODERN COLLIERY

In 1945 a Government Committee of Mining Engineers was appointed and later recommended a big programme of reconstruction and development in our coal mines. During the past few years a great deal has been done to modernise our collieries and this photograph shows the up-to-date pit-head gear at the Mosley Common Colliery in Lancashire.

face, such as steel arches, pit props and bars, timber and machinery, all reach their right place, and that the movement of the tubs is not held up in any way.

The pit pony is still used in some mines, but gradually the numbers employed below ground are being reduced. In 1951, however, there were still some 17,000 ponies working in our mines. Just as modern methods and modern ideas have improved the working conditions of the miners themselves, so have modern standards improved the conditions under which the pit ponies of to-day carry on with their work below ground.

Screening and Washing

When the cage of full tubs reaches the surface, the "banksman" pushes the empty tubs into the cage and the full ones out at the other side, though in some mines this is often done by pneumatic rams. The coal in the tubs passes to the screens where it is tipped out and sorted into sizes. The small coal goes to the washery where it is cleaned and again sized. This washing plant is a very important part of the equipment of most collieries. A stream of water is passed through the mixture of small coal and rubbish and drives the coal away as it is lighter than the stone, slate, etc., which is left behind.

Research work and experiments are being carried out continuously and experts believe that in various

National Coal Board.

IN THE LAMP ROOM

Before going down the pit the miner calls in at the lamp room. On his head he wears a black, light-weight helmet, and to the front of this the electric lamp is fitted. The accumulator is hung on his belt and is connected to the lamp by a length of strongly insulated flex.

branches of the industry big advances will be made in the next few years.

Roughly about half the total number of men employed underground are engaged in the actual task of getting the coal and putting it in the conveyors and tubs which take it away. At the time of the Reid Committee, whose report was published in 1945, it was considered that our old-fashioned haulage system was mainly responsible for keeping down the output of the mines. Since then the task of installing coal-cutters, mechanical conveyors and haulage locomotives has been a high priority and

THE MAN WHO FIRES THE SHOT

One of the most responsible jobs in the mine is that of the man known as the shot-firer. He carries all explosive charges in a locked canister to which there is only one key which never leaves his possession. Here he is seen unlocking the canister before fixing and firing the shot to dislodge the coal.

Photos: Mirror Features.

The shot has been fired and has done its work successfully, bringing down some thirty tons of coal. In some mines the mechanical loader moves forward and draws the coal into the electrically-driven shuttle-car. In others the coal is filled on to conveyor belts and later transferred to wagons.

A SAFE ROOF OVERHEAD

Mirror Features.

All the underground galleries in a coal mine must have adequate support for the roofs. In main roads near the shafts brickwork or metal rings similar to those used on underground railways may be used. Nearer the coal face, where the galleries are smaller, wooden pit-props are used to support steel girders. The pit-prop is cut to the required length, then hammered into position, wedges being used when necessary. It is essential that the steel bars supporting the roof shall be exactly horizontal.

has already brought about a great improvement.

Electricity to-day does all the winding and hauling in many mines, and the pumping in almost every mine. For every ton of coal that comes to the surface several tons of water may have to be pumped from the mine to the surface. In most mines the pumps never cease their work throughout the year.

Finding a Fault

On the whole the daily round of the miner does not continue uninterruptedly on the same job for so very long. Apart from the different tasks which are undertaken by each shift there may be changes at the coal-face itself. One day a last strip of coal is got from the face to leave a wall of solid rock confronting the next shift. A " fault " has been encountered ; a great crack in the earth's crust breaking the continuity of the layers of rock, the edges of which have slipped, bringing the coal on one side of the fault above the coal on the other side. The seam may continue at a higher level above the roof of the old face, or at a lower level, below the floor.

Drifts may have to be driven through the rock to get at the displaced seam so that coal-getting can begin again as soon as possible. The transport of the necessary materials and machinery, laying the sleepers and rails, track for new haulages, all these are jobs which the miner is called upon to do when necessary.

There is quite a wide variety of jobs, too, among the men who work underground. The Coal Cutter operates the coal-cutting machine, which is driven by compressed air or electricity; the

National Coal Board.

BOYS LEARNING THEIR JOB

Boys who enter the mining industry go first to a Group training centre which serves a number of collieries. Their training here lasts for 16 weeks, after which they go to their own colliery where they gain practical experience under their own training officer. Here we see a group of trainees down the mine where they are being taught how to clip the tubs to the haulage rope.

National Coal Board.

THE DEPUTY TESTS FOR GAS

In some coalfields the deputy is known as the " examiner," or " fireman." He is responsible for the safety of his district, and among his tasks is that of making tests for gas. One of the best methods is the use of the flame safety lamp. When the flame is turned down to a narrow line on top of the wick, a halo, or " cap," is formed above the flame if firedamp is present. A trained man can detect as little as $1\frac{1}{2}\%$ of firedamp.

Coal Hewer brings down the cut coal from the coal-face, either with a hand pick or by mechanical pick, while the Ripper cuts away rock over the seam to enable the roads to be made, levels roadways, and sees to supporting timbers or steel arches. On this work he uses power drills and explosives when necessary.

The train of tubs which carries the coal away from the coal-face is drawn by the engine under the control of the Haulage Engine Man, while there are Electricians and Fitters working down the mine to instal and service the coal-cutters, loaders, conveyors, ventilating fan motors, electric drills, and other underground machinery.

On the staff side there is the Agent who exercises technical and administrative control over two or more collieries, while the Colliery Manager looks after and directs the day-to-day work of his own particular mine. In charge of all underground workings during his shift is the Under Manager, while the Colliery Engineer is responsible for the maintenance of the mechanical and electrical equipment and the Surveyor keeps all the plans of the workings up to date.

The Overman is in charge of a section of the underground workings, and the Deputy looks after a district and is particularly concerned with safety. In some coalfields the Deputy is better known as the " examiner " or " fireman." He examines the district at

THE COAL-CUTTER AND THE SHUTTLE-CAR

In the Whitehill Colliery the most remote coal faces are over three miles from the pit bottom, and the mine itself is 2,750 feet underground. It is fully mechanised, and our photograph gives a view of one of the electrically-driven Sullivan coal-cutters which cuts into the bottom of the coal face to a depth of about six feet.

Photos : Mirror Features.

Once the coal-cutter has done its part the work of getting out the coal is very much easier. In some modern mines it is loaded into the shuttle-car and driven off to the conveyor belt. There is no pony or manual haulage in this colliery and the shuttle-car seen here is being driven by a young miner.

A NEW MINE IN SOUTH WALES

" South Wales Argus."

Many collieries have been reconstructed and remodelled in recent times. A number of new collieries have been sunk, while small pits nearing exhaustion have been closed. Among mines reopened and remodelled in recent years is one at Nantgarw in South Wales which produces a type of coal particularly suitable for carbonisation, producing gas, coke, and the various products of gas manufacture. The photograph shows Nantgarw during reconstruction.

least twice every shift to see that everything is in order and at the end of his shift he compares notes with the incoming deputy before going off duty and making his report to the manager. In testing for gas the " deputy " uses a flame safety lamp. He calculates the amount of firedamp from the height of the flame.

New Training Methods

There are many other jobs at a colliery : shaftsmen, boilermen, storemen, lampmen, pumpmen, safety officers, training officers, dust suppression officers. Then in the workshops above ground fitters are kept busy in repairing and maintaining the great variety of mechanical devices used, while in the blacksmiths' shop the tools are sharpened and tempered, steel

arches are repaired, and work which requires oxy-acetylene welding is carried out.

The training officer at the colliery, who is responsible for the welfare of the workers during their first six months at the mine, is able to give advice to any lad about the particular job for which he is best fitted. There are many opportunities for young men to take courses of advanced study to qualify them as technicians, under managers, and surveyors.

As long ago as 1920 a " Miners' Welfare Committee " was set up by Act of Parliament, and a levy was imposed on every ton of coal to provide the money. Much of the money has been used to build pithead baths so that the miner can leave the pit dirt at the colliery and travel to and from work

National Coal Board.

WORKERS AT THE SCREENS

In the picking sheds the large coal is sorted, any foreign matter, such as stones, shale or slate being thrown out by experienced men as the coal passes over an endless chain of trays known as screens. The position of these screens is shown in the diagram of the washery on the opposite page.

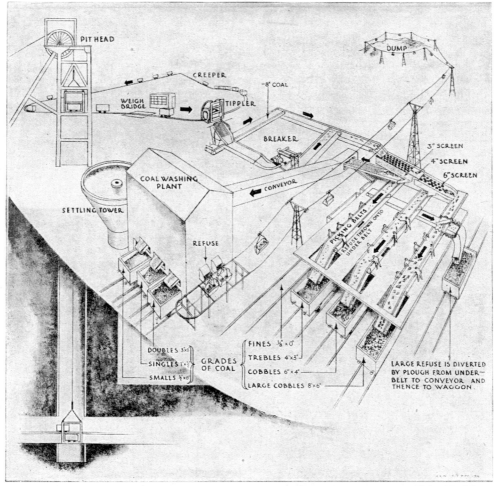

Labels in diagram:
PIT HEAD
CREEPER
WEIGH BRIDGE
TIPPLER
DUMP
-8" COAL
BREAKER
3" SCREEN
4" SCREEN
6" SCREEN
COAL WASHING PLANT
CONVEYOR
SETTLING TOWER
REFUSE
PICKING BELTS REFUSE THROWN ONTO UNDER BELT
DOUBLES 3"×1"
SINGLES 1"×½"
SMALLS ½"×0"
GRADES OF COAL
FINES ⅛"×0"
TREBLES 4"×3"
COBBLES 6"×4"
LARGE COBBLES 8"×6"
LARGE REFUSE IS DIVERTED BY PLOUGH FROM UNDER-BELT TO CONVEYOR AND THENCE TO WAGGON.

National Coal Board.

WHERE COAL IS SCREENED AND WASHED

The big brick and steel structure which is a prominent feature at many collieries is known as the washery. When the coal comes from the pit it is a mixture of large and small pieces and a certain amount of rock and dirt. This mixture has to be cleaned and sorted, and in the above diagram a general idea is given of the various stages through which the loads from the mine now pass. The smaller coal is tipped into tanks of water which are kept agitated. The stone and other impurities sink while the small coal floats off and over a miniature weir to grids, where it is dried.

clean and well-dressed. Apart from these pithead baths, over 1,000 welfare institutes and outdoor recreation schemes, as well as nearly a score of convalescent homes, have been provided.

Present coal-cutting methods result in considerable quantities of coal, amounting to about 10%, being reduced to dust or very fine, dirty coal. How to convert this into serviceable fuel has been the subject of recent experiments. Methods have now been devised whereby this dust can be efficiently cleaned and converted into top quality fuel in the form of briquettes. In due time this should lead to the addition of several million tons of coal to our yearly production of fuel.

There is no industry more important to Britain than coal-mining. Nearly 700,000 miners are employed and more are wanted to increase the output, which amounted in 1952 to over 212 million tons of deep-mined coal. A coal-miner's job may not have the glamour of certain other callings, but a great deal has been done in recent years to make the conditions under which the miner works as pleasant as possible.

In the old days a boy who went into the mining industry usually learned his job from a relative or older friend who was anxious to help him. Nowadays, with mechanisation changing the methods of working, this family party plan, excellent though it was, has almost completely disappeared.

Realising this, regulations have been introduced to ensure the proper training of all new entrants. A boy goes first of all to a Group training centre where films, charts and pictures are used to explain how coal is brought from the pit face, how the mine is ventilated, and many other details, including demonstrations on how the job is done. Part of his time is spent in school, where English, mathematics, mining science, as well as physical training, are among the subjects taken. Boys spend sixteen weeks on this part of their training, while older men take a shorter course.

After leaving the training centre the new mine-worker goes to his own colliery. His training at the coal face lasts for at least sixty days, and the new boy learns from a trained worker the best way of doing the job.

National Coal Board.

BY-PRODUCTS FROM THE COAL MINE

On an earlier page is a picture of work in progress at the new mine at Nantgarw in South Wales. In this picture we have a view of the coke ovens and by-products plant at Nantgarw. It will deal with some 1,500 tons of coal daily, yielding 1,100 tons of coke as well as 18 million cu. feet of gas for Cardiff and neighbouring towns, 4 tons of concentrated ammonia and 3,000 gallons of benzole.

ALL ABOUT IRON

AN IRONSTONE QUARRY IN NORTHAMPTONSHIRE

This photograph shows the first stage in the production of iron and steel. The big mechanical shovel removes the " overburden " to expose the ore. The lower shovel digs out the ore and loads it into wagons.

IRON and steel are inseparable from our everyday life whether we are awake or asleep. We sleep on beds with steel springs. On rising, we wash ourselves with water pumped through iron mains, and, if necessary, remove whiskers from our faces with a steel razor. At breakfast, the milk on our porridge or in our tea may have travelled over a hundred miles the previous night in a steel tank-wagon over steel railway lines and hauled by a steel locomotive. Then we go to school or to work, perhaps on a bicycle which is practically all steel except for the rubber tyres and leather saddle. The streets may be lined with iron lamp standards, there may be steel tramlines let into the roadway. Perhaps on the way we pass under a steel railway bridge. Cars and buses pass, made up almost wholly of iron and steel, except for the tyres and upholstery. Electricity and gas supplies depend upon iron and steel, and much of our food is imported from overseas in steel ships and cooked on stoves and in ovens made of iron. Iron and steel never cease to affect us intimately throughout the day until the steel bedsprings claim us again at night.

So important are iron and steel, that economists compare the material wealth of different nations by estimating how many pounds of steel are consumed in them every year for every one member of their populations.

Iron and steel are very closely related, but the words are not just different names for the same thing. There are three kinds of iron, and to understand the relationship between these and steel we may draw up a " family tree " like this—

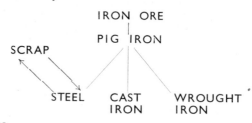

Cast iron, wrought iron and steel are finished products; that is to say, materials from which useful articles (machinery, etc.) are made. Iron ore is the raw material which occurs in Nature, while pig iron and scrap are intermediate products; that is to say, they are of no use in themselves except as a means of producing iron and steel.

In telling the story of iron and steel we shall first examine iron ore and see how pig iron is produced from this. Then we shall see how cast iron and wrought iron are produced and what they are used for. Finally, we shall see something of the more difficult and costly business of making steel, of which there are a great many varieties, and the kind of things it can do for us.

Iron Ores

Iron does occur in certain parts of the Earth as " native " iron, that is iron not in chemical combination with any other element, but the amount of such iron is so small and in such awkward places that it is not worth while to collect it and use it for any purpose. The sources of all our commercial iron are *iron ores* which for the most part are oxides of iron, *i.e.*, iron combined with oxygen and, to a lesser extent, iron carbonate, a compound of iron, oxygen and carbon.

The richest of these ores, which contains over 72 parts of iron in 100 of ore, is called *magnetite* because it is magnetic and is mined extensively in Northern Sweden at Kiruna and Gellivaare. There are other deposits in various parts of the world.

Next richest is *hematite*, which is red-coloured and is named after the Greek word for blood. It contains 70 parts of iron per 100. It is mined in Cumberland and North Lancashire and in South Wales. Enormous deposits have been worked in the American state of Minnesota at Mesabi on the western tip of Lake Superior, and further large deposits are being explored in Brazil, Venezuela, Labrador, etc. It is also mined and exported from Spain (Bilbao being the chief port) and N. Africa.

Limonite is similar to hematite but contains chemically combined water, making it a " hydrated " ore and therefore less rich. It is frequently found in marshy places as " bog iron ore " and derives its name from the Greek word for meadow. It contains 60 parts of iron per 100, and is extensively mined and smelted in Alsace-Lorraine (France) where it forms a large part of the great " Minette " ore deposit.

B.I.S.R.A.

AN EARLY BLAST FURNACE

Sussex was at one time the great iron-smelting district of England. This picture, from an engraving on an old clock-face, shows an early eighteenth-century blast furnace in the Weald of Sussex.

THE MODERN BLAST FURNACE

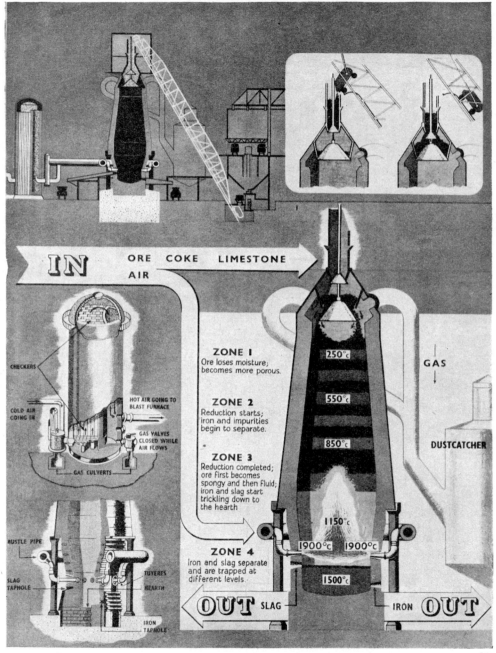

IN ORE COKE LIMESTONE
AIR

CHECKERS

COLD AIR GOING IN

HOT AIR GOING TO BLAST FURNACE

GAS VALVES CLOSED WHILE AIR FLOWS

GAS CULVERTS

BUSTLE PIPE

SLAG TAPHOLE

TUYERES

HEARTH

IRON TAPHOLE

ZONE 1
Ore loses moisture; becomes more porous.

ZONE 2
Reduction starts; iron and impurities begin to separate.

ZONE 3
Reduction completed; ore first becomes spongy and then fluid; iron and slag start trickling down to the hearth

ZONE 4
Iron and slag separate and are trapped at different levels.

250°C
550°C
850°C
1150°C
1900°C 1900°C
1500°C

GAS

DUSTCATCHER

OUT SLAG

IRON **OUT**

B.I.S.F.

This diagram illustrates the Blast Furnace of to-day, and its working is described in these pages. The circular tower is about 100 feet high and up to 27 feet in diameter across the bottom. The top of the furnace is quite cool while the hearth at the bottom is at white heat. As the smelting proceeds the molten iron collects in the hearth. The impurities which have combined with the limestone to form a molten mass, known as slag, are easily removed.

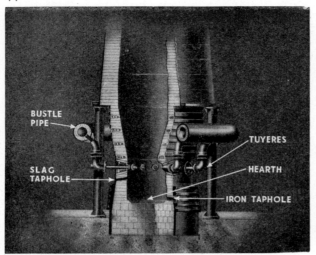

BUSTLE
PIPE

TUYERES

SLAG
TAPHOLE

HEARTH

IRON TAPHOLE

B.I.S.F.

A CLOSER VIEW OF THE HEARTH
In this diagram a closer view of the hearth of a blast furnace
is given.

Finally, there is the carbonate ore, *siderite*, named after the Greek word for iron. In its pure state it contains 48 parts of iron per 100. Large deposits of siderite of varying purity are worked in the English Midlands, the field stretching from North Lincolnshire, down through Northamptonshire and west to North Oxfordshire. It is also mined in the Cleveland Hills of North Yorkshire. It is now our most important British source of iron, and while the ores found here are not very rich they often contain lime which makes them more easily smelted.

Another common iron mineral is *pyrite* or *pyrites*, a compound of iron and sulphur. This, however, is not used as a source of iron since the sulphur makes it almost worthless for this purpose. Large quantities are mined, though, to extract the sulphur for the manufacture of sulphuric acid. It occurs as an impurity in some coals, where you may detect it as a brassy crystalline deposit on the surface.

The Discovery of Iron Smelting

How exactly men came to discover that iron ore could be smelted and would yield a metal we do not know.

Possibly, the discovery came when lumps of exceptionally rich ore were for some reason placed on a fire and the wood, burning down and forming charcoal, smelted them at least partially. Other people believe that iron ore may have found its way into an old pottery kiln, for we know that the art of " firing " earthenware is extremely old. At all events, there is definite evidence to show that iron was smelted as long ago as 1400 B.C. and possibly even before then.

The early iron smelters obtained iron by heating lumps of easily smelted rich ore in a charcoal fire either in the open or in a small brick or stone shaft, using the force of the wind to raise the temperature of the fire. By doing this the charcoal (which is carbon) combines with the oxygen of the ore to form carbon monoxide gas leaving the iron behind, which melts and trickles out at the bottom. The use of carbon in this fashion to reduce (as the chemist calls it) the ore, is the essential basis of iron smelting to this day.

Later on the bellows were invented which made the ironmaster independent of the weather and also enabled him to concentrate the wind or blast in a tube and put it exactly where he needed it. To this day it is possible to find some primitive native tribes in Uganda who still smelt iron in a tiny little shaft, using hand bellows to raise the wind.

Iron produced in this fashion was not like the iron the modern blast furnace makes because being smelted at a comparatively low temperature it did not take up much carbon from the charcoal and thus could be forged with the hand hammer and welded together almost as soon as it had been produced. In this fashion the iron which was forged into the wonderful

KEEPING THE FURNACE FILLED

The furnace shaft is kept filled with solid material up to the top and once a furnace is blown-in it goes on making iron night and day for a period of years. Here we see the " skip-track " running up to the top of the furnace. A skip loaded with iron ore and coke is on its way up.

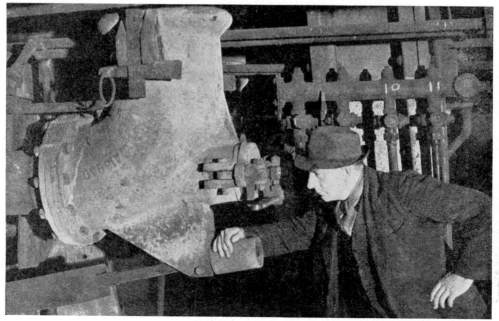

Photos : B.I.S.F.

Modern furnaces are charged mechanically and there is very little hand labour attached to them. As illustrated here, however, a watch is kept on what happens. The blast furnace " keeper " is seen taking a look inside through the blue glass let into the tuyere.

steel sword-blades made at Toledo and Damascus must have been produced, and the remarkable pillar of almost pure iron at Delhi in India. To-day, we have lost these arts, but we produce our iron on a gigantic scale in comparison.

Modern Blast Furnaces

As the years passed so the furnaces and bellows used grew larger, and iron containing carbon and, therefore, not immediately forgeable, was produced. By the fourteenth century iron made from the blast furnace was used for the most part for making cannons and similar items and was *cast* into moulds directly it was tapped from the furnace. Charcoal was still used as a fuel and from this time to the end of the seventeenth century the Weald of Sussex was the great iron-smelting and cannon-founding district of England. Siderite or *clay ironstone* was quarried locally and the forest systematically felled to make the charcoal.

In 1709 Abraham Darby of Coalbrookdale, Shropshire, first succeeded in smelting iron, using not charcoal, but *coke*, and from this point the development of our modern blast furnaces really begins. Coke is stronger and more porous than charcoal and the height of the furnaces, which formerly was only about 35 feet at the maximum could now be raised according to the strength of the bellows. With the coming of the steam engine these, of course, also became larger and more powerful.

The modern blast furnace is a circular tower about 100 feet high and up to 27 feet in diameter across the bottom. The shape of the interior you see illustrated on page 43. Air is blown in through a series of nozzles known as *tuyeres* set around the hearth, and the ore, coke and limestone enter at the top through an arrangement of two hanging cones or bells fitting into steel rings which are gas tight. One bell opens while the other is shut which ensures that as batches of solid material are put into the furnace no gas leaks out, and

Steel Company of Wales.

TAPPING BRITAIN'S LARGEST BLAST FURNACE

Pig iron derives its name from the way it always used to be cast into shallow troughs arranged about a central " runner " rather like baby pigs against the mother sow. Various other methods also are used nowadays. Here we see the 25-foot blast furnace at Margam being tapped.

RUNNING INTO THE MOULDS

Sport and General.

We have seen the molten pig iron being run from the furnace and in this photograph the molten metal is being run into shallow moulds or troughs in a gently sloping bed of sand. Here it is allowed to cool and become the solid pig iron.

all the furnace gas is led away by the big offtakes or pipes from the top.

The top of the furnace is quite cool; the hearth is at a white heat; and little discs of blue glass are set into the tuyeres to enable the man in charge to keep an eye on the interior. As the smelting proceeds so the molten iron collects in the hearth, and floating on top is the slag: that is, impurities which have combined with the limestone to form a molten mass which is easily removed. Iron and slag are run out at intervals through the slag-notch and taphole provided.

The furnace shaft is kept filled with solid material up to the top and once a furnace is " blown-in " it goes on making iron night and day for a period of years, stopping only when the lining, which is made of heat-resisting substance called firebrick, is worn out and has to be renewed. Modern furnaces are charged mechanically, there being very little hand labour attached to them.

Modern blast furnaces are nearly all provided with hot blast, after the invention of James Neilson, a gas engineer of Glasgow, in 1828. The method of providing this is illustrated on page 43. Some of the issuing furnace gas after cleaning is burned in a Cowper stove and heats up a column of firebricks to a bright red. After some hours the incoming cold air blast is diverted through this stove to pick this heat up while the furnace gas is burned in another stove, which was formerly heating the blast. Every blast furnace must have at least three stoves attached to it, two working to heat the blast and one standing spare, since the brickwork in a stove has to be repaired and cleaned every so often. The use of hot blast saves a great deal of coke.

The remainder of the furnace gas is used to raise steam to work the blowing engine or generate electricity and other jobs.

The smelting of iron ore in the blast furnace is the first stage in the production of all our items of iron and steel, and the material which issues from the blast furnace taphole is called *pig iron*.

Blast furnaces in Great Britain now produce about 9½ million tons of pig iron every year. About 7½ million tons of this are used to make *steel*, the remaining 2 million tons make *cast iron* and a very much smaller quantity of *wrought iron*.

What Happens to Pig Iron

We saw from the " family tree " on page 41 that pig iron is an intermediate product, and from it cast iron, wrought iron and steel are manufactured. Pig iron derives its name from the way it always used to be cast into shallow troughs in a gently sloping bed of sand, these moulds being arranged about a central " runner " rather like baby pigs against the mother sow.

In a number of ironworks this is still regularly done and the resulting iron

when cooled and solid is pulled out of the sand beds by chains attached to an overhead crane, the " pigs " being broken away from the " sow " by a blow from a sledge hammer. Since pig iron contains about 8 parts of impurity in every 100 it is brittle and breaks easily. This material is then known as " sand cast pig."

Many furnaces now, however, cast their iron into a casting machine which is essentially a long endless chain on which are supported a series of small iron moulds called " pallets." These move slowly along and the stream of metal fills each one as it passes. Further on they are sprayed with water, and by the time they reach the other end of the chain the iron is solid and may be tipped straight out into a waiting railway wagon. All the labour of preparing the sand beds, filling them, and then breaking up the solid iron is avoided. The " pigs " of iron (as they are still called) are also much cleaner.

In some cases, where the pig iron from

B.I.S.F.

RUNNING INTO THE CASTING MACHINE

Instead of running the molten metal into the shallow moulds as seen on the previous page, many furnaces now run the molten pig iron into a casting machine. Further up the line the pallets are being sprayed with water, and the clouds of steam can be seen in the background.

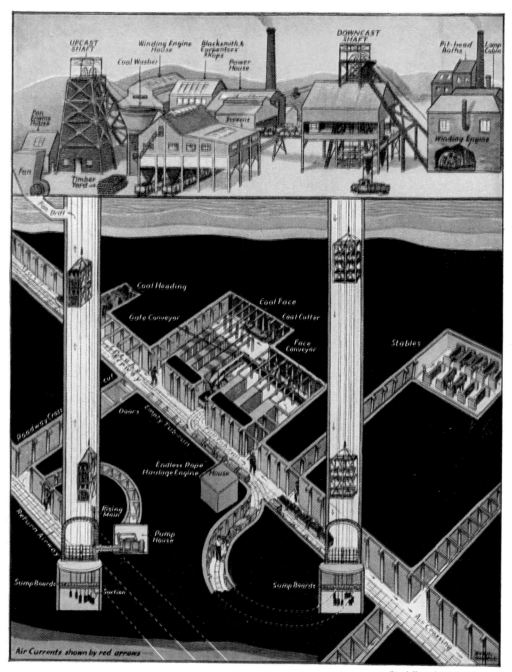

Specially painted for this work.

ABOVE AND BELOW GROUND AT A COLLIERY

On the surface a coal-mine has its power-house, screenings, railway sidings and gear for the shafts which give access to and egress from the pit. Fresh air for underground workers is drawn into the depths by way of the downcast shaft, circulated through roadways and along many passages, until it is withdrawn by means of the upcast shaft. Though tubs or trams may be drawn along the main roads by steam or electric haulage engines, ponies are still used near the coal face, their stables being always the subject of special care. Note the cages in the twin shafts.

Specially painted for this work.

A BLAST FURNACE IN ACTION

A blast furnace in an ironworks is a giant stove through which a current of air is driven to bring the ore, flux and coke with which the receptacle is charged to glowing heat. In this process the purpose of fireside bellows is carried into effect on a colossal scale. Thus, air from a reservoir passes through a heating stove and then enters the furnace from below. Gas generated in the furnace is used to operate the blowing engine ; and, as we see above, molten metal trickles like water to the furnace hearth from whence it is directed into troughs.

the blast furnace is to be used for making steel, and the steel-works is reasonably near at hand, the iron is never cast at all, but is poured into large holding vessels called "hot metal ladles," which are lined with fire-brick and mounted on railway wheels. The "hot metal," as it is then called, is hauled to the steelmaking furnaces while still molten and all the heat contained in it is thus saved. We shall see more of this when we look at steel being made.

B.I.S.F.

FILLING A LADLE

Here is molten pig iron pouring into a hot metal ladle. When full the ladle will be hauled along the railway to the steel works and the iron charged to open hearths or converters.

Making Things of Cast Iron

It is possible to cast pig iron straight into a mould as soon as it leaves the blast furnace, like the old Sussex cannon founders, in which case it becomes cast iron at once. This is still done occasionally, but it is not common, firstly because it is not often convenient to have to make up intricate sand moulds near a blast furnace and secondly because the iron from a blast furnace is not always of a suitable composition to make good castings.

Pig iron destined to become cast iron is usually re-melted in a kind of minia-ture blast furnace called a *cupola*. This is simply a shaft lined with fire-brick with a number of rectangular tuyeres let in near the bottom, a soft cold blast being provided by a fan blower. Coke and solid pig iron are fed in about three-quarters of the way up and molten iron tapped out at the bottom. As a rule no effort is made to reclaim the heat in the gases, which burn off at the top. About 4 cwts. of coke are required to melt a ton of iron. By adjusting the kinds of pig iron and

scrap charged, the chemical composi-tion of the resulting molten iron can be controlled within certain limits. The "nature" of cast iron is chiefly determined by the quantities of silicon and phosphorus it contains. Iron from the cupola is cast at about 1,200° C. temperature, a bright yellow-red heat.

Moulding and Founding

Making cast iron objects in sand moulds is called iron founding and the place where it is done an iron foundry. Iron foundries are to be found all over the country, ranging from small ones where castings only a few pounds in weight are made, to much larger ones where the castings may weigh as much as 20–30 tons and sometimes even over 100 tons.

First comes the operation of pattern making, a highly skilled job, where a replica of the object to be cast is made up in wood and varnished to protect it from the effects of damp. To allow for the iron shrinking as it cools, the pattern must always be made a little larger than the final casting.

dry. Shortly before the metal is due to be poured the two halves are put together again and holes are cut in the cope to allow the molten metal to flow in. After the metal has been poured in, the mould is left standing for a certain length of time to allow the iron to solidify sufficiently. Then the mould is "shaken out" by hammering the sides of the box or by placing the whole thing on a vibrating grating. The sand breaks up and the crude red-hot casting is revealed.

After cooling, the casting must be cleaned up or "fettled" to remove any sand sticking to it and cut off any unwanted bits such as the "gates" where the iron flowed in. If it is a complicated casting it is sometimes

Wellman Smith Owen Eng. Corp. Ltd.

A LADLE CRANE IN ACTION

We have seen the molten iron being poured into a hot metal ladle. The iron has now travelled to the steelworks and is poured into a big holding vessel called a "mixer." From here it will be taken out as required.

The pattern is then placed inside a stout iron frame called a moulding box, and special heat-resisting sand, very slightly moistened, is shovelled and rammed around the lower half of the pattern until it forms a solid mass. This makes the "drag" half of the mould. A sprinkling of fine dry parting sand is put over the surface of the moulding sand, then another moulding box is put on and more moulding sand rammed in to make up the "cope" half. The two sections of the mould are then parted, the pattern is withdrawn, and the two halves allowed to

placed in a furnace at a dull red heat to relieve any tensions which may have been caused during uneven cooling down.

There are, of course, many variations on what has been described above. For instance, the cope and drag may be moulded separately on separate patterns. Where a casting is to be hollow inside, a specially moulded piece of sand called a "core" must be inserted into the mould. For certain forms of long cylindrical castings (*e.g.*, water mains, sewer pipes and the like), the mould is spun around during pouring, making a " centri-fugal " casting. The entire subject of moulding and casting needs a whole book to describe properly. It is not, of course, confined to iron either; casting objects in copper, brass, bronze, zinc alloys, light alloys, etc., is very widely practised and has been so for a long time. A single pattern can be used to make a great many moulds, and casting iron as described above is very well suited to the making of a large number of the same item, or mass production as it is called. Foundries engaged on the mass pro-duction of small parts are often fully mechanised, the moulding being done by machines, the moulds when completed being placed on roller tables where a light push enables them to be

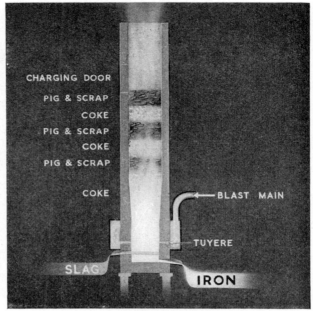

CUPOLA FURNACE

This diagram illustrates the cupola furnace used in making cast iron. The pig iron is re-melted with a certain quantity of scrap. By altering the quantity of scrap and using various sorts of iron, the founder can control the quality of the cast iron, within certain limits.

B.I.S.F.

FOR MAKING CAST IRON

Pig iron which is to be made into cast iron is usually re-melted in a kind of miniature blast furnace called a cupola. Here we see the iron being tapped from a cupola in a small iron foundry near London.

MODELS IN WOOD

The two curious objects seen here are wooden patterns for making
moulds in which metal will be cast.   To allow for the shrinking of the
metal as it cools, and for any machining of the surface, they are
slightly larger every way than the finished casting is to be.

run from one end of the shop to
the other. The sand is as far as possible
handled by conveyor belts.

This is, of course, impossible with
large mouldings which are made up on

the shop floor, while
very large ones have
to be made up in a
pit to enable the
men to get at them
properly.

Common cast iron
objects are fuse-
boxes, lamp stan-
dards, drainpipes,
house radiators, gut-
ters, gas-stoves,
kitchen ranges, etc.
In a motor car the
cast iron cylinder
block is most im-
portant. Cast iron
is not particularly
strong, or tough, but
it is cheap, and is
therefore used
where something
hard, solid and
weighty is wanted,
but where it will not be subjected to
shocks which might make it crack.
Unlike steel and wrought iron, cracked
cast iron is not easy to repair satisfactorily.

Photos: Foundry Trades Journal.

A COMPLICATED MOULD

This shows the " drag " portion of a large and complicated
moulding. Before the molten metal is poured in, the " cope " will
be placed over the top.

Cast iron is an
unspectacular
" maid of all work,"
but we should be
a lot worse off with-
out it.

**Making Wrought
Iron**

Wrought iron is
now something of a
rarity, since it has
so largely been re-
placed by steel, but
we should not ignore
it entirely, for a
certain amount is
still made and will
continue to be
made.

As we have seen,
the pig iron which
comes out of the
blast furnace is

brittle, and cannot be shaped under the blacksmith's hammer because it contains up to 8 parts in 100 of other elements or impurities, chiefly carbon and silicon which make it unweldable, and phosphorus and sulphur which make it brittle.

In 1784 Henry Cort invented a process called "puddling" which converted pig iron into an iron which could be forged, because, in puddling, the carbon, silicon, phosphorus and sulphur were removed, leaving an almost pure iron behind.

CASTING IN PROGRESS

The white-hot metal has been brought in the ladle held between side-shafts supported by a crane. It is now being poured into the mould where it will be left for a certain length of time to allow the iron to solidify.

A puddling furnace is illustrated on page 54. It is what is known as a reverberatory furnace, because the iron is heated by the flames above it, heat being reflected downwards from the roof. During puddling the iron pigs are placed on the hearth of the furnace and the heat of the flames is enough to bring them to a pasty, half molten condition. Men then push and poke the mass about with iron rods, and the oxygen in the hot air inside the furnace combines with the carbon to form carbon monoxide gas and with the other impurities to form a pasty slag. When the puddler considers that the iron is ready he gathers it up into a ball, pulls it out of the furnace and places it under a steam hammer. By the blows of the hammer the slag is

Photos: Foundry Trades Journal.

TO BE SMOOTHED BY MACHINE

In this photograph the casting is seen after shaking out. It must now be cleaned up or "fettled" and then smoothed to the exact shape.

British Iron and Steel Federation.

IN THE WORKS' LABORATORY

Here we see a corner of the chemical laboratory of a big iron and steel works. In here all the samples of steel taken during and after melting will be chemically analysed to make sure that they are within the specification.

squeezed out of the mass and the iron beaten out into a rod or strip.

Wrought iron has two very valuable properties; it can be welded at a red heat under the blacksmith's hammer, and it is remarkably resistant to rusting. It is soft but tough, and does not crack. It is nowadays used for making certain kinds of chain, each link being welded round the last one by the blacksmith; for bars which the blacksmith uses for making into horseshoes and mending farm implements;

and finally for ornamental "filigree" ironwork.

Between its invention in 1784 and the invention in 1856 of a method of producing steel on a large scale, wrought iron was of tremendous importance. The first railways, for instance, were all laid with wrought iron rails, and the first locomotives and steamships were largely built of this material.

We still speak of the "iron road" and the "iron horse" although they have both long since become steel. Steel can be made very much stronger than wrought iron, and it was the advent of steel which opened the way to the development of the railway's great competitors — the motor car and the motor lorry.

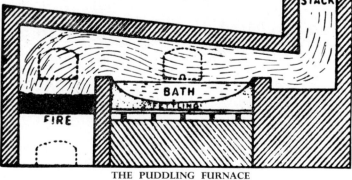

THE PUDDLING FURNACE

The process known as "puddling" was invented by Henry Cort in 1784. During the puddling the carbon, silicon and phosphorus are removed, leaving behind an almost pure iron.

THE STORY OF STEEL

Steel Company of Wales.

AT BRITAIN'S LARGEST STEELWORKS

This photograph was taken during the final stages in the erection of the Abbey Works at Margam in South Wales. On the left are seen Nos. 1 and 2 Blast Furnaces, while in the centre are the Hot Blast Stoves.

WE now come to look at steel and how it is made, and to understand this properly we must first be quite clear what steel is and how it differs from cast iron and wrought iron.

Cast iron, as we saw, is nothing much more than re-melted pig iron cast into sand moulds. It is not refined in any way and therefore all the impurities in pig iron find their way into cast iron in much the same quantities.

Wrought iron is pig iron which has been given a strong " dose " of refining in a puddling furnace until almost all traces of the four impurities have been removed. The iron, however, is never made completely molten, only pasty, and the refining has to continue until the puddler considers that it is all done. He cannot exercise any close control

over the progress of refining, or stop it any time he wishes.

Steel, however, differs from cast iron and wrought iron in two important aspects. Firstly, it is refined in the fully molten condition, and secondly we can exercise a very close control of the exact quantities of carbon, silicon, phosphorus and sulphur it finally contains. The most important of these is carbon, which is contained in steel in quantities varying from 1 in 100 to 1 in 1,000 and largely determines its hardness and toughness. In the last fifty years we have also learned how to add " alloy " elements (manganese, chromium, nickel, molybdenum, tungsten and several others) to steel and so increase its range of properties enormously, and we are still learning to make more and different steels every year. Steel is now quite the

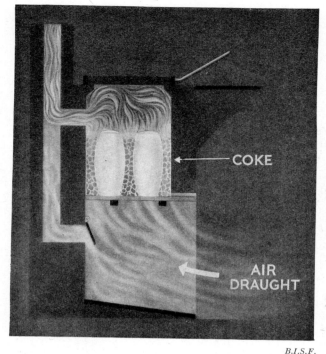

B.I.S.F.

MAKING CRUCIBLE STEEL

This diagram shows the principle of the Crucible Process.
The clay pots are immersed in a coke fire which heats them
to 1,600° C. and melts the steel.

most versatile structural material we possess.

The Crucible Process

Before the first proper " steel " was made, the nearest approach to it was " cemented iron." This was made from Swedish iron bar (a pure iron made in Sweden from magnetite ore smelted in a charcoal furnace) which was packed in air-tight boxes full of charcoal and then kept at a red heat for a period of weeks in a " cementation " furnace. In this way a certain amount of carbon could be made to re-enter the iron, which increased its hardness. The chief trouble with cemented iron, however, was the fact that the carbon did not always enter the iron evenly, and this non-uniformity often made it unreliable stuff to work with.

In 1740 a clockmaker of Doncaster named Benjamin Huntsman had grown tired of repeated failure in his clock springs of cemented iron and he determined to do better. He rightly considered that the cause of the trouble was the uneven distribution of the carbon and he decided that the only safe way to ensure an even distribution was to get the iron fully molten so that the carbon it contained could " diffuse " easily throughout the whole mass. After many unsuccessful attempts Benjamin Huntsman finally achieved this, and founded a steelworks in Sheffield which still bears his name. His process is called the " Crucible " process and the metal produced is " Crucible Steel."

Huntsman's process is essentially simple and is illustrated on this page. It is simply a clay pot (the crucible) embedded in a coke fire in which the steel is melted in much the same way as you might melt wax in an earthenware dish. The point is, though, that to get steel fully molten we have got to go to a temperature of nearly 1,600° C., a really *white* heat, and Huntsman's real problems were first to make a clay pot to withstand this and then to design a fire which would heat the pot evenly from top to bottom. (It should be noted that cast iron is fully molten at only 1,200° C. because its impurities lower its melting point. When these are removed the melting point is much higher.)

The great centre of cutlery manufacture—Sheffield—was built up on the crucible process of steelmaking. Three things all helped in this—deposits of a clay called " ganister " to make the pots, deposits of coal for the fires, and water power from the River Don to work the hammers and forge the knives.

Although we now have much less crude methods of making steel, the crucible process is still very much alive, though not, of course, anything like as extensively as it was. It is well suited for making small quantities of high-quality steel, but is not a "tonnage" process. Since the pot and its load of molten steel have to be manhandled out of the furnace and poured by hand, each batch of steel made cannot be more than about 80 pounds in weight at the maximum.

Making steel by the ton and more came just over a hundred years later, in 1856.

Invention of the Bessemer Process

Modern steelmaking may be said to have begun in the year 1856, when Sir Henry Bessemer showed the world how to make steel from pig iron in one stage and in large quantities.

Bessemer was the son of a type-founder and was a man of proved inventive ability even before he took out the patent which made his name famous. One day he noticed that some pieces of pig iron which had been left inside a special furnace of his own design were in fact altered to pure, and therefore malleable, iron; the carbon and silicon seemed to have been "burned-out" by the furnace blast. This gave him the idea that perhaps he could do the same thing in a more controlled fashion. His first test was performed on a batch of Swedish pig iron; he melted this in a Huntsman crucible and then inserted a tube and blew air through it. The idea succeeded; and to his surprise the air did not cool the molten pig iron, as one might have expected; it actually warmed it up, due to the heat of the chemical reaction between the oxygen and the "burned-out" carbon and silicon. Bessemer immediately realised the importance of this, namely, that provided he could blow fast enough he ought to be able to make malleable iron from molten pig iron without using any other fuel. Accordingly he arranged for a much larger vessel to be filled with molten Swedish pig iron and blew air through a series of holes in the bottom. Sure enough, when the flame of the burning carbon had died down the impurities had been removed and the metal was hot enough to be run out into moulds. The new process was born.

However, Bessemer's troubles were not altogether over. For one thing the new process would not remove sulphur and phosphorus from the metal, and a large-scale experiment in South Wales proved a costly failure before this was

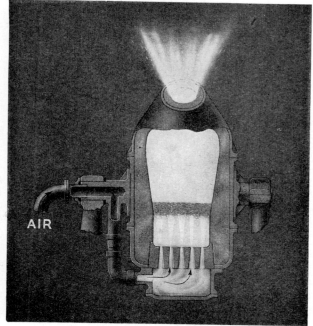

B.I.S.F.

A BESSEMER CONVERTER

Here we see the principle on which the Bessemer converter works. The blast enters the wind box through a hollow trunnion, so the blast may be turned on with the converter in any position.

POURING IN THE METAL

Molten pig iron is here being poured into a Bessemer converter. The converter lies horizontally while this is being done and the metal does not run down the tuyeres. By the Bessemer method, steel is made from pig iron in one stage.

realised. Only Swedish pig iron or pig iron made from Cumberland iron ore could be used. Then again the nozzles or "tuyeres" of the converter vessel did not last long and little commercial progress was made until a Swede named Goränsson advised raising the blast pressure and making narrower tuyeres. The worst trouble was, however, that "blown" metal which had had the carbon taken out of it in this way was full

Photos: British Iron & Steel Federation.

THE CARBON FLAME FROM THE CONVERTER

In this photograph the Bessemer converter has been swung rapidly to the upright position after filling. Reaction starts immediately and the "blower" judges how far it has gone from the appearance of the converter flame—that is, from the burning carbon monoxide issuing from the converter mouth as seen here.

of oxygen, and when it cooled down in the mould large volumes of gas were evolved. The metal, in fact, behaved very like ginger beer on a hot day—it climbed out of the mould just like " gassy " liquid climbing out of the bottle, leaving only about half of itself behind.

This problem was solved by David Mushet. He showed that if manganese was added to the iron after blowing, it would neutralise the effect of the oxygen and the metal could then be cast quite comfortably. Manganese is added to Bessemer metal in the form of ferro-manganese and spiege-leisen, both of which contain carbon, so that the final carbon content of the metal can be accurately adjusted at the time the addition is made, and thus the pure malleable iron becomes what we can properly call *steel*.

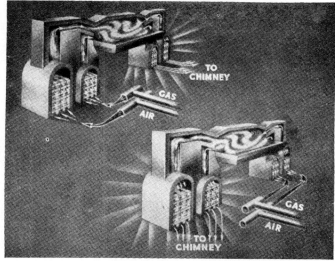

B.I.S.F.

THE OPEN HEARTH FURNACE

This drawing shows the general principles of the Open Hearth furnace. One of its advantages over the Bessemer converter is that it can melt and refine scrap. It is also a slower process and can therefore be more precisely controlled.

The Modern Bessemer Process

Early in his experiments Bessemer realised the advantage of conducting the " blow " in a vessel mounted upon pivots called " trunnions," so that it could be filled or emptied without having to keep the blast on to prevent the steel running down the tuyeres. He designed a pear-shaped converter, and the shape of this vessel has not greatly altered to this day. Modern converters usually hold about 25 tons of molten pig iron and complete the conversion of this to steel in about fifteen minutes. The hot metal which has come from the blast furnace in a hot metal ladle is poured in while the converter is lying horizontal and then the blast is turned on and the converter

swung rapidly to the upright position. Reaction starts immediately and the " blower " judges how far it has gone from the appearance of the converter flame—that is, from the burning carbon monoxide issuing from the converter mouth.

In the early stages the flame is weak but accompanied by a large number of bright sparks. This shows that the silicon is being oxidised. After about five minutes these die away and the flame brightens up and becomes longer. The carbon is now coming out, and this continues for about ten minutes. Small drops of white-hot slag fly out, making a brilliant display. Towards the end of the reaction the flame shortens, and the blower, watching it carefully, turns down the wind and brings the converter down to the horizontal position. First the slag is poured off and then the ferro-manganese and spiegeleisen are shovelled in. After a few moments to allow this to be absorbed the big steel ladle is brought underneath and the contents of the converter are poured into it.

The entire operation of turning 25 tons of iron into steel will have taken less than twenty minutes and the temperature of the metal will have been raised during conversion from about 1,300° C. to 1,600° C. The inside of the converter will be white hot, and in order to lose none of this valuable heat the converter is immediately re-filled and another blow starts. The converter will work day and night like this until it has to stop to have a fresh bottom fitted, after about fifty blows, or to be entirely re-lined, after about 200 blows. Thus Bessemer steelworks have some three to five converters installed, so that when any one of them has to be re-bottomed or re-lined the others can maintain production.

Getting Rid of Phosphorus

Bessemer's original process used a converter lined with silica, technically known as an acid lining, and he could not remove sulphur and phosphorus from pig iron. This rather serious drawback was overcome in 1875 by Sydney Gilchrist Thomas, who was a Magistrates' Clerk by profession and who studied chemistry as a hobby. He suggested using a basic lining of a material called dolomite and then adding lime to make a basic slag. Unlike the silica lining, the dolomite lining could withstand the chemical action of the basic slag. With his cousin Gilchrist, who operated a steel-works at Blaenavon in South Wales, this process was perfected and the Basic Bessemer or Thomas process is now extremely important, particularly in France, Belgium and Germany, where the iron ores nearly all contain a considerable amount of phosphorus. Not only does the process remove this phosphorus but the basic slag which carries the phosphorus away is a

B.I.S.F.

IN FRONT OF A TILTING OPEN HEARTH FURNACE

This picture of men at work in a large steelworks shows the front of a big tilting Open Hearth furnace which is being " fettled " after tapping. The regenerators which heat the air and gas are underneath the platform on which the men are working.

valuable fertiliser and a source of considerable profit to the steel-maker.

In Great Britain, however, there are now only three large converter steelworks, which between them produce about 1 million tons of steel every year. Converters have been replaced by Open Hearth Furnaces.

The Open Hearth Furnace

The invention of the Open Hearth Furnace in 1864 followed very quickly after the Bessemer converter, for open hearth steel-making has two advantages over the converter. The first is that it can melt and refine *scrap*, which the converter cannot, and the second is that being a slower process the analysis and temperature of the steel being made can be much more precisely controlled.

By 1860 the quantity of scrap becoming available was considerable. The Industrial Revolution and the coming of the Railway called for more and more ironwork and machinery, but no machine lasted for ever, and in time it had to be replaced by a new and more efficient one—and since there was no ready way of making use of the old iron, the scrap piles grew and scrap was very cheap. In addition, the very act of making and using steel creates scrap. Just as when a tailor has com-

Wellman Smith Owen Eng. Corp. Ltd.

UNDERHUNG JIB CRANE WITH LIFTING MAGNETS

Cranes with electro-magnets are used to lift the scrap out of railway wagons and then put it into the boxes used for charging the Open Hearth furnaces. The operator on the travelling platform controls the crane.

pleted cutting out a suit he is left with all sorts of odds and ends of cloth, so during casting, rolling, forging and building things of steel, odds and ends are left behind which all go to swell the volume of scrap.

Two men invented the open hearth furnace, though they worked independently—Sir William Siemens in Britain and Martin in France—and the invention is generally known as the Siemens-Martin open-hearth furnace. Of the 15 million tons of steel produced every year in Great Britain, over 13 million tons are now made in the open

B.I.S.F.

THE CHARGING MACHINE AT WORK

In modern steel works all the work of charging the Open Hearth furnace with pig iron and scrap is done mechanically. Here we see the charging machine as it swings round to face the open hearth. The door is raised and the box of scrap is pushed in and emptied.

hearth. Some 7 million tons of scrap are melted.

The essential features of the open hearth furnace may be best understood by going back and looking at the old puddling process. Like the puddling furnace, the open hearth is a reverberatory furnace. The charge is heated from the flames above it, the heat being reflected downwards by the roof. The temperature in the open hearth, however, has got to be some 400° C. to 500° C. higher than that used in puddling, since the steel is actually melted, not merely reduced to a pasty state. This is achieved by removing the coal fire from the furnace altogether and turning it into a gas producer, a blast of air and a jet of steam being blown up through a bed of glowing coal to make producer gas. This gas and the air to burn it are then conducted to the furnace through flues, but before they enter the hearth

both are preheated to some 800° C. to 900° C. by being passed through a checkerwork of red-hot firebricks very similar to the checkerwork in a Cowper Stove which heats the blast furnace wind. This hot air and hot gas then burn in the open hearth and make a flame hot enough to melt steel scrap.

The burnt gas leaving the open hearth is at a temperature of about 1,600° C. and it passes at once through a duplicate set of firebrick checkerwork, which it heats to about 900° C. Every fifteen to twenty minutes the furnace is reversed, i.e., the air and gas change direction, just as the two Cowper Stoves on a blast furnace exchange their functions every few hours. This method of gas and air preheating is called Regeneration and the sets of firebrick checkerwork are known as Regenerators.

Many open hearth furnaces are now

STEEL IN THE MAKING

At the stage shown in this photograph the scrap is now partly melted and the hot metal goes into the open hearth. The charging machine holds a special chute or "launder," and an overhead crane carries the ladle of metal and tilts it.

Photos: British Iron & Steel Federation.

Nothing is left to chance in the modern steelworks and at every stage tests are made. Here we see the temperature of the steel being measured by an immersion pyrometer to check the progress of refining. During the "boil" small samples of the steel are taken and sent to the laboratory for analysis.

ANOTHER VIEW OF THE OPEN HEARTH FURNACE

In this photograph the view from the back of the Open Hearth furnace is seen during " tapping."
On the right-hand side the molten steel can be seen as it pours over into the big steel ladle held
ready for it by the overhead crane.

fired with oil squirted into the furnace in a fine spray. Only the air need then be preheated.

The hearth of the open hearth furnace is a rectangular shallow " bath " with gently sloping sides, 10 feet to 15 feet across, 30 feet to 50 feet long and 2 feet to 3 feet in depth. It is lined with heat-resisting material similar to that used in the converter, silica in the acid furnace, and dolomite in the basic furnace. The roof is usually made of silica. The charge is inserted into the hearth through lifting doors in the front wall, and when fully molten and refined to exactly the chemical analysis desired, the steel is run out at the back, either through a taphole set in the bottom of the hearth, or, if the furnace is a large one, the hearth portion is mounted on rockers and rollers, and can be tilted so that the molten steel

flows out down a chute or launder. This is called " tapping."

Making Steel in the Open Hearth

In modern steelworks all the work of charging the open hearth furnace with pig iron and scrap is done mechanically. Scrap and solid pig are put into long rectangular boxes made of steel, which are then picked up one by one by a charging machine, pushed into the furnace on the end of a long rod and turned upside down. The contents fall out and the box is then withdrawn for a fresh load. Some furnaces melt down the charge all from cold, in which case they use about seven parts of scrap to three of pig iron, while the larger furnaces, and especially those made to tilt, will use molten pig iron. Sometimes equal parts of hot metal and scrap will be used, or as much as three-

The Wellman Smith Owen Engineering Corpn. Ltd.

CASTING STEEL INTO INGOTS

Here we give a scene in a big steelworks after the molten steel has been brought from the furnace in one of the big ladles, seen above, to the casting bay. The ladle is suspended from the overhead crane while the ingot moulds are filled with molten metal. The moulds are placed on stout steel " bogies " and these are then taken at once to the stripping bay. It is during this operation of teeming the molten steel into the moulds that the final and most important sample of the steel is taken for analysis.

The Wellman Smith Owen Engineering Corpn. Ltd.

AN INGOT CHARGING MACHINE AT WORK

The ingots of steel have been stripped—that is, removed from the moulds—as soon as they are sufficiently solid.   They are now picked up by the ingot charging machine and placed in a furnace called a soaking pit, the purpose of "soaking" being to bring the whole ingot to an even temperature all the way through.   At this bright-red heat the ingot is ready to proceed on its way to the first stage of hot rolling in the cogging mill.

quarters of the charge may be molten pig. The hot metal will, of course, have been hauled from the blast furnace in a hot metal ladle, and is poured into the open hearth by the overhead crane.

To make a batch of steel in the open hearth, anything from 40 tons to 300 tons according to the size of the furnace, takes from ten hours to twelve hours. For the first five hours or so the charge is loaded into the hearth and in another three hours it should be fully molten. Most of the impurities except carbon have by then combined with limestone or sand put in with the charge to form a fluid slag on top of the steel. The rest of the time is devoted to getting the carbon out of the steel to exactly the desired final content. To do this the men shovel in some pure iron ore, usually hematite or magnetite. The oxygen in the ore then combines with the carbon in the steel and forces it out as carbon monoxide gas. Since this forms bubbles in the metal the steelmaker calls it the " boil." The furnace is burning gas or oil the whole time. This method of refining steel is the " upside-down " version of making pig iron. In the latter we used carbon to take the oxygen out of the ore in a rather rough and ready fashion, now we use

Edgar Allen & Co. Ltd.

A MODERN ELECTRIC ARC FURNACE

Another type of furnace which is used for the high quality alloy steels, such as stainless, or nickel-bearing, or silicon steels, is the electric arc furnace. This photograph is of a 4-ton electric arc furnace at a Sheffield works.

the ore to take the carbon from the steel, but of course in a very precisely controlled operation.

During the " boil " small samples of the steel are taken out and sent to the chemical laboratory for analysis, and every so often the temperature of the steel will be measured with an " immersion pyrometer." In the old days the steelmaker merely relied on his judgment and the appearance of the steel to get the analysis and temperature right; now he has the aid of ingenious instruments to make absolutely sure. Sometimes, in order to speed up the refining of the steel, oxygen gas or compressed air is blown into the metal through steel tubes. This can often save quite a lot of time. When the carbon has been brought down to its final content the excess oxygen which has got into the steel is neutralised with additions of manganese and silicon, the taphole is opened or the hearth is tilted and the great mass of white-hot steel with slag on the top pours over into the ladle held ready for it. As soon as this is done the men inspect the inside of the furnace, patch up any holes in the lining with fresh silica or dolomite and spread a thin layer of fresh lining material all over the inside of the hearth (" fettling " as it is called), and within an hour the next charge is going in.

As long as the furnace is in a fit state the work of making steel goes on continuously day and night, the men working eight hour stretches or shifts. Every four months or so the furnace is cooled down and the roof and other worn-out brickwork is repaired.

The Electric Arc Furnace

Another furnace for making steel which is used for the high-quality alloy steels such as stainless (i.e., rust-proof) steel containing chromium, nickel-bearing armour-plate steels and silicon steels used for making the interiors of dynamos, transformers and electric motors, is the electric arc furnace.

When two pieces of graphite (a form of carbon) are connected to a powerful source of electric current and momentarily touched together and drawn apart a kind of " bridge " is formed between them. This is called an arc and is intensely hot, the temperature reaching over 3,000° C. It is also very bright indeed and is sometimes used as a source of light. Arcs may also be struck between graphite and steel and between two pieces of steel.

Sir William Siemens was the first to show that the electric arc could be used to melt steel.

The modern electric arc furnace is circular in shape with a hearth and a roof not dissimilar to the open hearth. The three graphite electrodes protrude down into the hearth through holes in the roof. The furnace is charged with steel scrap and then the electrodes are lowered until they touch the scrap and the arcs are struck. The heat melts the scrap which is then refined in very much the same way as steel in the open hearth, oxygen often being used.

Electric arc furnaces vary in size from about 3 tons to 30 tons capacity. They are mounted on rockers and are tapped by tilting. The refining in the electric furnace can be even more closely controlled than in the open hearth, and the absence of the flames means that alloying elements such as chromium, silicon, molybdenum, etc., may be added to the steel without the loss which occurs in the open hearth.

The High-frequency Induction Furnace

Another application of electricity to steelmaking is the modern version of the crucible process—the high-frequency induction furnace. This is the most recently invented steel-making furnace, being first put into commercial operation in 1922.

We have seen how steel can be made by melting it in a pot immersed in a hot coke fire, the heat passing through the walls of the pot from the fire to the steel. If, however, the pot is placed inside a copper coil which carries a high-frequency alternating current, that is a current flowing backwards and forwards between 500 and 2,000 times every second, then heat sufficient to melt the steel will be generated actually in the metal itself. (The current for electric light " alternates " at fifty times a second.) The pot need now act only as a container and will not wear out anything like so quickly. The outside of the pot and

FOR HIGH QUALITY ALLOY STEELS

Edgar Allen & Co. Ltd.

Sir William Siemens was the first to show that the electric arc could be used to melt steel. These electric arc furnaces vary in size from about 3 to 30-tons capacity, and the refining in this type of furnace can be even more closely controlled than in the open hearth. In this photograph oxygen is being blown into the steel in the electric arc furnace to remove the carbon. Great heat is developed in this process.

5—2

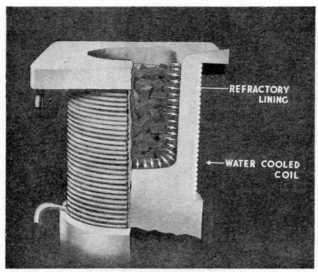

HIGH-FREQUENCY INDUCTION FURNACE

Another application of electricity to steel-making is the high-frequency induction furnace which is the modern version of the crucible process. As seen here, the pot is placed inside a copper coil which carries the high-frequency alternating current.

the copper coil may be cooled with water to give even longer life.

When this process was first publicly demonstrated in Great Britain the outside of the furnace used had a wooden casing. You can imagine the spectators' amazement when they saw white-hot steel emerging from an unscathed wooden box!

This is the process which has very largely replaced the old-style crucible furnace for the manufacture of very high quality steels for the best cutlery and tools, for instance. Since the entire pot and coil may be mounted together and mechanically tilted, all the

Photos: B.I.S.F

TAPPING A HIGH-FREQUENCY ELECTRIC INDUCTION FURNACE

This photograph shows a high-frequency electric induction furnace being tapped. The old-style crucible furnace has been largely replaced by this modern furnace for the manufacture of very high-quality steels such as those required for the best cutlery and tools, for instance. All the old man-handling has been done away with and the entire process is much cleaner and less arduous than the older method.

old man-handling has been done away with and batches of several hundredweights, or even tons, of steel may be made. The entire process is much cleaner and less arduous.

It is the high-frequency induction furnace which makes it possible to manufacture the remarkable alloy steels used in the gas turbine, the "jet" engine which drives aircraft at 600 miles an hour. These steels work at a red-heat and carry enormous loads without distorting even by a fraction of an inch!

Arc Furnaces and High-frequency Furnaces together produce about 600,000 tons of steel every year in Britain.

TESTING THE TOUGHNESS

To determine the toughness of steel an Izod testing machine is used. The big weight swings down and snaps the test piece in half. From the distance the weight continues to swing, the energy absorbed by the test-piece in breaking can be calculated.

Photos: B.I.S.F.

ALL MADE OF STEEL

We still speak of the "iron road" and the "iron horse" when speaking of our railways and locomotives although they have both been made of steel for long years past. Steel can be made very much stronger than iron, and the rails seen in this photograph are made of cast manganese steel which withstands tremendous wear. The scene is the railway crossing at Newcastle Station.

OUT OF THE FIERY FURNACE

B.I.S.F.

AT WORK IN THE ROLLING MILL

Steel billets are rolled into two general varieties of finished products: Sections and Rounds.
"Sections" are such things as beams, joists and railway lines. Here we have a finished rail
emerging from the last "pass" in a section mill. In front of the rolls are the guides to run the
steel between the grooves.

WE have now seen how steel is made, and we may now examine how this white-hot mass of molten metal is turned into something useful.

Steel, as we have said, is our most versatile structural material, and we can do a great many things with it. To understand this we may conveniently draw up another "family tree."

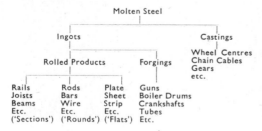

When it leaves the furnace the molten steel pours into a big steel bucket lined with firebricks and called a ladle. This ladle has in the bottom a firebrick nozzle about 1 inch or so in diameter, which is plugged inside the ladle by means of a long steel rod surrounded with firebrick reaching up to the top. By means of a lever arrangement this plug or "stopper-rod" can be raised or lowered as required to allow the metal to flow out when wanted.

If the steel is to make castings the ladle is carried into a position over sand moulds which are filled with steel in much the same way that moulds are filled with iron in the iron foundry to make iron castings. The difference is that whereas iron is always poured out quickly over the spout of the ladle, steel is "teemed," as the foundryman calls it, through the nozzle in the bottom, and since the temperature of steel is 300° C. to 400° C. higher than that of iron, so much greater care has to be taken in the making of the mould and in the filling of it to enable it to withstand this tremendous heat without cracking up or wearing away and thus spoiling the casting. Among the most important of steel castings are the centres of railway locomotive wheels, spoked wheels which have to withstand constant shocks and strains which would very soon smash cast iron. Another is ships' anchor cables, huge links being cast around each other very ingeniously to make up the length. In heavy engineering there are numerous examples of steel castings, particularly in steels like the enormously tough and wear-resistant *Manganese Steel*, which cannot be dealt with any other way. The huge jaws of rock crushers or the teeth of mechanical diggers are typical manganese steel castings.

The blades of the gas turbine, which are made of very high quality alloy steels melted in the high-frequency induction furnace, are formed by casting. Since they have to be so accurately shaped they are produced by a technique known as precision casting. This uses the centuries-old " Lost-Wax " method of moulding which was employed by the famous Italian silversmith Benvenuto Cellini in the creation of his masterpieces.

So it is that the combination of

Hadfields Ltd.

MAKING A STEEL CASTING

When steel is to be used in making castings the ladle is carried into a position over sand moulds in much the same way as iron in the foundry. Iron is always poured out quickly, however, while steel is "teemed" through the nozzle in the bottom of the ladle.

modern science and age-old craftsmanship has contributed to Man's conquest of space and time.

Making Steel Ingots

Casting is one way of treating molten steel and makes the finished product in one stage. But only 3 tons out of every 100 tons of steel are so treated; the other 97 tons are first made into ingots and then the solid ingots are mechanically worked into final shape by two general methods, rolling and forging. Not only can steel be shaped in this way, but the act of working red-hot or even cold steel improves its mechanical strength and toughness to a remarkable degree.

Ingots of steel are made by " teeming " the contents of the ladle into tall, narrow cast-iron moulds usually rectangular in section, sometimes octagonal. The size of each ingot depends on what it is destined to become finally. Steel to be made into wire or thin strip may be cast into small ingots of only about 1 ton in weight; sheets, plates, sections, rails, etc., into ingots of 4 tons to 10 tons; while the really big jobs such as high-pressure boiler drums or naval guns, which are forged, are made from ingots of perhaps 100 tons and more.

Ingots are " stripped," that is, removed from the mould, as soon as they are sufficiently solid, which time varies with size. Sometimes they are further treated in a separate works altogether, in which case they are allowed to go quite cold and are loaded on a railway wagon. More often, however, they are rolled in the same works, and they are immediately put into a furnace called a soaking pit. The ingots in a soaking pit do not get heated up to any great extent; the purpose of " soaking " them is to bring the whole ingot to a uniform temperature. When taken out of the ingot mould the centre of the ingot is still molten; the outside surfaces will be solid and at a red heat, probably about 1,100° C. to 1,200° C. temperature. When the ingot is withdrawn from the soaking pit it should be at an even temperature of 1,200° C. to 1,300° C. all the way through, and at this bright-red heat it proceeds on the first stage of hot rolling.

Rolling Mills

A rolling mill is in effect nothing more than a huge steel mangle, and if you take a piece of Plasticine and put it through your Mother's mangle (when she's not looking, of course!) you will get a fairly good idea of what a rolling mill does to red-hot steel. Out of every 10 tons of steel made, 9½ tons are rolled.

The first stage in rolling is called " cogging-down " and is done in a very large, stout and robust mill called a cogging mill. This reduces the size of the ingot to more manageable proportions, but of course lengthens it enormously. The long " bloom " of red-hot steel, as it is called, is passed back and forth through the mill until it is down to roughly the correct size, the rolls of the mill coming closer together for each " pass." The weight of the steel is far too much for man-handling, of course, so the cogging mill is equipped with long " tables " of electrically-driven rollers on either side, together with hydraulic rams and lifters which run the steel back and forth, turn it on its side, straighten it—all by the flick of a switch in the control cabin.

The noise is tremendous, and the shock when the rolls " bite " into the great mass of steel makes the whole building tremble. Sprays of water play on the rolls constantly to keep them cool. Huge electric motors drive the mill rolls, first one way and then the other.

Three Kinds of Rolled Steel

When the ingot has been cogged down, the " bloom " is cut into lengths of about 6 feet to 8 feet, which are called " billets " or " slabs " according to their shape. These are generally put into another furnace to get rather hotter before being rolled any more, since the steel may have cooled quite considerably during cogging down. If steel is rolled too cold it is not plastic enough and may crack.

Steel billets are rolled into two general varieties of finished products— " Sections " and " Rounds "—and slabs are rolled into " Flats." " Sections "

WHEN THE INGOTS ARE STRIPPED

B.I.S.F.

Ingots of steel are made by " teeming " the contents of the ladle into tall, narrow cast iron moulds, the size depending on their ultimate purpose. This picture shows the ingots as they are being stripped. The moulds are lifted off the red-hot ingots as they rest on the ingot bogies.

are such things as beams and joists for bridges, steel-framed buildings, ships' frames, etc., and of course railway lines.

" Rounds " are long steel rods such as those used for reinforcing concrete, other rounds are used for making bolts and nuts, and the smaller sizes may be later " drawn " through dies to become very small indeed and made up into steel hawsers. Most important of all, however, are " Flats," especially steel plates for locomotives, wagons, ships, etc., and sheets which are consumed in enormous quantities in the manufacture of motor cars and for making the tin cans which preserve food. " Tinplate " is thin steel sheet with a very thin layer of tin laid over the surface on either side.

Rolling mills which roll billets into sections and rounds have rolls with matching grooves cut into them in such a way that the steel passes through a series of cleverly shaped holes, finally emerging in the form that is wanted. The rolls do not move any closer together during the progress of rolling, the steel is guided into successively smaller grooves to reduce its size and bring it to shape.

In rolling plate and sheet, however, smooth rolls must be used. The steel is passed back and forth through the rolls of the same mill which are brought closer and closer together. To avoid constant reversing, the " three-high " mill with three rolls on top of each other may be used, the steel first going between the middle and lower rolls and returning between the middle and upper ones. Thus the mill runs constantly in one direction but the steel is reduced in thickness at each " pass."

IN THE MILLS AT MARGAM

Much of the steel in use to-day is in the form of plate and sheet, and in this picture we have a view of the giant cogging mill at Margam Abbey Works. This rolls the ingots to slabs. After shearing and trimming the slabs are re-heated and rolled in the continuous mills which are seen on the opposite page.

Photos: Steel Company of Wales.

Red-hot ingots are passed to and fro through heavy rollers which roll the ingot into a slab of anything up to 60 inches wide and $8\frac{1}{2}$ inches thick. Here the steel is seen passing through electrically operated slab shears, after which a separate edger mill will give the slab its correct width.

TOWARDS THE FINAL STAGES

After passing through a reheating furnace a slab is carried on rollers to the Hot Strip Mill. First it passes through a scale-breaker which removes the scale formed in the reheating furnace. It then passes through the four stands of the " roughing " mill. Here the slab is seen entering the first roughing stand.

Photos: Steel Company of Wales.

Here is the last stage in rolling steel strip in the 80-inch Continuous Strip Mill. This shows the Finishing Stands and run-out table. When it emerges from the last Finishing Stand the strip, travelling at a speed of up to 2,000 feet per minute, is carried down to one of the coilers,

The Continuous Mill

For the manufacture of the enormous quantities of steel sheet now demanded by the motor industry the continuous mill is used. Instead of passing the steel back and forth through a single stand of rolls, as many as five stands are placed immediately one behind the other and the steel goes straight from one to the next. The speed of rolling is very fast, the steel when it emerges from the last stand of rolls being shot out at something like thirty miles per hour. To see a long flat " snake " of red-hot steel tearing up the shop at this speed, to be caught and coiled up safely in a mechanical coiler, is a wonderful experience!

Not only is this method of rolling steel extremely fast but it makes the sheet tough and strong. In practically one single cold pressing operation in the motor-car factory the sheet is converted from a flat piece of steel into a motor-car body. Only steel which has been made to a very closely-controlled analysis and rolled in this fashion can stand treatment like this without cracking or winkling.

Small rounds and sections may also be rolled in continuous mills, in this case with grooved rolls. The steel emerging from the last set of rolls cannot be coiled, but is cut to lengths by an extremely ingenious machine called a " flying shear," which actually chops the steel while it is moving. Heavier sections such as rails are cut to length by a hot saw, a circular saw which bites through the red-hot steel in a matter of a few seconds.

In modern rolling mills, of course, all the handling of the steel to and from the mill is done mechanically on the long roller tables. Brute strength is not necessary, but a high degree of skill and speed in adjusting the mill setting and working the control levers most definitely is required.

Forging Red-hot Steel

If the steel is to be worked up into a shape impossible to make with rolls, and if it is needed in a much stronger condition than is possible when it is cast, then the ingot, or the billet in the case of a smaller item, is forged.

Forging is what the blacksmith does to red-hot wrought iron on his anvil; for steel we now use the hydraulic press and the steam hammer. In the first case we give the steel a mighty squeeze, in the latter we give it a series of hard blows. Another method of forging, which is used for making large tubes, is extrusion, where the plastic steel is made to flow through a hole, with the centre portion blocked out, and so take up the shape of a tube in a single pressing operation. Of course enormous pressures and very strong apparatus are needed for this. A 2,000-ton forging press is illustrated on page 78. The ingot rests on the " anvil " down below, and the ram, on which " tools " of various shapes and sizes may be bolted, slides up and down the four vertical pillars, being raised and lowered by tremendous hydraulic pressure. As forging proceeds, the ingot is turned a little bit further round at each squeeze and slowly takes up the shape required. In the case of a large forging of this kind it will have to be re-heated a number of times during forging. Special furnaces with removable front doors are used for this purpose, since the front of the furnace has to be torn down and re-bricked up every time such a large ingot is taken in and out.

The steam hammer is used for smaller items, and the manipulation of the billet is usually done by hand. The hammer is also used for drop forging, where both the hammer and the anvil carry a die—that is, a shallow mould of very tough steel—the die being in the shape of the final forging. The red-hot billet is laid over the die on the anvil and repeated blows from the hammer cause the steel to flow into the dies and take up the final shape desired. Motor-car crankshafts are

B.I.S.F.

THE MEN AT THE CONTROLS

We have seen the giant machines at work and here are the men who control them. Those seen in
this photograph are at the controls of a " cogging " mill. Their eyes never leave the mill and they
work the control levers by touch and at a tremendous speed.

produced in very large numbers by drop
forging. Hammer forging is, of course, a
noisy business as you can imagine, but is
a good deal faster than press forging.

Making Steel Tubes

Steel tubes may be made in various
ways according to their size. Medium-
sized tubes are extruded in one operation in the way already described.
Large tubes (apart from the very large
one being forged on page 78) are made
in what is known as a Pilger Mill by a
process which is a kind of cross between
forging and extrusion. A round billet
which has first been " burst "—that is,
spun around and squeezed to make a
hole appear along its central axis—is
pushed into a mill, the rolls of which are
eccentrically shaped and which revolve
in the opposite direction to the movement of the billet. These rolls both
squeeze and reject the billet, which is
then turned through a right angle and
pushed into the rolls again. This

constant squeezing, rejection, turning
and squeezing again slowly forces the
steel into the shape of a tube.

Small-sized tubes are made from
rolled steel strip in a continuous operation. The strip is caught up by a
machine, curled round until the two
edges are almost touching, the edges
are given a rapid heating and then
squeezed together to make a joint.
Provided the steel contains no more
than a very small amount of carbon
(*i.e.*, it is a very " soft " steel), the
edges will fuse together satisfactorily.
Automatic devices cut the tube to
length as it emerges continuously
from the outgoing end. " Pluto," the
famous pipe-line which carried petrol
underneath the sea during World War
II., was made in this way.

Heat Treatment of Steel

Steel, and especially alloy steel, is
capable of varying its properties according to the way in which it is heated and

cooled. By a combination of the right quantities of carbon and alloying elements with the right " heat-treatment " we can make a steel suitable for almost every conceivable job.

Ordinary " carbon " steels, such as are used for making rails and joists and similar sections, are " normalised." This is simply allowing them to cool in fairly still air after they leave the rolling mill. This imparts a certain degree of hardness and a certain degree of toughness, and before the rails are allowed out of the works a sample will be sawn off and tested for hardness and toughness. Only if the properties are sufficiently good will the rails be " passed " for service. Like men joining the army, they have to be pronounced " fit " for the arduous job they do.

Steel may be made extremely hard by " quenching "; that is, plunging it red-hot into water or oil and cooling it very rapidly, but such treatment is liable to make it brittle and it may crack easily. The necessary toughness may be recovered by " tempering "; that is, letting the quenched steel soak for a period in a gentle heat of about 400° C. to 500° C. The armour-plate in tanks and battleships, which has to be hard enough and tough enough to withstand shot and shell, is given an elaborate quenching and tempering treatment. It, too, is very carefully examined and tested before being passed for service.

Another thing we can do with steel is to " case-harden " it; that is, make it very hard on the outside but maintain a degree of softness and toughness inside. This is done by partially " cementing " it. A fairly low carbon steel, usually containing some nickel and chromium, is immersed in charcoal, or in a chemical called potassium cyanide, and is heated for a certain length of time. This causes some of the carbon in the charcoal or cyanide to diffuse into the steel,

B.I.S.F.

A 2,000-TON FORGING PRESS IN ACTION

When the steel is required in a much stronger condition than is possible when it is cast, then the ingot is forged. In this photograph a high-pressure boiler drum is being forged on a 2,000-ton hydraulic press.

UNDER THE STEAM HAMMER

Here we see a light forging being made under the steam hammer. The boy operates the hammer while the man works the steel into shape. For these smaller forgings the manipulation of the billet is usually done by hand.

forming a high carbon layer on the outside surface. Before this becomes too deep, the steel is taken out of the furnace and is normalised and tempered. The high carbon outer layer, which is extremely sensitive to heat treatment, becomes very hard, while the inside remains tough. This kind of treatment is given to the teeth of large cog wheels; the rubbing surfaces are thus made very hard and resistant to wear, while the body of the tooth remains tough and able to carry the load without cracking.

Cutting and Joining Steel

Finally, we may take a look at the ways in which steel, after we have rolled it into sections or plates or bars, can be utilised to construct machinery, bridges, ships, cars, locomotives, etc.

The first thing necessary is to cut the pieces of steel to the right length and shape, and for this we now possess a most valuable and useful tool in the oxy-acetylene cutting torch which can cut through steels over a foot thick. The cutting torch works with a mixture of two gases, oxygen and acetylene. The acetylene is burned in a flow of oxygen, and this makes an extremely hot flame which is played on the steel and rapidly brings a small area to a red-heat. Then another and finer jet of oxygen is turned on which actually shoots through the middle of the oxy-acetylene flame and strikes the red-hot steel. At this temperature the oxygen very rapidly turns the steel to molten iron oxide which is in fact blown out of the steel by the force of the jet. The operator then moves the torch slowly along and the jet of oxygen cuts a narrow slit in the steel. If the torch is mechanically guided a very smooth cut can be made. A flood of sparks pours out of the steel, and the operator must wear dark goggles to enable him to see what he is doing and protect his eyes from sparks.

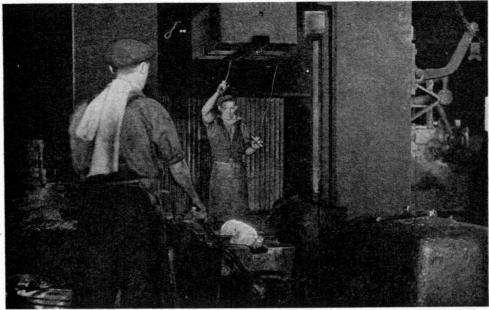

B.I.S.F.

DROP FORGING IN PROGRESS

In drop forging both the hammer and the anvil carry a die—a shallow mould of very tough steel—which is in the shape of the final forging. The red-hot steel billet is laid over the die on the anvil and repeated blows from the hammer force the steel into the shape desired.

Having cut our steel to size, it must be joined together in the way we want it. This can be done by drilling holes in the steel and joining the pieces either with rivets or nuts and bolts. A rivet is a little piece of steel shaped like a mushroom. The " stalk " of a red-hot rivet is pushed through the matched-up holes in two steel plates, and protrudes a short distance. One man then " holds-on " the head, while on the other side another man hammers the stalk and flattens it out to hold the rivet in place. As it cools and contracts, the rivet makes a very tight fixture. The big steel girders supporting railway bridges are generally made up of a number of steel plates riveted together, and the steel plates of ships' hulls are generally riveted to the frames and to each other.

Alternatively, nuts and bolts may be used, but these are, of course, very much more expensive and are used only where the joint must be undone

again, such as in joining railway lines together with " fishplates." When the track is worn out the joints must be released or the rails cannot be pulled up easily.

Electric Arc Welding

Over the last twenty years or so another method of easily and rapidly joining steel together has been developed and perfected—the process known as electric arc welding.

We saw when we considered the electric arc furnace how an electric arc may be struck between two pieces of steel and may actually melt them. Another practical use is made of this in arc welding. Two pieces of steel to be joined are brought close together and held firmly. Sometimes the edges are " bevelled " to form a groove. The welder then takes a rod of steel about $\frac{1}{2}$ inch in diameter, and often coated with a special material, and attaches it to one terminal of a powerful direct current dynamo. The pieces of steel to be joined are connected to the other terminal. The welding rod is then momentarily touched against the steel and withdrawn and an arc is formed. This melts the steel of the welding rod, and, to a lesser extent, the steels being joined together. Drops of molten steel from the rod fall into the space between the two pieces of steel, fuse with molten steel from either side and then, as the rod and arc are moved slowly along, they harden to form a solid and uniform joint. Welding in this manner is now very widely used for joining steel plates, castings and sections, both large and small sizes. It is quick, cheap and convenient, since no drilling and matching of holes is required. You must never look directly at the arc, though, as it is very bad for your eyes. The welder watches his work through a piece of dark glass set in the middle of a special piece of stout sheeting which protects both his eyes and his face from the dangerous ultra-violet rays.

Wellman Smith Owen Eng. Corp. Ltd.

MAKING STEEL TUBES

In making large tubes the method of forging which is used is known as the extrusion process. The plastic steel is made to flow through a hole, with the centre portion blocked out, and so take up the shape of a tube in a single pressing operation. Enormous pressures and very strong apparatus are required.

Our Most Dependable Metal

When Benjamin Huntsman made up his mind to try his hand at steel-making he did so because he wanted to make clock springs which were reliable. He was tired of hearing his customers complaining that the springs of his clocks didn't last properly and demanding that new ones be fitted. Right from the very start, therefore, steel was designed to be something on which the user could depend.

To-day, steel in all its numerous

A SOUTH WALES STEEL WORKS

The Steel Company of Wales was formed when four great companies engaged in the steel and tinplate industry pooled their resources. One outcome was the erection of the largest steel plant in Europe: the Abbey Works at Margam, Port Talbot. This photograph shows the Melting Shop Building; the eight chimneys correspond to the eight open hearth furnaces inside.

Photos: Steel Company of Wales.

The whole site of this new works, built on waste land near the sea where special grass was planted to bind the sand together, covers an area three times the size of Hyde Park, and is some four and a half miles long. Some idea of the land on which it is built is shown in this picture of the Cooling Tower and the Melting Shop ramp at Margam.

ALL MADE OF STEEL

Wellman Smith Owen Eng. Corp. Ltd.

In this picture we see some finished examples of the products of the steel works. The main structure shows the girders forming the spring arch of the famous Sydney Bridge in Australia. On top of these girders is a giant creeper crane, so called because it is able to creep along the top of the girders as the work of construction on the bridge goes on.

forms may rightly claim to be not only our most versatile material but also our most dependable. Everything in the manufacture of steel is kept under control, particularly the chemical analysis which plays such a large part in determining the properties of the final metal. If you ever have the good fortune to visit a modern steel works you will see on almost every side instruments and devices used to control the process, and one of the most important places in the whole works is the chemical laboratory where the samples of the steel are analysed.

Samples will be taken from the molten metal during refining, and the chemists will check the amount of carbon, silicon, manganese, sulphur and phosphorus they contain, and if " alloy " steels are being made then chromium, nickel, molybdenum and vanadium will be " assayed " as well. More samples will be taken when the steel has been rolled and treated, and if any analysis shows that a " cast " of steel is of the wrong chemical composition, then all the steel made from those ingots will be stopped from going to the customer.

Next door to the chemical laboratory you will probably find the " test-house." Here the samples of the steel are examined for their mechanical properties. The " tensile strength " of steel is determined by finding out how much force is needed to pull apart a sample of steel of a square inch in section. Hardness is measured by forcing a ball bearing or a diamond-shaped piece of very hard steel into the polished surface and measuring the indentation. Toughness is determined by breaking a sample by means of a heavy swinging weight and measuring how much the swing of the weight has been reduced. Only a simple calculation is needed to work out how much energy is consumed in breaking the steel sample.

In the same building the works metallurgists will be busy examining the inside of the samples of the steel through microscopes. What is called the " microstructure " of the steel is very important in determining its properties and making certain that the heat-treatment has been done properly.

All this care ensures that the steel will never let the customer down. Next time you see an express train thundering past— look down at the rails and especially at the rail joints. Watch how the rails bend under the weight and see how the wheels " hammer " the rail ends. If you count the number of wheels in each train and then find out how many trains pass that particular spot every day you can calculate just how many hammerings that steel rail has to put up with every twenty-four hours. It is the dependability of steel which ensures that this rail and all its fellow rails throughout the length and breadth of the railway system carry the load and go on carrying it.

G.E.C.

PROTECTING THE WELDER

An electric welder is seen here at work. The arc is " struck " at the end of the welding rod, and the worker watches it through a piece of dark glass, set in the shield. This protects his eyes and face from the harmful ultra-violet rays.

Treasures
Won from
the Earth's Crust

Metals that Serve
us in
A Hundred Ways

Transvaal Chamber of Mines.

WEIGHING BARS OF SOLID GOLD

The largest gold refinery is at Germiston, near Johannesburg, centre of the world's richest gold-fields. The precious metal is extracted from the ore by various processes and then formed into bars of almost pure gold. Our photograph shows the scene when these bars are being weighed. Approximately a bar contains 400 fine ounces troy.

THAT PRECIOUS METAL—GOLD

FEW words stir men's minds so deeply as "gold." Gold stands for wealth, power, royalty, excellence, value. Since the earliest days of history gold has been regarded as very precious, the metal fit for kings and priests to wear. Gold is the first metal mentioned in the Bible (Genesis ii. 11). The Tabernacle of the Israelites was richly decorated with gold; so, too, was the Temple of Solomon. In his Book of Revelation, St. John visions the Heavenly Jerusalem as constructed of pure gold: nothing baser seemed worthy.

Ancient legends are full of references to gold. You have read, for example, the story of Jason and the Golden Fleece; and that of Midas, King of Phrygia, who was granted the magic power of turning everything he touched into gold. We still speak of an extremely wealthy person as a Midas.

Almost Indestructible

Gold is a very beautiful metal. It is also practically indestructible, being affected by but very few other substances. The oxygen of the air does not harm it, so that it never tarnishes, and a thin layer of it gives a sure and beautiful protection against corrosion.

Gilding has been practised from the earliest times, being made possible by the ease with which gold, the most malleable of all metals, can be beaten out into thin, unbroken sheets. The gold-beater flattens an ounce of it into many square feet of " leaf "; and an ounce has a very small bulk, since gold weighs nineteen and one-third times as much as water and is over two-and-a-half times as heavy as iron.

Its beauty, permanence, ease of working and rarity have combined to render gold so greatly desired a metal that many dreadful deeds have been done to acquire it, and the alchemists laboured to find the Philosopher's Stone which would change baser metals into gold. The last quality—rarity—has perhaps had most influence. If gold were dis-covered in quantities equal, say, to those of copper, its present value would disappear. It has been estimated that all the gold produced since the discovery of America in 1492 would not amount to 25,000 tons.

During the four centuries elapsed since then the population of the world has increased very greatly; and, in spite of the fact that the gold output also has increased, there seems no likelihood of the metal ever exceeding the demand for it, or of its value going down. The steadiness of its price has made gold the most reliable standard of value by which to set the prices of all other commodities. In the form of coins, gold is a very convenient medium of exchange. During the forty-seven years following 1870 the Royal Mint in London converted into coins gold worth over £400,000,000. In 1914 the value of all gold currency in circulation throughout the world was put at about £1,660,000,000.

In later years gold coinage in Britain and elsewhere has been largely replaced by paper currency in the form of notes of the same value as the old gold coins, but gold still remains an international standard and national currencies have a definite value in terms of gold.

To be suitable for the hard wear that it gets as coins, jewellery, watch-cases, and other commercial articles, gold is alloyed with copper or

Specially drawn for this work.

GOLD MINING IN THE KLONDYKE

The men who won gold in the Klondyke had to work under conditions which only those possessed of the finest physique could stand. The ground had to be thawed before digging could begin. The above illustration shows miners at the windlass bringing up the earth excavated from the shaft.

THE TRAIL OF '98

Specially drawn for this work.

For three or four years, between 1897 and 1901, Klondyke, a district in Yukon Territory, north-western Canada, was the goal of a multitude of men, and women too, who were prepared to risk everything, even life itself, in a wild rush to stake out gold-mining claims. From this picture we gain some idea of the terrible hardships encountered by the miners in their journey over the Chilkoot Pass. Fortunes were made in the Klondyke, but many men and animals fell by the wayside, victims of exhaustion and the intense cold.

silver. Pure gold is 24-carat gold. A sovereign is of 22-carat gold; that is, it contains twenty-two parts gold out of twenty-four, the other two parts being another metal—copper. Jewellery is usually of 18-, 15-, 12- or 9-carat gold. A great deal of gold is used in the arts. Much is locked up as ingots (bullion) in banks, and in this condition may be passed to and fro between countries for many years in payment of debts. Of the remainder, the bulk is being used or hoarded away as coin.

Washing for Gold

Gold has often been found as loose grains, flakes, or lumps, called nuggets, in the sand and gravel which form, or once did form, the beds of streams and rivers. Gold occurring thus is called alluvial gold. It is usually separated from other substances by means of water.

"Washing," in its simplest form, consists in placing some of the gold-bearing sand or gravel in a shallow iron pan with water and tilting the pan slightly while giving it a circular motion. The lighter portions of matter are flicked over the lip with the water, while the heavier gold particles and pebbles settle. The pebbles are picked out by hand and the washing is continued till only a little sand remains with the gold. The residue is carefully dried, and the earthy dust can then be blown away.

Where large quantities of material

Transvaal Chamber of Mines.
AT WORK IN A SOUTH AFRICAN MINE
Most of the gold of the world is now obtained by deep mining from quartz rock, the superficial deposits having gradually been worked out. Primitive man obtained quite considerable quantities of gold from deposits near the surface, but to-day gold-winning involves deep mines and machinery, as seen in this picture of men despatching the gold-bearing quartz for crushing in the Modder Deep Levels of the South African Rand.

WITH THE GOLD SEEKERS

Topical Press.

Here is another scene of men at work in a gold-mine, but this photograph was taken in Australia. The men are working some 700 feet underground at the Red, White and Blue Gold Mine at Bendigo, Victoria. They are using a pneumatic drill for the removal of gold-bearing quartz, the white reef of which is visible in the background. It has been stated that miners who follow a big quartz reef successfully can earn very high wages.

have to be treated, a sluice is used. This is a long sloping wooden trough, with crossbars, named riffles, nailed to the bottom. A stream of water flowing through it carries away the rubbish. At intervals a " clean-up " takes place. The gold, whether " free " or amalgamated with quicksilver poured into the trough before operations began, to absorb it, is scraped from behind the riffles and washed in a pan. If quicksilver has been used, the amalgam is heated in an iron retort until the quicksilver passes off as gas into a condenser, where it turns again into liquid. Only the pure gold is left behind in the retort, in a very open or spongy condition. It is melted down into solid bars for sale.

The ease with which alluvial gold can be recovered, and the possibility of striking rich " pockets," or deposits, and nuggets of it, has caused a rush of miners and all kinds of other people to any district in which it has been discovered.

Mad Rushes for Gold

Stories of the great gold-rushes during the latter half of the last century seem almost incredible in these days when gold-mining has become a great industry. There are still alluvial deposits of gold but big finds are unlikely. Long before history was written man regarded gold as the most precious of metals and the search for it has never ceased.

To-day the recovery of gold from the earth is a job for expert metallurgists and mining engineers. The lone prospector

South African Railways.

TAKING SAMPLES FOR TESTING

There has always been a certain amount of hazard about the discovery of gold and in striking a rich vein of quartz, but in these days as little as possible is left to chance. In the picture above an expert is taking samples of the reef so that it can be properly tested for gold content. If the yield is poor then the reef is abandoned and another reef showing better prospects of a profitable return is sought.

Commonwealth of Australia.

SLUICING FOR GOLD

This photograph, taken in Victoria, Australia, shows another method of winning gold. A deposit of gravel is being broken up and washed away by a large jet of water, and made to pass through a succession of sluices in which the gold that it contains is trapped.

has disappeared and the well-organised mining company has taken his place.

The first of the great historical " gold-rushes " followed the finding of gold in a channel being cut for a water-mill on a tributary of the Sacramento river, in California. The discovery was made in January, 1848. The news of it spread like wildfire all over the continent of North America. People poured into San Francisco in thousands. Some came by ship round Cape Horn; others came overland across the mountains, suffering great hardships.

The " rush " lasted about five years and the lucky ones made rich strikes, washing out thousands of pounds' worth of gold in a few weeks. Most of the miners, however, barely made a living, or soon quitted the country in disgust. A considerable amount of gold was won, however,

before the shallow deposits had been worked out.

Among the Californian gold-seekers were many Australians. One of these thought that some of the districts of his home-country were very much like those in which Californian gold deposits occurred. He returned to Australia in 1850 to see if he could find gold there, and discovered it in 1851 near Bathurst, New South Wales, about 100 miles from Sydney. A terrific stampede took place. Sydney was left almost deserted. The same year gold was found at Ballarat, in Victoria, and a similar find occurred at Melbourne.

Fortunes were made by lucky folk very quickly, for the Australian gold was coarse, and a single stroke of a pick might reveal a nugget worth a large sum. One day in 1851 a black shepherd walked into Bathurst with a lump of gold that fetched £4,000. The discovery of other great nuggets from time to time helped to sustain the gold fever. In 1858 a nugget, suitably named the "Welcome," was dug up. It weighed 138 *pounds*, and was valued at well over £8,000 at that time, but the price of gold has risen considerably since then. An even larger one, "The Welcome Stranger," scaling 141 pounds, appeared some years later.

In the "Gold Boom"

In two years the diggers unearthed over £20,000,000 worth of gold. The output then fell off, but by 1895 gold to the value of over £300,000,000 had been produced in Victoria, New South Wales and Queensland, where gold was found in 1860.

Australia experienced another "gold boom" in 1882, when gold was discovered in the northern extremity of Western Australia; and yet another in 1892, when large deposits were found round Coolgardie, about 350 miles east of Perth, the capital. Since that time more than £150,000,000 worth of gold has been won from the East Coolgardie field, and its Golden Mile became famous.

Then, in 1897, came the rush to the Eldorado of the North, the wonderful Tom Tiddler's Ground in the part of North-West Canada and Alaska through which the great River Yukon flows. Australians who joined in it exchanged

South African Railways.

A GENERAL VIEW OF CROWN MINES, JOHANNESBURG

Even at the beginning of this century, and for long ages before, the winning of gold had been largely a matter of individual effort. Stories of good fortune and grim despair have been told of the great gold rushes. To-day, gold-mining is a big, well-organised industry, and some idea of the extent of the works erected is given by this picture of a well-known South African mine.

STAGES IN WINNING THE GOLD

When the gold-bearing quartz has been mined, it is broken up into fine powder by heavy stamps which are, in effect, powerful grinding machines. The powder is treated with mercury and passed on to the cyanide tanks. Our picture shows a stamp battery at a Johannesburg gold-mine.

South African Railways.

Here we see the cyanide tanks at the gold-mine. Most of the powdered ore is brought to these tanks which contain potassium cyanide. Zinc is added also during the process and the deposit which forms at the bottom of the tank is now nearer the stage when it will be pure gold.

South African Railways.

ANOTHER PROCESS IN GOLD-WINNING

Not all the powdered quartz from the stamp battery is conveyed to the cyanide tanks ; some of the dust containing particles of gold is collected and discharged on to corduroy blankets, as seen in the picture above. Over these a gentle stream of water trickles evenly. The heavy particles of gold remain in the corrugations while the light sand is washed away.

the great heat of their own country for the arctic winters of the frozen North.

The story of this rush is much the same as that of earlier rushes—great hardship, some enormous fortunes and many disappointments. Easily-reached alluvial deposits are soon exhausted. After the cheaply-won gold has been got, operations may be taken up by mining companies using dredgers to wash at a profit large quantities of gravel containing only a small amount of gold. Other companies may wash down river banks, with powerful jets of water, into large sluices.

In many districts the mining of alluvial gold has been followed by the mining of ore containing gold.

About Reef Mining

Various kinds of rock sometimes con-tain gold, distributed through them as pure particles or combined with other elements. Most of the world's gold now comes from the reefs of ore, sandwiched in between valueless rock. The working of reefs requires the sinking of shafts and the use of expensive machinery for winning and treating the ore, and is beyond the means of the " small " man.

The most famous gold-bearing reefs of the world are those of the Witwaters-rand, in the Transvaal, South Africa. The Witwatersrand is a low range of hills running east and west. In it, one edge of what may be called great basin-like strata of gold-bearing ore comes to the surface. The ore consists of quartz pebbles cemented together by silica and iron oxide. The Boer name for it is " banket," a word meaning almond-rock, which it resembles in appearance.

Very small particles of gold are distributed evenly through the cement.

The valuable feature of the goldfield of the Witwatersrand—or Rand, as it is called for short—is the reliableness of the reefs, as regards both their position and their gold content. One can be practically certain of striking the reef at the calculated depth, and of getting a profitable amount of gold out of it.

The reefs slope upwards steeply. In opening a mine, shafts are sunk to and through a reef, and then carried through the stratum underneath it, parallel to the reef. At different levels, about 150 feet apart, short tunnels, called cross-cuts, are driven into the reef, and horizontal drives or galleries made from these along the reef, in the ore. The galleries are connected by holes, named winzes, excavated up and down in the vein, so that eventually the ore is divided by galleries and winzes into " stopes " or blocks.

Now begins the stoping, which is the removal of these blocks of ore. The most usual method is to work downwards from one gallery to another, the ore being blasted away in great steps and shot down the winzes into trucks in the gallery below, which carry it off to the shaft. When a stope has been cleared, it is filled in with rubbish, a great deal of which is removed with the ore.

In what is called " overhand " stoping the miners work upwards, attacking

South African Railways.

POURING OUT LIQUID GOLD

Poets and writers have sometimes in their songs and stories likened a beautiful colour to liquid gold, but the workman in this picture is more concerned with the task in hand than anything fanciful. For the molten stream he is pouring is, in truth, worth a small fortune. The photograph was taken at a gold-mine on the South African Rand.

the roof from a sloping bank of rubbish which they build up as they rise.

After being carefully picked by hand, the ore is broken up by stamps into a fine powder. The stamps are, in effect, great iron pestles and mortars. The pestles weigh about a ton each and are raised and dropped ninety times a minute by machinery.

Gathered by Mercury

After grinding, the pulp is passed over copper plates coated with mercury. The mercury absorbs a good deal of the gold. The material that has been over the plates is " concentrated " to remove as much useless stuff as possible, and then placed in great vats containing a solution of potassium cyanide. The potassium combines with the gold. When the solution has been run off, zinc is added. The potassium now dissolves the zinc and leaves the gold deposit at the bottom of the vat ready for collection.

Mining on the Rand began in 1887. Since that year the mines have yielded gold to the value of, roughly, two thousand million pounds sterling.

They still produce nearly half of the world's gold yearly supply. If to their output be added that of the gold mines in Australia, Canada, and other parts of the British Commonwealth, it will be found that two-thirds of all gold now mined comes from lands forming part of the British Commonwealth.

Down to the year when the War of 1914–18 began, people in Britain as well as in other countries used sovereigns and half-sovereigns or other high-value coins made of gold, carried on the person in special purses or receptacles. Now, instead of gold coins, we depend on bank-notes and find them perfectly satisfactory.

Australian News & Information Bureau.

THE GOLDEN MILE AT KALGOORLIE

The richest square mile of gold-bearing country in the world is at Kalgoorlie in Western Australia. Since its discovery just over sixty years ago more than £150,000,000 worth of gold has been won from the East Coolgardie field, of which the Golden Mile forms the main producing centre. The Great Boulder Gold Mine is at one end of the Golden Mile and Kalgoorlie at the other end.

BEATING OUT GOLD LEAF

Photos by courtesy of Messrs. George M. Whiley Ltd.

ONE OF THE OLDEST OF THE ANCIENT ARTS

Here we have a general scene in the workshop of the gold-beaters of to-day, where a craft which has been exercised by skilled workers for forty centuries is still carried on. Though modern machinery has come to his aid, the gold-beater of to-day requires the same high skill as his forerunners, and English gold leaf now stands at the head of the world's markets.

FROM the days of the ancient Egyptians gold leaf has been in demand because of its durability and brilliance. In the tombs at Thebes wooden coffins were found profusely ornamented with gold, while samples of beaten leaf, ready for application, were found in the tomb of Tutankhamen.

So for forty centuries this craft, one of the world's oldest industries, has continued. In Britain the gold-beaters have long maintained their high traditions, and from all over the world come demands for their products. Among the public buildings in England with exterior adornment of pure fine gold (*i.e.*, without addition of any alloy) may be mentioned the Houses of Parliament, the National Gallery, Buckingham Palace, the Victoria Memorial, Windsor Castle and Tower Bridge, while the crown-

ing glory of St. Paul's is the gold cross " that shines over city and river."

Among articles of everyday use ornamented with the gold-beater's aid are shoes and hats, with the maker's name inside; pencils, typewriter covers, spectacle cases, combs and clocks, cricket balls, tennis rackets, bicycles, motor-cars and railway coaches, while bookbinders, artists, makers of picture frames and furniture, as well as dental surgeons and others, all use the product of the gold-beater's art.

Stages of Production

In a modern gold-beating factory, such as the one of George M. Whiley Ltd., at Ruislip, the processes of gold beating are similar to those of the past, but modern machines also have been introduced. The production of gold leaf at Ruislip is now mostly by means

FROM BARS TO RIBBONS

The fine gold (24 carats) is melted 60 ounces at a time, mixed with small quantities of copper or silver as an alloy, according to the colour required in the finished leaf.

After being melted in a plumbago crucible, the gold is cast into bars measuring 11 inches long, 1½ inches wide, and ¼ inch thick. One of these bars is seen here.

Each bar is then passed many times between highly polished steel rollers, and, with steadily mounting pressure, a ribbon eventually emerges 330 feet long and 1/1000th inch thick.

From this long ribbon squares of 1½ inches are cut ; these are then filled or interleaved into a " cutch " consisting of specially-prepared 4-inch square pieces of paper,

WITH CARE AND SKILL

Gold-beaters' skins require careful cleaning and pressing after being used, and in this photograph the skins are being lightly rubbed with an Arctic hare's foot, dipped in calcined gypsum.

Some 1,100 gold-beaters' skins, 5¼ inches square, form a mould, and the delicate quarters of gold are lifted most carefully with foot-long boxwood pincers and filled into the mould.

In the mould the gold leaves receive the third and most vital beating. The skill of the gold-beater is concentrated for 3¼ hours on transferring the thickness of the leaf outwards.

The leaves are taken from the mould with pincers, cut with a "waggon" of sharpened slips of cane to 3¼ inches square, and then placed in books of twenty-five leaves each.

7—2

of machines capable of making a leaf to the highest standards.

The raw material—that is, "fine" gold, or gold of 24 carats—is melted 60 ounces at a time, mixed with small quantities of copper or silver as an alloy, according to the colour required in the finished leaf. This is melted in a plumbago crucible from which bars measuring 11 inches by $1\frac{1}{2}$ inches are cast.

Each bar is then passed many times between highly polished steel rollers, and, with occasional annealing and softening, and with mounting pressure, a ribbon emerges $1\frac{1}{2}$ inches in width, $\frac{1}{1.000}$th inch thick, and approximately 330 feet long.

Two hundred and twenty pieces $1\frac{1}{2}$ inches square, are cut from the ribbon and filled or interleaved into a "cutch"; this cutch consists of 4-inch square pieces of French paper, manufactured by the French firm of Montgolfier, who made the first practical balloon. These squares are bound together with two bands of parchment. In this cutch the gold receives its first beating for about thirty minutes, during which the original $1\frac{1}{2}$-inch pieces are extended to 4 inches square. The cutch being taken out of its bands, each of the 4-inch pieces of gold is separated from the interleaving sheets of paper and laid out on a cushion of calf skin, then cut with a steel "skewing" knife into quarters.

Between Gold-beaters' Skins

These quarters are now "filled" into 4-inch square skins, made of specially prepared ox intestine, called gold-beaters' skins, an operation done by women and demanding absolute accuracy. The 880 pieces now comprise a "shoder" and this is beaten for $1\frac{1}{2}$ hours with a 14-lb. cast-iron hammer on huge marble blocks, with leather aprons attached to catch the "shatts" or particles of gold.

From the shoder the delicate leaves of gold are lifted by means of boxwood pincers and quartered with a sharpened reed. These quarters are now filled into a mould, consisting of 1,100 very fine gold-beaters' skins $5\frac{1}{4}$ inches square, and this time the beating is done with an 8 lb. hammer. This is the most skilled of all the operations, as the gold-beater's object is concentrated for three and a quarter hours on transferring some of the thickness outwards to form a thicker edge. At the end a fine remainder, as it were, has been beaten out to an even degree of thickness. When this final stage of perfection has been reached the leaves are approximately $4\frac{3}{4}$ inches square.

An Arctic Hare's Foot

The next stage again depends on the skill of women workers, who take the leaf from the skins of the mould with their boxwood pincers, and then, with a "waggon" of sharpened slips of rattan cane (normally set in a square-shaped frame of $3\frac{1}{4}$-inch sides) cut off the thick edges from the leaf. The square leaves of gold are now standard size, $3\frac{1}{4}$ inches square, and are picked up and placed in books of twenty-five leaves each, in which the final product is sold. The interleaving tissue paper must be acid free and coated with red ochre—"rouge"—to prevent adhesion of the gold.

The cleaning of the skins after the gold has been removed is also a highly skilled task, carried out with an Arctic hare's foot dipped in calcined gypsum ("brime"). Both the powder (from Derbyshire) and the hare's foot are essential to the gold-beater. After cleaning, the skins are dried in hot presses. At no stage is the metal touched by hand. The texture of the gold leaves can only be indicated in figures as about $\frac{1}{250.000}$th of an inch in thickness.

Machines are taking the place of the gold-beater to some extent, but the delicacy and skill of the old craftsmen is to-day being merged with the newer skills of the engineers and technicians, and the ancient craft, reinforced by modern science, goes on unchanging.

SILVER, THE QUEEN OF METALS

Mondiale.

A PILE OF PURE SILVER

Silver, though much less valuable in comparison with gold, is still among the " noble metals " as it was when the ancient alchemists first classified it. Mexico, U.S.A., Canada and Australia are among the chief producers of this metal, and in this photograph is seen a pile of " cement silver " at a Canadian refinery. It is recovered in this form from the electrolytic process and is then melted and cast into bars.

SILVER was one of the earliest metals discovered by prehistoric man; it was also one of the first to be used by women for the making of ornaments with which to adorn themselves, and throughout its long history one of its regular uses has been in the making of endurable articles for personal adornment and practical use.

With gold it has been one of the romantic metals, and to obtain it men have been prepared to endure hardships and to risk their lives. From quite early times it has been used in the form of coins as a basis for payment. If gold is the king of metals then silver can justly claim to be the queen. It has a fine metallic lustre, pleasing to the eye, and, with the exception of gold, it is the most ductile and malleable of metals.

Though it is now much less valuable compared with gold, being worth about six shillings an ounce to-day, it is still valuable for coinage and for making ornamental goods as well as more useful articles such as dishes, forks and spoons. We still speak of the child of wealthy parents as being " born with a silver spoon in his mouth." In industry the increasing demand for silver in the electrical and photographic trades was one of the factors which led to the British silver coinage being replaced gradually by cupro-nickel coins. Silver has become too valuable to the electrician, the photographer, and in other industries, to be used in Britain as a token of exchange.

In Search of El Dorado

In the early years of the sixteenth century the Spaniards sent their explorers and adventurers to the New World to search for El Dorado, the fabled Land of Gold. Their conquests did indeed yield great quantities of gold which had been gathered by the rulers of Mexico and Peru, and millions of pounds' worth of the precious metal were shipped to Spain.

But it was the discovery of the fabulously-rich silver veins in the conquered lands which presently made Spain the richest country in Europe. These early Spanish explorers were experts in the use of divining-rods and were not long in discovering the mineral wealth contained in the mountainous regions of Mexico. The first silver taken from a Mexican mine by Europeans came from the still celebrated mines of Jaxco, in the state of Guerrero, in 1521. From that time onwards Mexico has been the chief silver-producing country of the world, though to-day the United States vies for leadership with her neighbour.

Many stories are told of the struggle between the Spaniards and the English in those years when the New World was being exploited. On a certain day in 1573, Francis Drake, with a band of sailors reinforced by a small body of Indians, landed from their ships to raid a convoy of mules, guarded by a handful of soldiers. In a few minutes Drake's men had sent the soldiers and the mule-drivers fleeing for safety, and the mules with their burdens were left as prizes for the victors. Altogether there were 30 tons of silver, worth at that time well over £200,000. By the time Spanish reinforcements reached the scene of the brief encounter Drake's men were well on their way to their ships with half the spoil,

TAPPING A SILVERY STREAM   *High Commissioner for Canada.*

The process being watched with so much interest is the making of silver ingots or bullion. The shining, liquid metal is flowing white-hot from the crucible into a ladle, from which it will be transferred like freshly-made jam to the moulds on the left. The great silver mines of Canada were discovered quite by accident.

Australian News & Information Bureau.

SEPARATING THE SILVER FROM THE LEAD

Although huge nuggets of practically pure silver have been found on rare occasions, most of the world's supply of silver comes from other ores such as lead and lead-zinc. Here we see a Continuous De-silvering Kettle in the Broken Hill Company's refinery at Port Pirie in South Australia. Zinc acts as a collector for the silver, which is then recovered by distillation.

while the other half had been safely hidden for future recovery.

Lost and Found Again

One of the mines of the Estrella del Norte Mining Company was lost for many years. The only record was a note on an old Jesuit map which said that the opening of the tunnel could be seen from the door of the mission church. For years the hills in front of the door were searched in vain. Then in 1905 a side wall of the old church crumbled to ruins and disclosed the existence of a door which had never been suspected. From this door the hillside was searched with the aid of glasses, the lost mine was traced, and a big fortune was obtained.

Chance indeed has played a big part in the discovery of silver mines. To-day the U.S.A. is one of the chief silver-producing countries of the world. Gold was discovered in California in 1848, and

for years after that prospectors roamed in likely spots in search of the precious metal. Two Irish miners accidentally discovered traces of gold in Carson River Valley. Another wanderer, Henry Comstock, pegged out a claim close by, but, watching the Irishmen at work, he was interested in the black rock they dumped aside. He came to an arrangement with them whereby they took the surface gold and he had the rest. Pieces of the black rock were assayed and found to contain £600 in silver and £175 in gold to the ton of rock. In this way was discovered the famous Great Comstock silver lode, and more fortune hunters flocked to the district.

In 1873 a syndicate of miners found the great ore body which was later known as the Big Bonanza. For three years this silver mine yielded £600,000 a month, and in about twenty-five years had turned out ore worth £26 million. It should

When the silver ore has been won from the mine it is in the form of large rubble, which has to be crushed almost into dust. The old-time method of crushing is still in use in many of the Mexican mines, and consists of rolling a massive boulder over the ore till a sandy deposit remains. About 35 per cent. of the world's silver comes from Mexico.

Photos: G.P.A.

This dusty, sandy matter must then be put into a pond or " buddle," about 5 feet in depth, where it is thoroughly mixed with the water by means of the rotating wheel in the centre. In this manner a kind of sticky mud is formed. There are several different methods of extracting silver from the ore, dependent upon the type of ore treated.

EXTRACTING THE QUEEN OF METALS

When the mud-like ore is taken from the buddle it is placed in a square box, the bottom of which is a fine screen, like that of a cinder sieve. This box is then submerged in a trough containing water and the process causes the heavy silver dust to settle at the bottom of the trough and it can then be easily collected.

Photos : G.P.A.

Having emerged from one complete washing the ore that has passed through the meshes of the sieve is removed from the trough and placed this time into running water. In this stage of the treatment the heavy metal settles at the bottom of the water and such dirt as remains is washed away. The workers at the mine here illustrated are mostly negroes.

be noted that silver mines are usually situated in dry, barren districts, such as the deserts of Old Mexico, the arid table-lands of Chile, the rocky fastnesses of Peru, or the desert lands of Nevada, Arizona, New Mexico and Colorado.

In Canada and Australia

During the present century big silver mines have been opened in Ontario, Canada. The first discovery was, as in so many cases, accidental, but before long Canada stood fourth in the list of silver-producing countries. In 1923, James Campbell Miles, prospecting in tropical Queensland, Australia, near the Northern Territory boundary, noticed the prominent outcrops of rock in the hills. With a good prospector's curiosity he went over and knocked off some chips of rock. Their heaviness impressed him and he put them in a sample bag and sent them to the Government assay office.

Not until he arrived back some months later did Miles learn that his samples were rich in silver and lead. Soon afterwards Mount Isa Mines Ltd. had been formed. The development of this field is one of the highlights of the story of twentieth-century mining in Australia.

If the discovery of this big silver-lead ore deposit was romantic, the growth of the Mount Isa Mines is a story of hard work. A company was formed and a railway was built to the mines and a large treatment plant erected. At Rifle Creek a great dam was constructed to supply water to the mine and town. The first ores contained more than half lead and about 35 ounces of silver in every ton of ore.

Later, in 1941, underground drilling indicated large copper ore veins near the silver-lead deposits. Copper was urgently needed at the time for the Allies in the war, and for some years Mount Isa changed over to the production of copper. To-day silver, lead, zinc and copper are produced at the Mount Isa Mines.

At Broken Hill in New South Wales is one of the richest ore deposits in the world, and here silver is mined with lead, zinc and cadmium.

Although some huge nuggets of practically pure silver have been discovered from time to time—one of them weighed well over a ton!—most of the world's production now comes as a by-product from other ores, lead and lead-zinc ores being the chief. The silver is separated from the less valuable parts of an ore by one of several processes. The cyanide process, which was first introduced into Mexico in 1905, is similar to the cyanide process for gold, but the principal method of dealing with lead ores is by what is known as the Parkes process. This consists of stirring a small quantity of zinc into the molten lead and silver. The zinc acts as a collector for the silver which is later recovered by distillation. The Williams process, developed at Port Pirie in South Australia, is a modification of the Parkes process.

Silver is also recovered from copper ores, and this is usually done by electrolytic methods.

Its Many Uses

In industry, silver is used in large quantities as an electrical contact material. It is used also for lining chemical plant for acetic acid, dyestuffs, essential oils, and in preparing foodstuffs containing vinegar, or for jam making. For the manufacture of mirrors a thin film of metallic silver is deposited on scrupulously clean glass; this is later varnished and backed with a protective paint coat.

The plates and films used in photography are coated with a compound of silver which is affected by light if exposed to it for even a tiny fraction of a second. Bromide and other papers used in producing the finished prints depend also on the sensitivity of a silver salt. It would be possible, though very difficult, to take photographs without the aid of silver, but anything in the nature of high-speed photography would be out of the question. Your holiday snapshots owe their existence mainly to the queen of metals— Silver.

NICKEL, THE GOBLIN METAL

THE " SLUSHER " AT WORK

Many of our modern inventions would not have advanced beyond the theory stage but for the part played by nickel in the improvement of other metals. In this photograph is seen an early stage in nickel production. The " slusher " is really a huge, heavy rake which is hauled backwards and forwards over the broken rock and ore until it has raked all the broken material to the top of the chute.

IN the minds of most people the progress of industry is associated with the names of the great inventors, such as Stephenson, Watt, Marconi and many others. It is not generally realised that the real factor on which advance has been dependent has been the quality of materials. Many of the ideas that were developed by the great inventors had been thought of before, sometimes hundreds of years before. Not long ago the 500th anniversary of Leonardo da Vinci was celebrated, and in the exhibitions of his drawings many devices and machines were shown which did not work in his time, and have only become available to mankind during the present century. This is because materials were not then good enough, or strong enough, to build the things which entered into his brilliant visions. In the story of the improvement of materials nickel is one of the elements which plays the biggest part.

Nickel was not even known 200 years ago. It was then discovered by a Swedish scientist, Cronstedt, but remained a curiosity until well into the last century, particularly because they could not, at that time, extract it from its ores. In fact, it obtained its name because of this difficulty. Its ores had been mistaken for copper minerals and named kupfernickel, meaning bedevilled copper—the goblin metal.

Big deposits of nickel were first found in 1865 in New Caledonia, a French island in the Pacific. These deposits supplied the world with its relatively small needs until the end of the last century, when enormous deposits of ore were found, by chance, during the building of the Canadian Pacific Railway through Northern Ontario. This field took a long time to develop, because once more great difficulties were encountered in getting the nickel out of the ore, which had to be done in several stages.

Armour Plate to Jets

The last of these stages involved a most interesting process invented by Ludwig

Mond, whereby the nickel is combined with carbon monoxide into a gas, and then re-deposited in its pure form by heating the gas. This method of refining is still used to-day. When the treatment problems were solved the Canadian field grew, and is still growing, and to-day it produces over three-quarters of the free world's requirements.

The first big use of nickel was for adding to steel for armour plating on battleships, but this use has been far surpassed by a multitude of other applications in almost every industry there is. Nickel is mainly used as an addition to other metals to alter and improve their properties. The two biggest groups of applications are the toughening of steels and irons, and the addition to steels, irons and many other metals to prevent their decay in the form of corrosion.

Nickel is also used in the manufacture and construction of watches, radio sets, cars, electric fires, railway engines, farm-ing implements and hundreds of other essential items of modern life. More recently, with the coming of the jet engine, the ability of nickel alloys to operate at very high temperatures has become very important. Here is an example where the invention has awaited the material, for the idea that a gas turbine would be efficient is not very new, but the world awaited a suitable material in which to build it. The great inventor, Whittle, succeeded because the materials available to him resisted the very high temperatures at which they had to operate.

Measuring Ocean Depths

Nickel has itself, or imparts to its alloys, many unusual properties. One example is that nickel changes its shape when magnetised, and this property has been used to construct an instrument with nickel sheets called the Echo Depth Sounder, for measuring the depths

Mond Nickel Co. Ltd.

PREPARING A " DRIFT ROUND " BLAST

The hard rock which contains the nickel ore has to be blasted, and here two workers are setting the fuses in readiness for a charge. This is what is known as a " drift round " blast and is used to drive horizontal passages (drifts) towards an ore body.

THE LAST STAGE IN REFINING NICKEL

Mond Nickel Co. Ltd.

The tower-like objects seen here are called decomposers. Each contains a charge of nickel pellets which are constantly being lifted to the top and allowed to fall again. Nickel, combined with carbon monoxide to form a gas named nickel carbonyl, is passed through the decomposers. When great heat is introduced the gas breaks up. The nickel is deposited on the pellets and the monoxide is drawn off.

THE USES OF NICKEL

The addition of nickel to iron renders it stronger and easier to shape with tools. As the molten iron is run through the discharging trough of a cupola, the nickel, in the form of pellets, is allowed to fall into it from a funnel over the trough.

Photos : Mond Nickel Co. Ltd.

Nickel is much used for nickel-plating articles to protect them from corrosion and to improve their appearance. In this photograph the covers of motor-car radiators are seen coming out of the nickel-plating vats in the radiator factory of a well-known motor-car works,

Mond Nickel Co. Ltd.

ORE CARS IN A CANADIAN NICKEL MINE

The largest nickel mines in the world are in Canada, which supplies over three-quarters of the free world's requirements. Here we have a scene in one of the big Canadian mines in which the largest underground ore cars in the world are used. The trolley loco. weighs 20 tons, while the cars are 14½ feet long and nearly 7 feet high. There are more than 280 miles of track in this mine.

of the ocean. Nickel is able also to change the vary of expansion in its alloy with iron, according to the amount that is mixed with the iron. By using one alloy it is possible to obtain a metal which has practically no expansion on heating, and this is very useful for making steel measuring tapes, or in other scientific instruments.

It is even more useful to be able to choose a material of exactly the expansion required, and this property is used to make alloys which will seal into any kind of glass, making a firm joint that remains airtight on heating. Even greater variety in properties is obtained in combining nickel with other metals in the manufacture of magnets. On the one hand, permanent magnets of a high strength can be manufactured from nickel alloys, but on the other hand, for many electrical uses it is important to have materials which can be quickly magnetised and de-magnetised, and here again nickel alloys fill the need. Finally, it is possible to make an alloy of nickel with iron that

is practically non-magnetic ; a strange result when it is remembered that both metals are, in themselves, magnetic.

Nickel is essential to almost every alloy that is made to resist corrosion, and stainless steels are well known to everyone. Alloyed with copper or chromium, and sometimes molybdenum, the hottest and most potent chemicals will be unable to attack the mixture, except so slightly that the container will last for years. These materials have made many of the great chemical industries possible.

Even things in your daily life are protected from decay by nickel. Your bicycle will have parts which are plated with nickel, though there may be chromium on top, more to maintain the finish than to help with protection. Taps and other domestic fittings are similarly protected.

It is because nickel finds its way into so many places that the amount that is used for every person forms an indication of the level of civilisation which a nation has achieved.

COPPER—THE RED METAL

International Nickel Company.

DRILLING HOLES FOR BLASTING COPPER ORE

Until about 1850 Britain was the world's largest copper producer, but the supply of ore fell rapidly, and no copper is mined in this country to-day. In most cases copper deposits, wherever found, must be reached by some form of mining. The usual method is to drill holes into the ore body and then load with an explosive charge. This article, which has been prepared with the kind assistance of the Copper Development Association, explains the production and many uses of copper.

THE only coloured metals, copper and gold, were the first worked by man, and have been in continuous use down the centuries. Of the two, copper is the more abundant and decidedly the more useful metal. Primitive man discovered that a lump of the naturally occurring metal, or native copper as it is called, could be hammered to any required shape and that it became harder and stronger in the process. Thus he was able to replace stone implements and weapons by copper ones. This use of copper probably continued for many centuries before bronze was intentionally made. One of the tombs of the ancient Egyptians, when opened some years ago, was found to contain a hoard of hundreds of copper tools. Although they were fashioned thousands of years ago, these copper tools were in excellent condition, for copper does not rust and is practically indestructible.

Bronze, which is mostly copper with the addition of a small amount of tin, was discovered later in history, and was found to be harder and stronger than copper. Brass, which is obtained by adding zinc to copper, was known to the Greeks and Romans. Such combinations of metals are called alloys, and copper forms the base of a great many alloys which are widely employed in industry. This is because copper and its alloys are easily worked and become stronger in the process, and have long-lasting qualities. They are also good conductors of heat and of electricity.

A Conductor of Electricity

The astonishing growth of most industries in the past hundred and fifty years has been due largely to the availability of electrical power, and electricity depends on copper. Next to silver, copper is the best conductor of electricity. It was soon discovered that the presence of impurities, in amounts so small that they were regarded as of no account, affected

Specially painted for this work.

A PIONEER GOLD PROSPECTOR IN AUSTRALIA

Gold has been found in nearly all parts of the world and has been regarded as a precious metal from the days of the early civilisations. At different times rich deposits have been accidentally discovered and a " gold rush " has followed, such as that which took place in Australia about 1851. Machinery has now largely taken the place of the methods of the early pioneers, one of whom is seen here " fossicking " for alluvial gold. The gold-bearing sand is placed in a shallow pan, partly filled with water ; the pan is tilted and given a circular motion so that the lighter material is washed away while the heavier gold particles remain.

By permission of the British Aluminium Co. Ltd.

HOW SCOTLAND'S WATER DRIVES AN ALUMINIUM WORKS

In recent years the use of Aluminium, especially in the form of alloys with other metals, has steadily increased, being particularly valuable in the manufacture of aircraft, motor-car castings and body work, cooking utensils, and even in bridge-building. Bauxite, chemically treated to give alumina, is subjected to electrical treatment, the power used for generating the electricity being that of falling water. In this picture is seen the 6-pipe water track, each pipe 39 inches in diameter and over a mile long, which drives the dynamos at the great aluminium works at Kinlochleven, Argyllshire.

the ability of copper to conduct electricity.

So a great demand arose for high purity, or high conductivity, copper. Although large amounts of copper in the native state have been exploited, as in the Lake Superior region of North America, nearly all the copper now produced comes from copper-bearing rocks called copper ores. Such ores are widely distributed throughout the world. They are found in the United States and Canada, Northern Rhodesia, South Africa, Spain, Chile, Australia, Turkey, India and Japan and in parts of Russia.

It is of interest to recall that copper was once mined in Britain, in Cornwall and Anglesey, and that until 1850 this country was the world's largest copper producer. World production of copper to-day averages about 2½ million tons a year, of which nearly a quarter is derived from the British Commonwealth.

Scattered in Grains

Copper ores are found at various depths, from near the surface where they are quarried like stone, to many hundreds of feet below ground level where they are mined like coal. Sometimes the ores occur as layers or veins in the surrounding rocks, but mostly they are scattered as minute grains of copper minerals in large bodies of rock. As a rule, the deposits do not contain more than 1 or 2 per cent. of the metal. That is to say, 100 tons of ore may yield less than 2 tons of copper.

Copper combines readily with sulphur, and its ores are generally sulphides; either combinations of copper and sulphur, or copper, iron and sulphur, with small amounts of other elements included. Chalcopyrite, a sulphide of copper and iron, is stated to account for one half of the world's total supply of copper. The deposits of this glistening yellow mineral in Spain

Mufulira Copper Mines Ltd.

UNDERGROUND HAULAGE IN A COPPER MINE

In many mines coarse jaw crushers are used to reduce the larger lumps of copper ore while still in the mine, after which the ore is loaded into trucks drawn by a locomotive and taken to the bottom of the shaft to be hoisted to the surface. This picture gives a good idea of the underground haulage system in a modern copper mine.

contain so much sulphur, that large amounts of both sulphur and copper have been obtained from it. Bornite, another sulphide ore, is known as " peacock ore " on account of its brilliant colours. Other classes of ores, the oxidised or weathered ores, include such minerals as malachite, which is bright green, and azurite, which is blue. Although such minerals may contain anything from 30 to 90 per cent. copper, not one of them occupies much of the ore body, but must be extracted from large masses of useless rock.

Although large deposits of copper ores are found at or near the surface of the earth, as at Utah in the United States and at Rio Tinto in Spain, the vast majority of ores are reached only by deep mining. New deposits are found by drilling boreholes by means of hollow drills. The nature of the different layers of rocks can be told by examining the drillings collected inside the hollow drill as it descends.

Reduced to Fine Powder

When the prospectors have indicated by borehole samples the nature and extent of a promising ore body, mine shafts are sunk to appropriate levels, and from these, tunnels are driven into the ore body, with cross-cuts to facilitate the removal of the ore. In this way a vast network of passages is made, connected by sloping ways or " raises." Large storage spaces are also made, and sometimes machinery for rough crushing is installed below ground. The main tunnels have light railways or conveyor belts to carry the ore from the inner workings to the mine shafts, whence the ore is raised to the surface.

To mine the ore, a chamber is excavated in the ore body and holes are drilled into the walls and roof. Charges

Rhokana Corporation Ltd.

GRINDING COPPER ORE IN BALL MILLS

Before the copper ore can be concentrated and taken to the furnaces for smelting, it must be crushed and then ground down to powder. The grinding is done in rod or ball mills which are steel containers holding some tons of loose steel balls or rods. By their rotating and cascading as the mill revolves these gradually grind the ore to powder.

HOW THE ORE IS SMELTED

The finely-ground ore passes through a series of flotation cells which separate the valuable part, the sulphide grains, from all the worthless matter. After the valuable part, called the concentrate, has been dried, thickened, filtered, and smelted in a reverberatory furnace, the "matte," as it is now known, is charged into a converter. This photograph shows a converter after being charged.

of explosives are rammed into the holes, and by means of long fuses groups of charges are exploded simultaneously, bringing down large masses of ore at a time. The ore obtained in this manner falls down chutes into storage spaces or into trucks. Coarse jaw crushers may reduce the larger lumps of ore before it is hoisted to the surface.

At the top of the mine, the ore is tipped on to an ore dump, from which it is drawn as required. Before it can be melted to extract the copper from it, the ore passes by conveyor belt to a series of crushing machines. Finally, it is mixed with water and fed into large cylinders containing tons of loose steel balls or rods which cascade down on the pieces of ore and grind them to a fine powder. Ore which is still not fine enough is separated by classifiers and returned to the grinding mills. A classifier is an inclined trough with a series of rakes, or a metal spiral, by

which the coarser material is pushed over the top and returned to the ball or rod mills. The now finely ground ore in water is allowed to flow to flotation cells, where the copper-rich particles are separated from the worthless rock. In each cell, pine oil is added to the mixture of ore and water, and air is forced up through the mixture, causing it to froth. The copper-bearing particles adhere to the froth and overflow the cell, while the useless rock particles sink to the bottom. A single plant may contain hundreds of these cells.

Ready for Smelting

The valuable matter, which is made up of copper and iron sulphides, is called concentrate. It is sent to thickeners, which are large tanks with revolving arms which draw the solid matter to the centre and allow most of the water to drain away. The remaining water is removed by suction filters. Excess sulphur may be removed from the concentrate at this stage by roasting.

The copper ore is now ready for smelting in a reverberatory furnace, in which the flames from a set of burners at one end pass over heaps of ore and fluxes spread over the hearth. The fluxes form a slag which takes up some of the impurities from the molten ore which is now called matte. The matte is still a mixture of copper and iron sulphides, and while in the molten state it is removed in ladles and charged into converters. In a converter, air is forced through the molten matte, and as it combines with the sulphur great heat is generated. The sulphur escapes as a gas, sulphur dioxide, and the iron goes into the slag, leaving crude copper. As the copper is poured into moulds, it bubbles, and the resulting large cakes of copper are known as "blister copper" from their blistered appearance.

Refining by Electrolysis

Blister copper is not fit for commercial use, as it may still contain small quantities of iron, sulphur, bismuth and other impurities, so it must be refined. The refining is done in another reverberatory furnace where the blister copper is melted. Air is blown through the molten metal to remove the impurities, and the final removal of oxygen is done by inserting long poles of green wood into the metal, a process called "poling." The refined copper is then tapped, the flow of metal being directed to a casting wheel carrying heavy moulds of the required shape to

Rhokana Corporation Ltd.

POURING THE MOLTEN COPPER

The copper "matte" is in the converter for about three hours, during which time all the iron is oxidised and slagged off, and the remaining sulphur is blown out. The converter is then tilted, as seen in this photograph, and the molten copper is poured into ladles and transferred to a heated holding or casting furnace.

International Nickel Company.

IN THE ELECTROLYTIC TANK HOUSE

To produce copper of high purity the electrolytic refining process is used whenever necessary. Here we have a view in the Electrolytic Tank House, showing the copper cathodes being removed from the tanks. In this process the insoluble impurities in the copper, including gold, silver, lead and tin, sink to the bottom of the tank, to be recovered later.

produce wire bars, billets, cakes or anode plates.

Copper of high purity can be obtained by fire refining, but if further refining is required this is done by electrolysis, using anodes made by fire refining. The anodes have lugs by which they hang in tanks between thin sheets of pure copper called starting sheets. The tanks contain dilute sulphuric acid and dissolved copper sulphate, and when an electric current passes through the tanks, the copper anodes dissolve and the copper passes to the starting sheets which grow in thickness, forming cathodes of pure copper. The impurities in the anodes, and any gold, silver or other valuable metals which may have remained in the copper through all the refining stages, settle to the bottom of the tanks as a sludge which is treated separately to recover the precious metals. The copper cathodes are taken to a furnace where they are melted, and the refined copper is poured into moulds, to form wire bars, billets or cakes.

Electrolytically refined copper, being of the highest purity, is specially suitable for electrical uses and for making high grade copper alloys.

Copper for the manufacturing industries is supplied as sheet and strip, bars, rods, wire and tubes. Over 180,000 tons of copper wire is made every year in Britain alone, to provide cables for electricity supply, telephones and telegraphs, submarine cables, and special cables for radio and television transmission. Copper sheet is widely employed as roofing for buildings, large and small, and for many kinds of chemical and other plant. Tubes of copper and copper alloys are used in buildings for water, gas, and sanitation services, and in many industries. Heavy copper tubes are employed as engraved rollers for printing.

The addition of other metals to copper produces a wide variety of copper alloys which are important in many industries. Mention has already been made of bronze, an alloy of copper and tin, and brass, an alloy of copper and zinc. These have many applications as castings, stampings and pressings, as well as in wire and tube forms.

FOR POWER AND PROTECTION

British Electricity Authority.

The electrical industry is largely dependent upon copper, particularly in the form of wire, because the electrical conductivity of copper is greater than that of any other metal, except silver. Actually, more than half of all the copper produced is now used in the electrical industry, and this photograph gives some indication of the miles of copper wire used in the transmission of electric power.

Copper Development Association.

In Roman times copper was used as a roofing material. Remains of this, after the passage of hundreds of years, were removed and again put to good use. The dome of the British Museum is roofed with copper, and so are the domes on the Old Bailey and the Bank of England, among other London buildings. Our photograph shows the copper roofing on Liverpool Cathedral.

A GREAT LINER'S PROPELLER

J. Stone & Co., Ltd.

In the shipbuilding industry copper and its alloys are used extensively. Here we see one of the four great propellers of the *Queen Elizabeth*. These propellers are made of high tensile brass, and each of them weighs over 30 tons. Brass, one of the best-known of the hundreds of copper alloys used in industry to-day, contains at least three-fifths copper, the remainder being mainly zinc,

Copper nickel alloys, familiar to us as coins, are highly resistant to corrosion and for that reason are employed in making chemical plant and for condenser tubes. Another copper alloy which does not corrode, aluminium bronze, has many industrial uses and has such an attractive appearance that it has been used for powder compacts and inexpensive jewellery. Nickel silver is a copper alloy which contains nickel and zinc but no silver, although it gets its name from its silvery appearance. Besides making handsome tableware it is produced in large quantities for electrical purposes. Cadmium copper is specially suited for trolley wires as it stands up to rough usage.

The list of copper alloys is almost unending, and includes special alloys such as tellurium copper, beryllium copper, chromium copper, and many others, each having its own combination of desirable properties while retaining for the most part the qualities which make copper itself a material so essential to modern civilization.

It is not only as a metal that copper is of great value in modern life. Copper chemicals are sprayed on potato and other plants to protect them from pests and diseases. Copper is a constituent of some anti-fouling paints used to protect ships' bottoms against marine growths. Copper is used to make coloured glass, in metallic printing inks, and for hundreds of other purposes.

One may safely say that there is scarcely an industry in which copper is not used in one form or another, and that it is as essential to-day as it has been all through its long history.

Copper Development Association.

A LOCOMOTIVE FIREBOX OF COPPER PLATE

In this photograph is seen a new locomotive firebox, made of heavy copper plate, and on a smaller scale is inset a modern locomotive in which, besides the firebox, many fittings are made of copper or of one of its alloys, such as brass.

ZINC, THE GALVANISING METAL

CHARGING THE RETORTS WITH BRIQUETTES

The most modern method of extracting zinc from its ore is by pyro-metallurgy (extracting by heat) by the American Vertical Retort process, and in this photograph the vertical retorts are seen while being charged with coked briquettes.

THERE are a number of ores from which zinc is extracted, but only two can be considered of importance; blende, the sulphide of zinc, and calamine, the carbonate. Blende is the more abundant and therefore the principal source to-day.

Unlike many metals which are mined, zinc does not occur on its own, but is associated with the ores of lead, silver, copper and sometimes tin, often forming extensive deposits of a very complex nature.

Extraction of Zinc

There are two main principles in operation for the extraction of zinc from its ore:

(1) Pyro-metallurgy, or extraction by heat.

(2) Electrolytic, or extraction from a solution of zinc salts by an electric current.

The most modern method of zinc extraction by pyro-metallurgy is the American Vertical Retort process.

There are three such plants in America, one in Germany, and one in England, at Avonmouth, near Bristol.

Applications of Zinc

Though one of the most important metals in everyday use, zinc often passes unrecognised and thus is not treated with the respect it so richly deserves.

Brass, that ubiquitous metal, is an alloy of copper and zinc; it is manufactured in the form of sheets, tubes, rods and wire, castings and forgings; it is used for making anything from brass buttons to the propellers of R.M.S. *Queen Mary*.

Think of the number of items which one sees daily that are galvanised. A galvanised article is one of iron or steel which is fabricated and afterwards dipped into a bath of molten zinc. The reason for galvanising is that zinc will not rust, and when enveloped the iron and steel are efficiently protected from rusting. A galvanised article will withstand the rain and damp atmosphere for many, many years.

We will take a few examples which will indicate the wide sphere of usage. To ensure a long and perfectly safe life, the pylons which carry electrical current across the countryside are galvanised. The farmer enjoys longevity of much of his equipment by the fact that it is protected from rust: his buckets, food stock bins, feeding troughs, barbed wire, and even the roofs of his barns. At home many examples can be found; such items as buckets and watering cans are galvanised, and most likely the steel window-frames of the house, before they are coated with paint.

Though galvanising is the most used method of coating with zinc, there are other methods which have their own particular applications, such as when a bridge is to receive the protection of zinc. This is far too large to be galvanised; it is therefore sprayed with zinc. Small objects such as screws and nails are sherardised; this entails the ob-jects being placed in a container in which there is a quantity of zinc powder. The container is sealed and slowly revolved in a furnace. The zinc impregnates the surface of the iron, forming an inner iron-zinc alloy, merging into a zinc-iron alloy, and finally, on the surface, pure zinc.

Another method of coating articles with zinc is by plating; this method is limited to components of such size that they can be disposed conveniently in a plating tank. Electro-deposited zinc coatings find wide application for protecting from rust many articles fabricated from sheet steel. They are also employed on wire and on nuts and bolts and similar small components.

Rolled zinc, which is made by rolling slabs of zinc into sheets, is used extensively in the building industry for roofing, gutterings, and waste-pipes. Large quantities are used for the cases of dry electric batteries owing to its special electro-chemical properties. Printers use sheet zinc widely for their

ROASTING THE ZINC ORE
This photograph shows the sintering machines which roast the zinc ore and extract the sulphur-dioxide gas before the ore is distilled.

CRUSHING MILLS AND COKERS

In these four Chilean mills the mixture of sintered zinc, crushed coal and binding material is crushed and bound together to make the briquettes in the first stages of extracting the pure zinc from the blende.

There are several ores from which zinc is obtained, but blende (sulphide of zinc) is the main source of supply. After the ore has been crushed, it is pressed into the form of briquettes. These are then " coked " before going to the vertical retorts, where the pure zinc is extracted. This photograph shows the briquettes being discharged from the cokers.

lithographic plates owing to the fact that the material is easily etched.

Small quantities of other metals are added to zinc of the highest commercial purity, which is 99·99 per cent., to produce a zinc alloy sold under the trade name of Mazak. Mazak is used for pressure die casting. Pressure die casting is the name given to describe the action of forcing molten metal under pressure into a steel mould for the production of castings, which can be extremely complex. It is a process which is unexcelled for rapid production of parts.

The number of articles produced from Mazak is legion. They vary from zip fasteners to motor-car radiator grilles, carburettors to model railway engines. It is a durable material to which organic or chemical or plated finishes can be applied.

Though zinc is applied in various forms to many other everyday uses it cannot be left without some mention of the very important zinc pigments. One of these is zinc oxide, a fine white powder which is used in paints and enamels as a pigment, and as an ingredient in rubber to make it tough and resilient; it is used in linoleum and leathercloth too. In pharmacy its antiseptic qualities find outlet in zinc ointments, adhesive plasters, soaps and cosmetics.

Another product is zinc sulphide; this is the basis of one of the most important white pigments, known as lithopone. Lithopone was invented by Mr. John Bryson Orr, a Scottish chemist, in 1898. Mr. Orr, when experimenting, discovered that a mixture of sulphide of zinc and sulphate of barium made a white pigment of great opacity. Its chief uses are in the paint, linoleum and rubber industries, where it is used as a basis for bright colours; it is used also in many other manufactures, such as cable, leathercloth, celluloid, asbestos and paper.

CASTING ZINC SLABS

The number of articles of everyday use which have been " galvanised," or coated with zinc, is legion, while sheet zinc is used extensively in many trades. Here we see high purity zinc being cast into slabs, in which form it is easily handled.

TIN AND TIN PLATE

Photos by courtesy of the Tin Research Institute.

IN A MODERN FRUIT-CANNING FACTORY

Canned foods have become an essential part of our daily menus, and the " tin-opener " is an important item of kitchen equipment. For fruit-canning, high-grade hot-dipped coatings of tin are used, and here we see the " tin cans " being filled with fruit. How tin is obtained and its many uses are dealt with in these pages.

TIN is found in the form of oxide, cassiterite, sulphide, and stannite; very rarely is it found as native tin. The ore is usually sparsely scattered through igneous rocks, of which granite is typical, as an intrusion into the cracks which developed when the rock was cooling after solidifying from the molten state. These intrusions take the form of thin veins, or, occasionally, of small isolated lodes.

In Cornwall, these veins or lodes are generally at a fairly steep slope to the horizontal; they vary in thickness from a millimetre up to several inches, but each vein may be many yards in width. Veins and lodes of tin are located at all depths down to 3,000 feet or even lower.

In Bolivia similar granite masses containing tin form a high plateau of the Andes mountains, rising from 12,000 to 15,000 ft. Other lode mining areas are in the mountains of Czechoslovakia, and in the north of Spain; there is also a lode mine at Pahang in Malaya.

The alluvial mining areas in Malaya, Indonesia, and elsewhere, have come about by the granite rock being reduced during millions of years to fine sand, and in some cases to kaolin (china clay). The cassiterite is found in fine particles in alluvial mud and gravel brought down from the mountains by the rivers.

At present the total world production of tin in ore is some 167,000 tons a year. Lode mining in Bolivia yields 31,000 tons; in Europe, including Cornwall, 2,700 tons are produced; from alluvial mining Malaya produces 58,000 tons; Indonesia 32,000; Siam 10,000, while the Belgian Congo produces some 15,000 tons annually. China 3,600, Nigeria 8,000, Australia

2,000 tons, with another 5,000 tons from other countries, completes the world's supply.

It is obviously cheaper to recover the tin ore from alluvial deposits, already naturally disintegrated, than from lode mines where miners have to blast and hew tunnels through one of the hardest of rocks.

Mining Alluvial Ore

Various methods are used in mining alluvial tin ore, but usually it is done in open-cast quarries or by dredging. In open-cast working the top soil is removed to expose the tin-bearing clay or gravel, and the pit is continually enlarged and deepened in terraces. Where bull-dozers, scrapers, drag-lines, and power-operated shovels can be used, the open-cast terraces are worked simultaneously at several levels, and the crude ore is carried away to the washing station nearby. In some areas mechanised methods are unsuitable and hand shovels are used, the ore being transported in baskets.

Another method is to wash away the sides of the pit with powerful water hydrants; the mud bearing the tin collects in sumps and is brought by gravel pumps to the top of a long ramp (or palong, as it is known in Malaya) sloping down into the pit, and divided every few yards by a cross board where the tin ore can sink while lighter material passes over.

The most effective method, however, is to form a lake or paddock in the deposit and launch into it a bucket-dredge assembled beside it. The boom with its chain of huge buckets may be capable of reaching 150 feet depth, and the dredge is firmly tied to the bank so as to enable the buckets to scrape away the tin-bearing earth. The sand and clay brought up by the buckets is discharged into a rotary sieve or trommel in which jets of water free the heavy tin ore.

Crude tin ore obtained by these methods is crushed, washed, and sieved; it may contain some iron and copper oxides and sulphides, or other valuable metals, which are then separated. This is done by a flotation process in which oil is used. Further processes are used to obtain a good separation, after which the dry "concentrate," containing about 70 per cent. of tin, is sent to the smelter.

Refining is generally done in a reverberatory furnace where the molten metal lies in a shallow pool a little below the arched ceiling of fire-clay from which the heat of burning gases is reflected into the metal. Further purification is effected after this treatment in the furnace, and, indeed, the refining operations are repeated many times before the highest quality of pure tin is obtained.

Properties and Uses

Tin has a low melting point (232° C.); is able to resist corrosion, and, when molten, to "wet" cleaned surfaces of steel, copper, brass and other metals, and to adhere to them after cooling down; it is ductile (flexible), and it will alloy with many common metals. Its main uses are for coating, for alloys, and in chemical compounds. Coatings are applied by either electrodeposition or by hot-dipping. In addition, tin coatings may be produced on articles by spraying them with fine particles of tin, or by immersing them in solutions of certain tin compounds.

In the electrodeposition method the cleaned article is suspended as the cathode in a tank containing the electrolyte, which is a solution of sodium stannate ($Na_2SN O_3$) or of stannous sulphate ($Sn So_4$). Anodes of pure tin are suspended two or three inches from the object. A current of about 15 to 30 amperes per square foot, and at from 3 to 5 volts usually, is passed for a few minutes, or, if a thick deposit (one-hundredth of an inch) is required, for as long as an hour. The sodium stannate bath works at 80° C., but the stannous sulphate bath can be

DREDGING FOR TIN

Nederlandisch Foto Bureau.

The larger part of the world's tin supply is got from tinstone, black oxide of tin, found near the surface mixed with gravel or earth. This huge floating dredge is scooping up tin-bearing gravel with its great steel buckets. These dredges are so efficient that it is worth while treating deposits containing as little as one pound of tin ore in three tons of sand and clay.

IN A CORNISH TIN MINE

Cornish tin was used by the ancient Phoenicians and the Romans. To-day, Cornwall still produces tin, but the mines have become deeper and water seeps in, as seen in this photograph of trimmers hauling trucks in the East Pool Mine.

wiping (" wiped " tin coatings).

Hot-dipped coatings generally range from one-thousandth of an inch down to half this when freely drained. In tin plate manufacture, coatings down to about one tenth this thickness can be obtained by squeezing off surplus tin between rollers working in hot palm oil.

Tinplates usually carry about 70-millionths of an inch of tin upon each side. The manufacture of tinplate began three or four centuries ago with the hand-tinning of small sheets of iron, and then about a century ago the process became mechanised. Twenty-five years or so ago, methods of producing steel sheet in continuous coils were developed in the U.S.A. This continuous sheet is preferred for tinplate manufacture because it is purer, more ductile, and more free from defects. It has to be cut up into sheets before it can be tinned.

The electrolytic variety of tinplate is always produced in continuous coils. The steel coil passes at speeds of five to ten miles an hour through long, shallow baths containing tin compounds in solution. Current passes in from pure tin bars (anodes) immersed in the solution, causing them to dissolve, and passes out through the strip of steel, depositing tin on it at the same time. After washing and drying, the strip is " flow-brightened " by passing the coil quickly through a zone which is just hot enough to fuse the tin coating.

The rate of deposition of tin is slow and very long baths would be needed to deposit the same thickness of tin as there is on ordinary tinplate. Electrolytic tinplate coatings are therefore thinner, generally about a third of the coatings with hot-dipped tinplate.

worked cold. This process is much used for tinning parts which are to be soldered later.

Coatings of tin can be produced also on steel, copper and brass without passing any external current, merely by tying round them a wire of aluminium and immersing in hot sodium stannate for a few minutes, or up to two or three hours if necessary. This method is useful for inaccessible places.

Tin coatings by the hot-dipping process are produced by cleaning the surface, covering with a flux solution, and heating in contact with molten tin. The tin may be molten in a pot, or applied as a wire or powder which is then melted on the metal surface; excess tin is drained off by gravity, or by spinning the article, or by

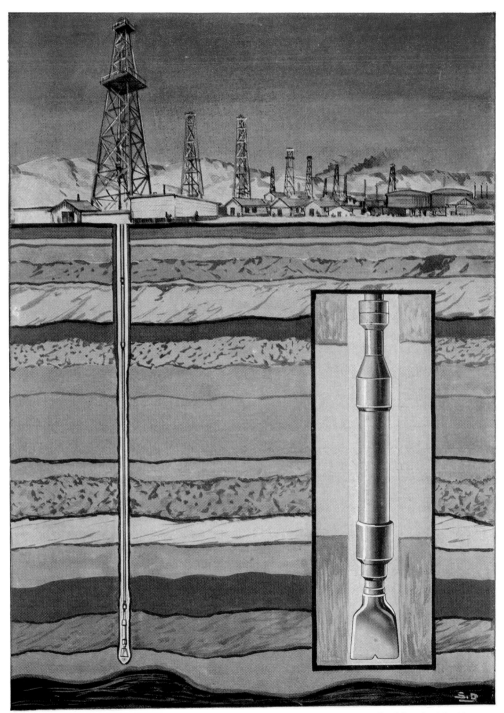

Specially painted for this work.

BORING FOR OIL BY TURBINE

This picture illustrates one of the modern methods of drilling oil-wells. Liquid mud is pumped at high pressure through a non-revolving pipe to a " turbo " drill (shown on an enlarged scale on the right) at the bottom of the well. The casing of the " turbo " which is fixed to the pipe and therefore cannot revolve, contains a small turbine. As the mud flows through the turbine it makes it turn. The turbine's shaft is connected with the drill through gearing, so the drill also is rotated. Having done its work, the mud escapes at the bottom of the casing and flows back to the surface outside the pipe.

Specially painted for this work.

COSTUMES THROUGH THE CENTURIES

The manufacture of woollen cloth for wearing apparel is one of Britain's oldest industries, and to-day both woollen and cotton goods are among our most important exports. In this picture we have a pageant of the dress worn in this country at different periods. It will be seen that until comparatively recent times men as well as women favoured brightly-coloured costumes. Trunk hose, reaching from foot to thigh, were succeeded by breeches, and it was not until the nineteenth century that trousers became the fashion. For women, the long skirt persisted until modern times.

For canned foods of the more corrosive types, such as fruits, hot-dipped coatings of high-grade are used. The electrolytic grade, with or without the addition of one or more coats of lacquer, has a large field in packing less corrosive foods and for dry materials such as coffee.

Hot-dipped coatings are generally used for milk cans and other dairy equipment, whether of steel, copper or gunmetal, and also for kitchen equipment such as mincers, sieves, mixing-bowls, etc.

Sprayed tin coatings are commonly used for large pieces of equipment that cannot be handled by ordinary means, such as large dough mixers, milk tanks and food-preparing vats.

Immersion coatings are extensively used on pins, eyelets, and similar small articles, particularly screws and other threaded parts where clogging of the thread must be avoided.

Tin coatings as a preparation for soldering are preferably of the hot-dipped kind, but may be of tin-lead alloy instead of tin.

Steel and copper wire are tinned by drawing them through baths of molten tin or tin-lead alloy and wiping off the excess tin by means of a rubber or asbestos wiper.

Pure tin is used for the manufacture of high quality foils for electrical condensers and for wrapping cheese and a few other food products. Additions of less than 2 per cent. of antimony and copper are made to the tin in such cases.

The addition of about 4 per cent. antimony and up to 2 per cent. of copper produces pewter and Britannia metal, which are mostly used for decorative purposes, but are also useful as corrosion-resisting alloys for contact with vinegar and certain other common substances.

Jewellery can be cast quite cheaply in this alloy, using rubber moulds. The addition of 7 to 10 per cent. antimony and from 2 to 7 per cent. copper transforms tin into bearing metal of the

GOING DOWN IN THE LIFT

A good deal of the world's supply of tin is now obtained from alluvial mining, but lode mining also produces 34,000 tons annually, of which Cornwall supplies some 2,700 tons. In this photograph a group of miners is seen just before going down in the lift to the deep workings.

highest quality for use in reciprocating engines. With even higher proportions of antimony, the alloy is harder and is much used for soda siphon tops and pressure die-cast counter mechanisms, valves for gas meters, etc. Other alloys of tin are used for the bearings of such appliances as electric motor dynamos, ships' propellers, and railway carriages and wagons.

Solders may have 100 per cent. tin down to about 20 per cent., and even much lower for special purposes. It depends on the work for which the solder is required.

One might go on at considerable length in mentioning all the articles in which tin and its alloys are used. Type metals are made of lead hardened with 15 per cent. of antimony, and toughened with from 4 to 12 per cent. of tin; the more tin the tougher the type and the longer it will last without becoming worn and flattened.

Bronze is an alloy of about 90 per cent. copper and 10 per cent. tin. Gunmetals are similar but contain from 2 to 5 per cent. of zinc as well. Bell metal is bronze with about 20 to 25 per cent. of tin. The colour is a greyish pink, and this alloy is extremely hard and resonant.

Since the introduction of the electrolytic process of manufacturing tinplate, the most important compounds of tin are those needed for electro-deposition: stannous sulphate and sodium stannate. More stannous sulphate is used than stannate.

Tin oxide is generally prepared from tin metal or tin recovered from scrap, since the natural oxide (cassiterite, tin ore) is not capable of being purified sufficiently. It is a dense white powder, insoluble in water and acids, and only slightly soluble in strong alkalis, but is dissolved by fused caustic soda. Its chief use is in ceramics and in porcelain enamels used on iron and steel, for which it is unsurpassed. Organic compounds of tin, such as dibutyl tin maleate, have in recent years become important in the manufacture of clear plastics, as they prevent the spontaneous clouding and darkening to which some types of plastic products are liable.

A TIN MINE IN BOLIVIA

High up in the Andes, granite masses containing tin form a plateau at 12,000 to 15,000 feet. Working at this altitude is difficult and inevitably costly, but some 31,000 tons of tin are produced annually in Bolivia. Our photograph shows the portal and main haulage level of a Bolivian tin mine.

THE STORY OF ALUMINIUM

Topical Press.

THE FIRST BRIDGE MADE OF ALUMINIUM ALLOY

Many experiments have been made to combine the lightness of aluminium with other materials having strength and toughness. These experiments have produced valuable alloys and in this photograph is seen the first aluminium alloy bascule bridge in the world. It spans the junction between the Hudson and Hendon Docks at Sunderland, and was opened in November, 1948.

ALMOST every kitchen nowadays contains some saucepans, kettles and other cooking utensils made of aluminium. And for a very good reason, since this silvery-looking metal is only about one-third as heavy as iron, conducts heat excellently, does not tarnish or rust, can be cleaned easily, and will stand a lot of knocking about.

The qualities of lightness and freedom from rusting make aluminium useful for many other purposes, such as the crank-cases of motor cars, name-plates, mats, ornamental fittings, reflectors, telescope tubes, and so on. The metal conducts electricity so well that large quantities are made every year into wires for insulated cables and overhead conductors, and parts of electrical apparatus.

Aluminium is one of the commonest elements in Nature. An acre of clay-land contains tons of it; even in a small back-garden aluminium lurks in no mean quantities.

But it is always combined with other elements—oxygen, hydrogen, sodium, chlorine, silicon—and the difficulty of separating it from them made it a very expensive metal, costing at one time much more than silver. About the year 1890 a method of parting it from its companions by means of electricity came into use. The price then fell with startling rapidity, and to-day aluminium costs hardly more than copper.

Between Rods and Lining

The story of aluminium begins in a deposit of a kind of clay, named bauxite, near Arles, in France, or Larne, Ireland, in the U.S.A., or in British Guiana, and recently in Australia. This mineral is white or red in colour, and a chemist would describe it as impure hydrated oxide of aluminium, which means a combination of oxygen, aluminium and water.

To pick up all the threads we have also to go to Greenland, where is found a great abundance of another compound of metal, called cryolite or Greenland spar. This substance can also be produced artificially for use in making aluminium.

We must next put on our list a great electrical power-station, where electricity is generated cheaply by falling water—at Niagara, at Kinlochleven, in Scotland, in Tasmania and elsewhere.

Imagine, then, the bauxite and cryolite brought together at the factory, which itself is near the power-station. In the factory are large carbon crucibles, each having an iron plate in the bottom, and over each box is a bundle of carbon rods. The iron plate is connected with the negative pole of the electric generators and the rods with the other pole.

By Electric Flame

A man lowers the rods against the lining and draws them away again. An intensely hot arc, or electric flame, is created between the rods and the lining. Cryolite is thrown in, and the intense heat melts the cryolite. Then bauxite is added in a steady stream. The aluminium in it is melted out and sinks through the cryolite to the bottom of the crucible, from which it is drawn off at intervals. The oxygen in the bauxite combines with the carbon of the rods to form a gas, which passes off into the air.

Aluminium is a very " kindly " metal to work. It allows itself to be rolled out, or drawn into wire, or squeezed and hammered to any desired shape. For saucepans, it is rolled into sheets, out of which circular pieces are stamped. Then each piece is placed between dies and its edges are turned up, and, behold! the body of a saucepan. To this a handle is riveted to make the article complete. The saucepan is a good thick one, holds half a gallon, and weighs 14 ounces. Its cast-iron com-panion, of the same size, weighs over 3 pounds.

As an Alloy

Pure aluminium is not a very strong metal. But if mixed with a small proportion of other metals, such as copper, zinc and iron, it makes a very light but strong alloy. These aluminium alloys are used for the pistons and connecting-rods of motor car engines. Engines of this kind have to run at very high speed, and they may make up to 5,000 revolutions a minute. Every time a piston reaches the end of a stroke it and its connecting-rod have to be stopped and moved in the opposite direction. The saving of even a few ounces is therefore a great gain, as the engine then has to waste much less power in repeatedly checking and speeding-up these parts.

Aluminium is used in an interesting way for welding tramline rails together end to end. A mould of fire-clay is first arranged on each side of the join and below it, to prevent the escape of the metal poured in to fill the space. A large crucible, rather like a flower-pot in shape, is placed over the joint and filled with a mixture of powdered aluminium and oxide of iron.

When the mixture is set alight by a special fuse, the oxygen in the oxide combines with the aluminium so fiercely that the iron is melted out and heated far above the melting-point of iron. The workman now presses down a lever, which makes a hole in the bottom of the crucible for the iron to run out through. The liquid iron not only fills the gap between the rails but melts their ends, so that when the joint cools the two rails become one.

Hundreds of experiments have been made by metallurgists to discover ways in which the desirable property of lightness which distinguishes aluminium from most other metals could be combined with other properties such as high strength, toughness, and freedom from corrosion. The first important discovery which was made was that if a small amount of copper and a still smaller amount of manganese were added to pure aluminium, the hardness and strength were considerably improved. It was also found that if this metal is heated and quenched and then left to " age " for some time, its properties improve very considerably. This metal is known as Duralumin.

Many other aluminium alloys have been developed, and a method has also been perfected for producing Duralumin sheet with pure aluminium on each side to protect it from corrosion. This material, which has been largely used for aircraft, is called " Alclad."

British Aluminium Co. Ltd.

A " BREAKING-DOWN " MILL

The first stage of the flattening-out process, known as " breaking-down," is done in this machine, which shows the hot rolling of strong alloy strip in a 96 in. wide " breaking-down " mill at the Falkirk Rolling Mills.

Lighter than Aluminium

A metal which weighs even less than aluminium is magnesium. Practically every schoolboy will remember the laboratory experiment with magnesium ribbon which can be set on fire to give a blinding white light accompanied by clouds of white smoke. Although magnesium is so readily inflammable when it is in the form of a ribbon or a very thin strip, it can be used quite safely when it is formed into the shapes and sizes required by engineers in the construction of aircraft and aircraft equipment.

By mixing small quantities of other metals with it, *e.g.*, aluminium and manganese, magnesium can be used for the production of alloys which have extreme lightness combined with reasonable strength. One of the best known of the aluminium-magnesium alloys is Magnalium.

The problem of light-weight metals has become increasingly important in recent years. In the construction of aircraft and motor-cars its advantages are obvious, but the use of aluminium alloys is extending steadily in many directions. In the building industry, for example, gutterings and downpipes made of aluminium last much longer than the older types. Then in all

Planet News.

FIRST SKYSCRAPER BUILT OF ALUMINIUM

This 25-storey skyscraper has been erected at 99 Park Avenue, New York, the first ever to be built entirely of aluminium. The building is completely air-conditioned and all windows are kept locked. One floor, the sixth by British reckoning, has been taken by the British Consulate-General and the British delegation to the United Nations. It is within walking distance of the United Nations building.

Sunderland, and in 1950 the first all-aluminium highway bridge in the world was opened in Canada near the big hydro-electric plant at Shipshaw belonging to the Aluminium Company of Canada.

Australia's New Industry

The biggest producer of aluminium in the world is the United States. Among the countries importing all their aluminium supplies from the U.S.A. has been Australia, where about 10,000 tons of the metal are needed every year. During the war there were many difficulties in obtaining this quantity, and Australia decided in 1941 to produce her own aluminium at home.

It was not possible to go ahead with a project of this kind during the war years, but between 1946 and 1953 the Australian Aluminium Production Committee set to work. Aided by the experienced advice of the British Aluminium Company, field surveyors searched throughout the country for deposits of bauxite and many thousands of samples were tested, while other experts studied methods of production. Deposits of bauxite were found at Inverell in New

branches of the food industry, including the manufacture of dairy utensils, aluminium is used increasingly, as it is in engineering for making pistons, cylinder blocks and other engine parts. In 1948 the first bascule bridge of aluminium was opened in Britain, at

South Wales, in Victoria, and at Ouse (near Hobart) and St. Leonards (near Launceston) in Tasmania. These deposits will be sufficient for at least 100 years of production. Other sources for the supply of bauxite are Wessel Island, some 400 miles north-east of Darwin, and from Malaya.

It is in Tasmania that the first aluminium manufacturing plant in the southern hemisphere has been built. Bell Bay, thirty-four miles by road north of Launceston, is the site of Australia's new addition to her ever-growing list of industries. The electric power is supplied by the Tasmanian Hydro-Electric Commission. A new town is growing at Bell Bay, and here 13,000 tons of aluminium ingot will be produced every year. Whatever difficulties may arise in the world, Australia will no longer be dependent on other countries for the aluminium which is so important in many of her industries. All the aluminium she needs can be produced at home.

The uses of aluminium are extending in every direction, particularly in the making of lightweight fittings, as already noted. In New York, however, an all-aluminium skyscraper was built in 1953–54 and may possibly lead to new methods of building in very restricted areas. In Britain, railway companies have been experimenting with electric trains built almost entirely of aluminium, and the results so far have been very promising, to put it mildly.

Aircraft and trains, bridges and skyscrapers, as well as many hundreds of smaller things, are all making use of aluminium. There has been nothing sensational about the steadily expanding use of this remarkable metal and its alloys, but few limits can be placed upon it to-day regarding the part it will play in the future.

Aluminium Company of Canada.

AN ALL-ALUMINIUM HIGHWAY BRIDGE

Britain had the first all-aluminium bascule bridge connecting two docks at Sunderland, but the first all-aluminium highway bridge, 504 feet in length, was opened in Canada in 1950. It spans the Saguenay River at Arvida, Quebec. In the background can be seen one of the power houses of the Shipshaw hydro-electric plant which supplies current to the works of the Aluminium Company of Canada.

THE METAL OF SATURN—LEAD

Photos by courtesy of Associated Lead Manufacturers, Ltd.

LEAD WORKS AND SHOT TOWER AT CHESTER

Lead was one of the metals known to the ancients and its uses are many. The Shot Tower seen in this photograph of the lead works at Chester was constructed about 1800 and is over 156 feet high. Inside it is a spiral steel staircase having 198 steps. This tower is still in operation making shot to-day.

ONCE I had to examine the sea-bottom round the end of a pier. To do this it was necessary for me to get into a diving-dress, a costume which I had never before had occasion to wear. When it was on me, my feet were encased in boots with leaden soles, weighing about 16 pounds apiece. The last items of the outfit to be attached to me, as I stood on the ladder leading down into the water, were two flat plates of lead, each scaling 40 pounds, fixed one on my back and the other on my chest.

"Heavy as Lead"

At this stage I realised the full meaning of the expression, "heavy as lead." I felt almost crushed under the unusual load. But as soon as I was in the water, with the dress blown out by the air pumped in, I knew that every pound of it was needed to keep me on the bottom and reasonably steady on my legs. Had the weights slipped off, I should have bobbed up to the surface like a cork.

Heaviness, then, is a very obvious quality of this metal, and one that makes it useful wherever a great deal of weight without very much bulk is needed at reasonable cost. Racing yachts, for example, carry many tons of it—anything up to 100 tons—in their deep keels to overcome the capsizing effect of their huge sails. We use leaden bullets and shot because, among other reasons, they travel farther than would bullets and shot made of a lighter metal, if discharged at the same speed.

Lead is not, however, by any means the heaviest of metals. Let us just see where it stands in this respect among its fellows: A block of lead measuring a foot every way weighs 710 pounds, which is about eleven and a half times the weight of the same bulk of water. One of zinc would scale 427 pounds, one of

VEINS OF GALENA

This close-up photograph of lead ore on top of a loaded wagon shows the veins of galena, from which the lead is extracted, in the large stone before crushing.

cast iron about 470 pounds, one of copper 547 pounds, and one of silver 650 pounds. So lead has all of these metals well beaten as regards weight. But it is easily outweighed by quick-silver, with its 847 pounds to the cubic foot; by gold, at 1,200 pounds; by platinum, at 1,260 pounds; and by the very rare metal, iridium, which, when compressed by hammering, weighs just twice as much as lead.

Lead and its Uses

Besides great weight—which is not always an advantage—lead has other qualities which make it useful to us. It is easily melted and cast into any desired form. It is so soft that it can be readily rolled or moulded by beating while cold. It is acted upon hardly at all by air and water, and is wonderfully durable. You may see to-day in the British Museum lead pipes and fittings used by the Romans 2,000 years ago, and still practically " as good as new."

About 1½ million tons of lead are used up every year. Of this over 500,000 tons a year are used in the manufacture of electrical accumulator plates, while about 300,000 tons are forced in a semi-molten state through dies to form pipes or in making electric cables. In addition, considerable quantities of lead are rolled out into sheets

for covering the flat parts of roofs and for lining tanks, while about 250 tons are used in red lead and litharge and another 50,000 tons in white lead.

Then there are the valuable alloys of lead, including pewter and solder, while a mixture of lead and antimony gives us type-metal, without which the printing industry could scarcely exist.

Lead plays a very important part also in connection with our water supplies, for when water mains are laid the joints between the pipes are made water-tight by hammering lead tightly into them. We have its help even when drinking water, since tumblers, like many other glass articles, contain a large proportion of lead—though it is quite invisible. Even our teacups and saucers may have lead in them, as lead forms part of some glazes used on chinaware and pottery. Lead was at one time used in making the popular " tin " soldiers and many similar toys, but other lighter materials, particularly plastics, are more generally used to-day.

It will be seen, however, that if some magician could by a wave of his hand banish all lead from the world we should be in a sorry plight as water burst in or

CONCENTRATING THE LEAD

Much of the earthy material is separated during the crushing of the ore; later, the lead is concentrated by the flotation process which is seen in this photograph.

IN THE LAKE DISTRICT

It is very probable that the Greenside Mine was first discovered in Roman times. Situated about a mile from Lake Ullswater on the eastern slopes of the Helvellyn range, it is the oldest producing mine in the North of England.

out upon us in all directions, electrical cables broke down, paint peeled off on every hand, and a number of other very unpleasant things happened.

A Little Word-family

The Latin word for lead, *plumbum*, is the father of several English words in common use. Two of them, " plumb " and " plummet," signify a heavy weight (usually of lead) attached to the end of a cord, to plumb (in the sense of find the depth of) water or deep holes. A sailor plumbs the sea when he takes soundings by " heaving the lead." A mason plumbs a wall when he tests its uprightness by means of his plumb-bob. To plumb may, again, mean to work in lead. A man who does such work is called a plumber, and his work is plumbing.

Then we have the word plumb as an adjective, meaning vertical. The famous Leaning Tower of Pisa, in Italy, is out of plumb—out of the perpendicular—by rather more than 16 feet. Plumbago, called also blacklead, has crept

into the family under false pretences; for plumbago has nothing whatever to do with lead, being pure carbon.

We have already mentioned small-shot. Have you ever wondered how the pellets came to be as perfectly spherical as if each had been cast separately in a tiny mould? One cannot imagine shot-makers using moulds and making a profit. As a matter of fact, they let Nature do the moulding for them.

Molten lead, mixed with a little antimony to make it more fluid, is poured through a sieve fixed at the top of a tall tower or old mine-shaft. The sieve is punched with holes as large across as the shot is to be. The lead flows through these holes in many streams, which break up into drops as they fall, and each drop has time to obey a law of Nature and become a sphere before, after travelling 150 feet or 200 feet, it reaches a tank of cold water and hardens instantly.

Now some of the pellets get knocked out of shape. They are sorted from the perfect shot in a simple but ingenious way. All the shot is sent down a sloping chute. The perfect shot get up enough speed to leap over a gutter lurking at the bottom, while the badly-shaped ones, hobbling along at a slower gait, fail to do so, and are trapped.

Where Lead Comes From

At one time British mines yielded over 70,000 tons of lead a year, and a large army of miners was employed in the lead-mines of Derbyshire, Northumberland, Cumberland, Yorkshire, Somerset, the Isle of Man, and several places in Wales and Scotland. To-day the British output is not much more than about 4,000 tons a year, but it is still carried on, with modern machinery. One of the largest lead mines in England is the Greenside Mine situated in the Lake District, about a mile from Lake Ullswater, on the eastern slopes of the Helvellyn mountain range. It is probable that this mine was discovered in the days of the Romans, though modern operations date only from the latter part of the eighteenth century. In the early days horses were used to carry the ore from the mine to the neighbourhood of Keswick for smelting.

To-day the United States is the largest producer of lead and over one-quarter of the world's supply comes from there; Mexico supplies 230,000 tons, Australia 200,000 tons, and Canada 150,000 tons. No other country produces more than 100,000 tons, and Spain's output is now only about 40,000 tons annually.

The two chief lead ores are named galena and cerussite. The first of these, which is sulphide of lead, has a sparkling crystalline and silvery appearance. Small pieces of it were often used in the crystal detectors of early wireless sets. Cerussite, which is carbonate of lead, occurs as white or coloured crystals. The metal is extracted from the ore by smelting in a furnace.

Queer Beliefs about Lead

Most lead contains more or less silver, which is separated from the lead if the quantity present justifies the expense of doing so. The oldest of the several processes used is named cupellation. The lead is heated in a furnace and air is blown over it. The oxygen in the air joins forces with the lead and forms lead oxide, also called litharge. The silver refuses to combine and is left behind. The lead in the litharge can be recovered by mixing the substance with carbon and heating it, when the oxygen in it goes into partnership with the carbon as carbonic acid gas and parts company with the lead.

In his " Canterbury Tales," the old English poet, Chaucer, tells us that each of the seven metals then known was connected with one of the heavenly bodies. Gold belonged to the sun, silver to the moon, quicksilver to Mercury, iron to Mars, tin to Jupiter, copper to Venus, and lead to Saturn.

WITH THE TAPPING GANG
Here we have a view inside the Refining Shop at the Associated Lead Manufacturers' works at Millwall, showing the tapping gang at work as the molten lead runs into the moulds.

The last-named planet had a very bad reputation among astrologers, for Saturn was none other than old Father Time, who reaps away men's lives with his scythe. And lead was looked upon as the worst of metals, because many compounds of it are very poisonous to man, beast and vegetation. So, in the sharing out of metals, Saturn very properly was made a present of lead.

The old alchemists taught that lead, like all other solid metals, was derived from quicksilver and sulphur. They hoped that, by purifying the mixture, they would change the " base " metals, of which lead is one, into the " noble " metal gold. In their hunt for a short cut to wealth they used up great quantities of lead; and it is not surprising that, instead of adding to their riches, many of them had to part with such gold as they already possessed.

Lead, however, has figured in history both for its harmful as well as its many useful properties. It is mentioned in the Old Testament in Numbers and in Job, and it constituted part of the spoils which the Israelites took from the Midianites. The Romans, as we have seen, worked lead mines in England, and the archæologists have found some fine examples of the lead work of early Saxon times.

On the dark side is the danger of lead-poisoning which was at one time a serious threat to workers in industries where the metal is used. Workers in the Potteries employ lead glaze, while painters, plumbers, printers and others have suffered unpleasant consequences due to minute quantities of lead being absorbed over a long period. Among the ill-effects was a kind of paralysis which attacked the nerves of the arm and produced a condition known as " wrist-drop."

Preventive measures are now taken to protect workers liable to be affected; these include the wearing of overalls, and, where necessary, respirators; baths are provided and employers must see that they are used by the workers where it is considered necessary; frequent medical examinations are made, and acid drinks are provided : these tend to remove any lead from the system.

In such ways the ill-effects of lead among those who use it have been greatly diminished; it may be assumed that among the many wonders science has wrought in recent years, the elimination of lead-poisoning among those who work with it will be recorded in due time. Lead is far too valuable a metal to be allowed to retain its reputation for evil.

IN THE SHEET ROLLING MILL
Lead, being very malleable, is easily rolled into sheets after first being cast into cakes about 5 feet square. This shows the sheet rolling mill in operation at the Millwall works.

URANIUM—SOURCE OF ATOMIC ENERGY

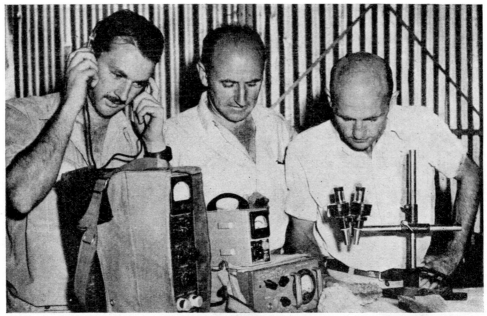

Central Press.

AT AN AUSTRALIAN URANIUM MINE

A geologist and two mining officials study a lump of ore from the Rum Jungle Mine, in the Northern Territory of Australia. The Rum Jungle uranium deposits, which are among the richest in the world, were first discovered in 1949. They are now the property of the Australian Government.

AS these words are being written, adventurous men in Australia, Canada and many other parts of the world are searching for uranium ore with all the fervour of the prospectors of the gold rush days. In both Australia and Canada aircraft are used to speed the search, but prospecting is also a full-time job for men with more modest equipment: men who have little more than a means of transport, a camping outfit, and that essential of the hunt, the Geiger counter which will show the presence of radio-active ore.

You can probably guess why the search is so important and why it is conducted so vigorously. The reason is that uranium is the source material of atomic energy. In Volume VII, you can read more about this amazing new power that Man has just discovered. Here it need only be said that atomic power is produced when the centre, or nucleus, of an atom is split (this is called nuclear fission), and that a certain kind of

uranium, called U-235, is the most suitable fissile material. Plutonium may be used, but it is an extremely rare element and can really be made available only by creating it from natural uranium. So uranium remains the wonder metal of the age and probably the most precious that we know.

In its pure metallic form, uranium is bright white in colour and looks rather like steel, but is, in fact, softer. It was discovered in 1789 by a German chemist named Martin Klaproth, who was also the discoverer of zirconium and titanium. He found uranium while he was examining Saxon pitchblende and named his discovery after the planet Uranus, which had been discovered by Sir William Herschel in 1781. Although uranium chemistry may be said to date from about 1840, when Eugene Péligot carried out experiments with the new element, it was not until 1896 that uranium was found to be radio-active by a French chemist named Henri Becquerel.

When we say that a substance is radio-active we mean that it sends out radiations, or rays, which can penetrate substances that resist ordinary light. It was during their experiments with materials left over from the manufacture of uranium at Joachimstahl (then in Austria, but now in Czechoslovakia) that Professor Curie and his wife discovered polonium and radium.

Although uranium is a rare and much sought after substance, the earth's crust actually contains more uranium than it does more common substances such as iodine and silver. But there are, in fact, only two minerals which contain large deposits of uranium. One is carnotite, a yellow crystal-like powder, and the

other is pitchblende which, as its name suggests, is bluish-black in colour and lustrous in appearance. Pitchblende is the source of the uranium from the Katanga region of the Belgian Congo and from Great Bear Lake in Canada's Northwest Territories. The presence of carnotite in the sandstone rock makes south-western Colorado and south-eastern Utah, in the United States, another uranium-producing region.

The discoverer of the hidden wealth of Great Bear Lake was a Canadian prospector named Gilbert LaBine, who had been so successful in discovering valuable deposits of gold and other metals that he had become head of an important mining company. His prospecting

George Hunter.

IN A CANADIAN URANIUM MINE

These miners are at work on the picking belt of the Port Radium Mine on the shore of Great Bear Lake, in the Northwest Territories of Canada. The ore that they are handling is pitchblende, from which uranium oxide can be obtained. The instrument hanging from the roof is a Geiger counter. Uranium from Port Radium was used in making the first atomic bomb.

in the Northwest Territories during 1929 and 1930 was hazardous work, for he penetrated these lonely and little-known lands by air, using maps that were often found to be inaccurate and relying on Indians, sent off well in advance, to establish fuelling points for his aircraft.

His first trip was made in the summer of 1929, when his pilot landed him at Great Bear Lake, but led to no stirring discoveries, although he saw enough of the eastern shore to make him want to return. So back he came in the spring of 1930, with a colleague named St. Paul. And this time, fortune was with him.

Not far from where he and St. Paul camped one day was the promontory now known as LaBine Point, and there LaBine made a rich strike of pitchblende bearing unmistakable signs of the presence of uranium. As he investigated farther afield, he realised that he had come across a real treasure house of mineral wealth. Manganese, copper, cobalt, nickel and high-quality silver were all present, but more important than any of these were the rich, bluish-black outcrops of pitchblende, which to LaBine meant radium. Thanks to his discovery, radium, which is so important in treating certain diseases, became available to hospitals and institutions at much lower prices.

Then, in 1939, scientists discovered a way of splitting the uranium atom, and raw material for atomic research became of supreme importance. The pitch-

George Hunter.

ANYTHING HERE?

This geologist is using a Geiger counter, which will tell him whether or not there is radioactive ore in the ground. He is working in the Beaverlodge Lake district of north-west Saskatchewan, where there have been very rich finds of uranium. The presence of pitchblende in this area was first reported in 1930, but only since the war has there been extensive prospecting and development.

blende of Great Bear Lake was yielding almost pure uranium oxide as early as 1942, for none knew better than LaBine how important it was to build up stocks of this substance. The world was then at war and victory might well go to the side which produced the first atom bomb. And it did, in fact, come about that uranium from Great Bear Lake was used in making the first of these terrible weapons—the atomic bomb dropped on August 6th, 1945. Before this, Port Radium (the mining centre on Great Bear Lake) and the secret uranium refineries at Port Hope, Ontario, were officially taken over by the Canadian Government.

Canada's " Uranium Rush "

Great Bear Lake is by no means the only part of Canada where uranium has been found. In recent years many Canadians, professional prospectors and enthusiastic amateurs alike, have joined in the search for new fields, and in 1953 at least one important Canadian department store was advertising " a handy portable Geiger counter " for sale. Said the advertisement: " It's so easy to use. Requires no experience at all. Ideal for campers, tourists and cottagers. Just snap on the earphones, press the button and away you go! "

By October, 1953, nearly 50,000 claims had been staked by uranium prospectors in the horseshoe of the " Canadian Shield." It is certainly a fact that uranium is comparatively easy to find in the Dominion because there is so much of it; but only a few of the claims staked are likely to represent uranium deposits that are workable and worth working.

Districts where important finds have been made include Sault Sainte Marie-Sudbury, in Ontario, where Algoma Mills is one of the main centres; and the old fur-trappers' town of Maniwaki, in Quebec Province, north of Ottawa. But the richest finds have been in the Beaverlodge district of Saskatchewan, where a new prospecting town called Uranium City has been built. Uranium City is about 500 miles south of the Arctic Circle and in 1953 its links with the outside world consisted of an air service, except in the summer when travellers could also use the rough road to Bushell, on the shores of Lake Athabaska. The first buildings to be put up in Uranium City were not, in fact, built there! Indeed, it is wrong to say that they were " put up " at all. For they came from the derelict mining town of Goldfields and were dragged to Uranium City across the winter ice of Athabaska and other lakes by bulldozers fitted with caterpillar tracks.

Among the men who have helped to develop the uranium deposits in this part of Canada is Gilbert LaBine, whose Gunnar mine in the Beaverlodge region is said

George Hunter.

A TEST DRILLING

There are many diamond drills of the kind seen in this picture at work in the Beaverlodge district of north-west Saskatchewan, in Canada. They are used by the large mining companies to confirm the presence of uranium-bearing ore and to show at what depth the ore lies.

to be the richest in the Dominion. So the great prospector, who was the first man to discover large deposits of pitchblende in the Western Hemisphere, still leads the way. It is not surprising that Canadians call him "Mr. Uranium."

Another part of Canada where prospectors are vigorously seeking uranium is the Noranda area of Quebec Province, where more than 500 claims were staked in the first eighteen days of 1954. Canada is now second only to the Belgian Congo as a leading uranium producer.

Where Uranium is Used

The centre for atomic research in Canada is Chalk River, about 130 miles west of Ottawa, where

The Times.

THE CHIEF CENTRE OF A RICH URANIUM-ORE DISTRICT

This is part of Uranium City, the new mining town which is to be the centre of the Beaverlodge district. The building seen in the picture is the post office. Uranium City is about six miles from Bushell, on the shores of Lake Athabaska, but aircraft provide its chief link with the south, the flight from Edmonton taking about three hours.

Canada established her third atomic pile in 1951 for the production of radio-active isotopes for use in industry and science. An isotope is the chemical "twin" of another element, differing only in its atomic weight; thus U-235 is an isotope of natural uranium. Canada's first atomic pile, the ZEEP (Zero Energy Experimental Pile), was used by Canadian and British physicists for much of their nuclear research during the Second World War. The Zeep, like her second atomic pile (the NRX), forms part of the Chalk River plant.

Some of the largest and most remarkable atomic research centres and factories are to be found in the United States. At Oak Ridge, Tennessee, the research and production buildings are scattered across a wide valley. The largest unit in the

Oak Ridge establishment is known as K-25 and is itself the size of a small city. The largest of the seventy buildings that it occupies is over one and a half miles long and is claimed to be the largest factory in the world under one roof. Here, the isotope U-235 is separated from ordinary uranium (U-238). Materials produced by Oak Ridge are used at the Hanford, Washington, plant for the manufacture of plutonium. The Hanford plant stretches for miles along the valley of the Columbia River and is thought to contain at least six atomic piles.

Research in atomic energy is carried on at Berkeley, California, at Ames, Iowa, and at many universities and laboratories. The National Reactor Testing Station at Arco, Idaho, became widely known in

December 1951, when it succeeded in producing electric power from atomic energy.

A closely-guarded centre is Los Alamos, New Mexico, where the main activity is research in atomic weapons.

Los Alamos is one of the strangest cities in the world. It stands on a lonely plateau, 7,500 feet high and cut off from the surrounding country by a steep canyon, except on one side where a constantly guarded road links it with the outside world. This inaccessible place was chosen as the site for an atomic centre by the United States' government in 1943 and the town which has been built there for the scientists and technicians, and their families, is almost self-contained. Guards continually patrol the boundaries of the place, which is known locally as "The Hill," and workers and visitors coming to Los Alamos from the outside world have to show special passes at the entrance gate built across the single approach road. On the plateau, not far from this gate, is Los Alamos' own air strip, and beyond, the town itself with its 12,000 inhabitants. It is claimed that the physics laboratory in this place of secrets is the finest in the world. The name "Los Alamos" means "the poplars" and was chosen because trees of this kind grow on many parts of the plateau.

Britain's New Industry

Britain's chief research centre is at Harwell, in Berkshire (see Vol. VII, "Atomic Energy and Its Meaning"), while nearby Aldermaston specialises in research on atomic weapons. The first British-made plutonium was produced at Harwell in 1949, in Britain's first "Gleep" (graphite low energy experimental pile). Uranium itself has been found in Britain; in the Dolgelley district of North Wales, where, a few years ago, geologists discovered radioactive rock. Under present conditions, however, it is not considered worth-

Central Press

WHERE THE MINERS OF RUM JUNGLE LIVE

This is the miners' camp at Rum Jungle, in the Northern Territory of Australia. The scrub gum trees give a little shelter from the intense heat. The corrugated iron round the foot of each tent helps to keep out the tropical rain during "the Wet."

while to work these deposits.

Britain's new industry for producing atomic energy material for both peaceful and warlike purposes at present comprises four major units. Risley, near Warrington, is the headquarters where production is planned; at Springfields, near Preston, pure uranium is produced from uranium concentrates; isotope U-235 is separated from ordinary uranium in the plant at Capenhurst, Cheshire; and at the Windscale Works, near Sellafield, in Cumberland, atomic piles are used to separate plutonium from uranium.

The building of these factories has been described as "probably the largest, certainly one of the largest, engineering projects undertaken in Britain since the war." You can read more in Vol. VII about the processes used at these factories.

Central Press.

BRITAIN'S PLUTONIUM FACTORY

These impressive buildings are the two large natural uranium atomic piles of the Windscale Works near Sellafield in Cumberland. From the piles come highly radioactive slugs, or lumps, of uranium. Each slug contains a small amount of plutonium, which is extracted and purified in another part of the factory. Built and operated by the Ministry of Supply, Windscale covers about 300 acres. When the factory is in full production, it requires more than 5,000 staff and workpeople.

The Secret of Rum Jungle

Among the many brave explorers of Australia during the last century was a hardy Scot named John McDouall Stuart, who made many attempts to cross the vast continent from Adelaide in the south to the shores of the Indian Ocean in the north. He found success on his sixth and last attempt. And on July 24th, 1862, he and his companions reached the shores of Van Diemen's Gulf, where they hoisted the Union Jack and gave loud cheers—for the success of their journey, for the Queen, and for the Prince of Wales. In his journal, Stuart described these northern lands as "splendid country," and not long after the government of South Australia tried to establish a settlement in the district now known as Rum Jungle.

Rum Jungle is on the Edith River,

some fifty miles south of Darwin; and at first it was merely called "The Jungle" and was principally a supply centre for prospectors and miners. They had hoped for gold; instead they found copper and tin, which they mined in rough workings that remain to this day. At that time no one realised what great wealth Rum Jungle held, for to these early miners uranium was valueless. For them, "The Jungle" meant tin, copper and the store where they could buy provisions. One night—or so the story goes—some miners who were unable to pay their bills broke into the store and broached a large cask of rum. Its contents spouted over the floor of the place and flowed from the store into a nearby pool. That, it is said, is why "The Jungle" became Rum Jungle.

Later, the road and railway were built, but Rum Jungle guarded its secret until 1949, when an experienced prospector named Jack White came across uranium ore in the old tin and copper mines. He had found uranium deposits that proved to be among the richest in the world.

Her Own Uranium Plant

The first shaft at Rum Jungle was the work of Jack White himself. The only tools he used were pick and shovel, and his first loads of ore were brought to the surface by a primitive windlass and bucket. Larger shafts and better equipment were afterwards put in by the government, and the development of Rum Jungle was later helped by advances amounting to over £A.1,000,000 by Britain and the United States jointly. It was expected that about £A.2,000,000 would be spent on the development of Rum Jungle. This development will include a uranium treatment plant. Such is the value and importance of uranium in the modern world that an act was passed making all deposits, whether found or still to be discovered, the property of the government.

Rum Jungle is only one of many places in Australia where uranium has been discovered. This precious ore is also being mined at Radium Hill, in South Australia, south-west of Broken Hill (New South Wales), and at nearby Crockerswell. Deposits suitable for deep mining have also been found at Yankaali, in the hills south of Adelaide; at Ernabella, near the border of the Northern Territory; and at Wallaroo and Moonta. Early in 1954, the first pitchblende ore sample taken from deposits in the Adelaide Hills, South Australia, was processed at a pilot plant in Adelaide. In many States, aerial survey is playing an important part in finding new areas likely to contain uranium. The aircraft used for prospecting are fitted with scintillometers. These devices can detect radiation from radioactive minerals under the ground and so help in the pinpointing of radioactive areas. In South Australia, no fewer than 200 indications of radio-activity were discovered in an area of fifty square miles by this modern method of prospecting. The aerial detection service also pointed the way to extensive deposits about 230 miles from Darwin and well to the east of Pine Creek, in the Northern Territory. Ground parties located the new field on Coronation Day (June 2nd), 1953, and it was therefore called "Coronation Field." At first, it was considered to be the most important find since Rum Jungle, but a few months later the potentially more valuable deposits near Katherine (also in the Northern Territory) were found by three local residents who had bought themselves a Geiger counter. In the same month it was announced that prospectors had proved the presence of radio-activity in the Weld Range, 400 miles north of Perth, the capital of Western Australia. Another Northern Territory field was discovered at Brock's Creek, about 130 miles south of Darwin, in November, 1953. The Northern Territory is thus especially rich in uranium, and many people believe that the recent finds may herald a new era of prosperity for this rather desolate part of Australia.

It was arranged that until Australia had her own atomic piles and factories, her uranium should be shipped to the United States for use under the direction of the Joint Agency for Atomic Energy (this is an official body which deals with the uranium supplies of the western countries). But by September, 1953, a factory for treating uranium had been built at Port Pirie and it was then expected that this plant would be working by May, 1954. Speaking in Adelaide on July 22nd, 1953, the Premier of South Australia said that the next large power station to be built in the State would use atomic energy and that it would be needed within seven years.

Meanwhile an Australian Atomic Energy Commission has been set up to take charge of all matters relating to uranium and atomic energy, including surveying and prospecting, mining and refining, scientific research, and the use of atomic energy for defence and in industry.

Australia has been the scene of a number of important experiments in the warlike uses of atomic energy. In early October, 1952, the first British atomic bomb was exploded in the Monte Bello islands, about eighty-five miles off the West Australian port of Onslow. On October 15th, 1953, a British atomic

Central Press.

THE ENTRANCE TO THE RUM JUNGLE URANIUM FIELD

Rum Jungle is about fifty miles south of Darwin, in the Northern Territory of Australia. Uranium ore was first discovered here in 1949 by a prospector named Jack White. It has since been established that Rum Jungle is one of the richest uranium fields in the world. It is now controlled by the Australian Government and is, of course, subject to security measures, as the notice in our picture shows.

weapon was successfully exploded at Woomera, South Australia, and a second atomic explosion was staged here about a fortnight later.

Woomera lies about 300 miles northwest of Adelaide in the desolate interior, and this was undoubtedly why it was chosen as the place for research into rockets and guided missiles. In 1947, Woomera boasted a solitary farmstead, but by 1953 it had become a township of 500 houses, with its own store and hospital, electricity supply and airfield, and water piped 250 miles across the desert from the Murray River. The railway has also come to Woomera, which is now connected by a branch line to the east-west transcontinental route.

This secret place was called Woomera because that is the aboriginal word for "throwing spear," and what was a throwing spear but a primitive form of rocket or guided missile? But as we have seen, the work of the Woomera range has now been extended to include atomic weapons, which are tested here under conditions of great secrecy. Take as an example the first detonation of a British atomic weapon, an experiment which was known by the code-name "Project X-200"' For this test, 80,000 square miles of South Australia were proclaimed a security area and the explosion was staged on the remote "Emu field" of the range by a team of over one hundred scientists from Great Britain and Australia under the direction of Sir William Penney. What the weapon was and what the scientists sought to discover were not revealed.

From South African Gold Mines

Another nation of the British Commonwealth which produces uranium is South Africa, whose gold ores are rich in this mineral. The mines chosen to produce uranium were West Rand, Daggafontein, Blyvooruitzicht, Western Reefs, West Dreifontein and Stilfontein, and by July, 1953, recovery plants were extracting uranium at three of them.

Europe, too, has important deposits of uranium. Some years ago signs of its presence were found near Limoges, in France, and more recently, in the Black Forest and the Fichtelgebirge in Western Germany. These last may be developed quite soon to provide nine tons of uranium a year for peaceful purposes. It was said that these nine tons would provide as much energy as 24 million tons of coal.

Some of the most intensively worked uranium mines are to be found in Eastern Europe, especially in the Erzgebirge—a mountain range along the frontier of east Germany and Czechoslovakia, where Johanngeorgenstadt is one of the chief centres. The Erzgebirge (" Ore Mountains ") have long been worked for a number of metals. Freiberg, near Chemnitz, is said to be one of the atomic research centres in this part of Europe, but much of the Erzgebirge uranium goes, with uranium mined in Poland and Czechoslovakia, to the Soviet Union.

The Soviet Union

Another part of the world which supplies uranium to the Soviet Union is the Chinese province of Sinkiang, which has a common frontier with the U.S.S.R. The uranium mines are in the north and north-western regions of Altai, Illi and Chuchal. Since 1950, the development of mineral resources in this Chinese province has been handled by China and the Soviet Union jointly.

Within the frontiers of the Soviet Union, uranium is produced in the Alma-Ata region of Kazakhstan and in Tadzhikistan (both in Soviet Central Asia), and at the new centres of Komsomolsk, Magadan and Khabaravsk in eastern Siberia. But beyond telling the world that she, too, holds the secret of the atom bomb, the Soviet Union has said little about her atomic research.

The Uranium Age

In one of his broadcasts in 1953, Mr. Menzies, the Prime Minister of Australia, spoke of the challenge of " the uranium age." He said that so far the emphasis had been on the military value of uranium; but he also spoke of its more peaceful uses. Tremendous heat could be produced from uranium, which might therefore become a valuable substitute for coal and other fuels.

It is, indeed, the fact that atomic power can be produced from uranium and harnessed in the peaceful service of mankind that makes the work of prospectors and scientists worthwhile.

Magnetism
and
Electricity

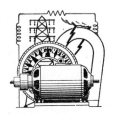

A Great Discovery
and its
Many Developments

Specially drawn for this work.

HOW ELECTRIC CURRENT FLOWS

These boys represent the atoms of a conductor through which a current is passing, and the oranges that they are handing to one another stand for electrons being transferred from atom to atom. The atoms themselves do not travel as wholes.

ELECTRICITY AND ITS USES

THE Greek poet Homer tells us of an "old man of the sea" named Proteus, who looked after the seals which made up the flocks of Poseidon, king of the oceans. He had the power of prophecy, and would tell the future of anyone who could hold him fast. This was very difficult to do, for he changed into one shape after another, and proved himself a "very slippery customer."

Electricity is rather like Proteus. It is very difficult to keep hold of. If you are not very careful it will wriggle out of your grasp, often without making any sign of how it does so, and you are left wondering where it has gone. Even its very nature has puzzled men for a long time past. One theory after

another has been built up, and then, hey presto! it has had to take another shape, and previous ideas about electricity are all upset.

Electrons—What are they ?

The present view held by learned men about electricity is that *all matter* is electricity. Rather a shock, is it not, to have to look on oneself as all electricity, which one had before thought to be confined to wires, batteries, motors, and things of that kind ?

Still, one has to respect this view of wiser people. Let us examine it a little. Matter is made up of atoms, it is said. It is also explained that every atom is a group of particles of positive and negative electricity. The negative particles are called electrons, so this theory of matter is known as the electron theory.

Each atom may be likened to a core of paired-off positive and negative particles, with one or more rather loosely attached electrons revolving round it, as the planets revolve round the sun. The atoms of iron, gold, quicksilver, carbon, and the other elements differ only in the number and arrangement of electric particles they contain. As our bodies are made up of elements mixed together, it follows that—if the theory be correct—we are in effect electricity.

Boys, Oranges and Electricity

We have mentioned this new theory about matter only because it helps to explain in an understandable way what we speak of as an electrical current.

Imagine a number of boys arranged in a ring, each holding an orange in his hand. A boy represents an atom, and an orange represents one of those electrons which is not very closely bound to its atom. At a given signal every boy passes his orange to his right-hand neighbour and takes that of his left-hand neighbour. Each boy-atom still has an orange, but there has been a movement of oranges, and if the signal be repeated again and again the oranges will circulate right round the ring.

From Atom to Atom

When a current passes through a wire, then, we must regard it as a passing-on of electrons from atom to atom of the material of which the wire is made. A big current means that electrons are being passed in large numbers; a weak current that the exchange is limited.

Now an electric current does not flow without a reason: let us see if we can find this reason. Going back to our ring of boys, let us suppose that the ring is broken at one point and that the passing continues in one direction,

WHEN ELECTRIC CURRENT CEASES   *Specially drawn for this work.*

The circuit has here been broken. The two-orange boys are the part of a circuit into which electrons are being pumped from the other part, the no-orange boys. Immediately the circuit is completed again there will be a flow from the over-electroned " negative " side to the under-electroned " positive " side, and the passing along will be re-established.

until half of the boys have two oranges apiece, and the other half none. The two-orange boys now separate from the no-orange boys. If things were left in this condition there would be dissatisfaction. The boys without any oranges would feel that they were owed one apiece by the two-orangers; and the latter, being nice boys, would be quite willing to give them up. Everything is ready for a flow of oranges when the ring is re-formed.

In like manner an electric current is due to there being atoms in one place with electrons to spare (these are called "negative" atoms), and in another place "positive" or electron-hungry atoms which are short of electrons. The current is merely a distribution of electrons until matters are evened up.

Specially drawn for this work.

A SIMPLE EXPERIMENT

Rub a glass or ebonite rod with a silk handkerchief and hold it near small fragments of tissue paper. This is what will happen.

Specially drawn for this work.

THE DANCING PUPPETS

Or place a sheet of glass thus over tissue-paper puppets, and rub it well. Here again, the thing rubbed attracts light, loose objects, to make good a shortage of electrons.

Electrified by Friction

Whence does electricity get its name? From the Greek word *elektron*, meaning amber. More than 2,000 years ago the Greeks had noticed that if a piece of amber were rubbed it became able to attract small, light bodies. For a long time people took little interest in the fact, but when it became an object of serious study this peculiar power was called electricity.

We know now that all bodies may be electrified by friction. If one rubs a fountain pen against the sleeve it will pick up small fragments of paper. Some kinds of cloth become electrified if brushed, and attract dust in an amazing manner; and the paper running through a printing press at high speed is apt to give trouble by its highly electrified condition.

A Simple Experiment

Tear up a piece of tissue paper into small bits and lay them on the table. To right and left of them place a thin book, and bridge the gap with a sheet of glass. If the glass be now rubbed with a silk handkerchief the bits of paper will jump up from the table and cling to its under side, some hanging on for a long time.

In an earlier paragraph we spoke of electrons as parts of atoms. When the glass is rubbed, some of the looser electrons in it are picked up by the silk, leaving the glass rather short of elec-

trons. The glass therefore attracts the bits of paper to extract electrons from them. As soon as they have given some up, and are no "richer" than the glass, they fall off again.

The Wonders of the Wimshurst Machine

One can steal electrons, as it were, without actual rubbing. Perhaps you have seen an apparatus called a Wimshurst machine. The chief parts of it are two flat circular glass plates, revolving close to each other in opposite directions, and two Leyden jars. The last are glass jars covered part way up, both inside and outside, with tinfoil. A rod passes through the centre of a stopper of insulating material in the mouth of each jar, and a chain hanging from its bottom end touches the inner tinfoil.

Stealing the Electrons

The action of the spinning glass plates is to steal electrons from one jar and store them up in the other. If two knobs, connected with the jars, are brought close together, the electron-hunger of the robbed jar becomes too great to be borne, and there is a discharge of electrons to it from the other jar through the air, accompanied by a loud crackling noise and brilliant flash. This flash is really a succession of sparks, for the first discharge overdoes matters, making the hungry jar overcharged ; and many jumps to and fro may take place before the

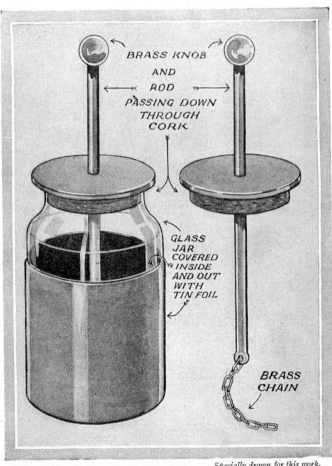

BRASS KNOB AND ROD PASSING DOWN THROUGH CORK

GLASS JAR COVERED INSIDE AND OUT WITH TIN FOIL

BRASS CHAIN

Specially drawn for this work.

A JAR FOR ELECTRONS

This picture shows a complete Leyden jar on the left, and the insulated centre-rod separately on the right. The chain makes connection between the rod and the inside lining of tinfoil, which is completely insulated from the outside coating of foil by the glass of the jar.

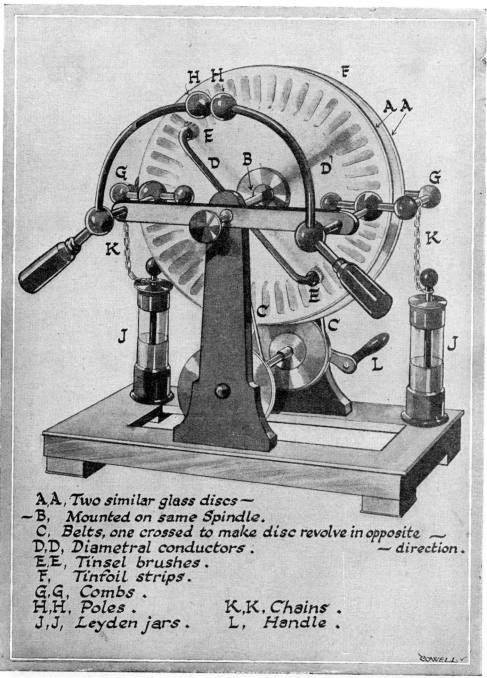

A.A, *Two similar glass discs —*
—B, *Mounted on same Spindle.*
C, *Belts, one crossed to make disc revolve in opposite —*
D,D, *Diametral conductors :* — *direction.*
E,E, *Tinsel brushes .*
F, *Tinfoil strips .*
G,G, *Combs .*
H,H, *Poles .* K,K, *Chains .*
J,J, *Leyden jars .* L, *Handle .*

Specially drawn for this work.

This is a Wimshurst machine. If the knobs HH be separated and the handle L be turned, the effect of the machine is to steal electrons from the inner lining of one Leyden Jar J, and transfer them to the lining of the other, till one is highly negative and the other highly positive. On HH being brought close together again, a crackling spark discharge takes place between them, while the electrical balance is being restored in the jars.

ARTIFICIAL AND NATURAL LIGHTNING

This flash of artificial lightning occurred in a laboratory. It is about 14 feet long, and to create it a tension of 2,200,000 volts was needed. The shadows of the great balls and their supports are thrown sharply on to the wall behind.

But the greatest flash ever produced by man's agency is insignificant in comparison with the displays given by Nature. How extensive a really fine lightning flash is has been recorded here by the camera, which can capture what evaded the human eye.

BIG SPHERES FOR BIG EXPERIMENTS

In this picture we get a close view of the spherical electrodes seen on the opposite page. They are the terminals between which electrical discharges take place in the course of experiments with very high tension currents. Their size may be judged by comparing them with the man on the step-ladder.

balance is restored. But as the whole operation occupies perhaps only a millionth of a second, one seems to see but a single spark during a discharge.

Some Wimshurst machines have many pairs of plates, and are what may be called electron-pumps of great power. When they are in action they produce streams of sparks a foot or more long, and a deafening noise. A spark from one of these monsters would have very serious, if not fatal, effects on any living creature.

Nature's Fireworks

But Nature, as a spark-producer, puts all human inventions completely into the shade. If during a thunderstorm two clouds, one overcharged and the other undercharged with electrons, come near each other, there is a terrific exchange between them, seen as a flash of lightning, and followed by a clap of thunder. Sometimes the discharge takes place between a cloud and the earth; and a steeple, house, or tree through which the current flows may be destroyed. Lightning sparks are to be measured not in inches or feet, but in hundreds of yards.

The Mysterious Stone

Probably 1,000 years at least before the Greeks noticed the peculiar behaviour of rubbed amber, the Chinese, who were advanced in science while Britons were still savages, made the discovery that a certain kind of stone had the property of attracting iron, and that a splinter of it, floated on water, turned north and south. In other words, they had discovered natural magnetism and the mariner's compass.

The " stone " in question is a kind of iron ore called magnetite by us, and lodestone, that is, " leading-stone," by our ancestors. Long ago it was mined at a place named Magnesia, in Thessaly, and so it came about that a steel needle or bar which has been given the properties of lodestone by being rubbed against it, or in some other way, is known as a magnet.

A magnet does not give out electricity, but, as we shall see, it has a very important connection with it.

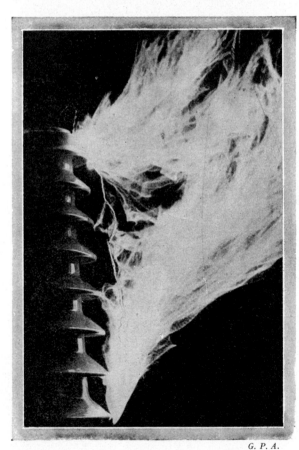

G. P. A.

FIREWORKS ROUND AN INSULATOR

An enormous electrical pressure was needed to cause this discharge between points at the top and bottom of this many-storied insulator, which is under test.

Fountains of Electricity

Electricity produced by rubbing is of little practical use, being very unmanageable, and

HOW WE GOT THE DYNAMO

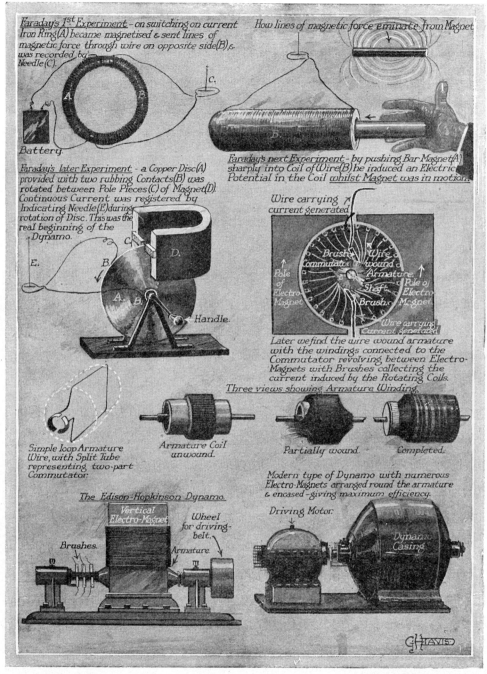

Faraday's 1st Experiment - on switching on current Iron Ring(A) became magnetised & sent lines of magnetic force through wire on opposite side(B) & was recorded by Needle (C).

Battery.

How lines of magnetic force emanate from Magnet

Faraday's later Experiment - a Copper Disc(A) provided with two rubbing Contacts(B) was rotated between Pole Pieces(C) of Magnet(D). Continuous Current was registered by Indicating Needle(E)during rotation of Disc. This was the real beginning of the Dynamo.

Handle.

Faraday's next Experiment - by pushing Bar Magnet(A) sharply into Coil of Wire(B) he induced an Electric Potential in the Coil whilst Magnet was in motion.

Wire carrying current generated

Brush. Wire wound Armature. Commutator. Pole of Electro Magnet. Staff. Pole of Electro Magnet. Brush.

Wire carrying Current Generated

Later we find the wire wound armature with the windings connected to the Commutator revolving between Electro-Magnets with Brushes collecting the current induced by the Rotating Coils.

Three views showing Armature Winding.

Simple loop Armature Wire, with Split Tube representing two-part Commutator.

Armature Coil unwound.

Partially wound.

Completed.

Modern type of Dynamo with numerous Electro-Magnets arranged round the armature & encased - giving maximum efficiency.

The Edison-Hopkinson Dynamo.

Vertical Electro-Magnet

Wheel for driving-belt.

Brushes.

Armature.

Driving Motor.

Dynamo Casing.

G H DAVIS

Specially drawn for this work.

The great machines used in power stations to supply us with electricity are the result of discoveries made, rather more than a hundred years ago, by Michael Faraday in connection with magneto-electric induction. This term means the creation of current in a circuit by moving part of it through a magnetic field, or by moving a magnetic field through it. Our artist here explains, by a series of sketches, Faraday's famous experiments and the development of the dynamo.

escaping in a moment if given the chance. Not till about the year 1800 was a way found of producing a *steady* electric current, by means of what we call an electric cell. This has two different substances—one usually carbon and the other zinc—standing in a fluid which causes electrons to collect round one much more than round the other. If the two substances are joined by a wire, there is a steady flow of electrons through the wire until the energy of the cell is exhausted.

By Chemical Means

For a very long time this method — the chemical method — of producing currents was the only one with which electricians had to work. The electric cell is still very useful for many purposes requiring only a small current, as for working telegraphs, telephones and electric bells.

But it would be ruinously expensive to apply it to tasks which used very strong currents.

Electricity has to-day become a giant which moves our trams, trolleybuses and electric trains, lights our houses, cooks for us, keeps millions of machines running, pumps water from mines, smelts metals, and does other jobs too numerous to mention.

We could never have obtained sufficient power to do all these things just by using electric batteries. The use of electricity on the present-day scale became possible only when men had discovered how to build electric generators. The story of this advance is closely bound up with the discovery of the electro-magnet. Indeed, the history of electricity is, like so many modern wonders, a story of one discovery linking up with another and leading to a big advance.

General Electric Co. Ltd.

ELECTRIC LIGHTING OF KINGSWAY, LONDON

Electricity was known and studied for many years before methods of using it for lighting were discovered. The arc lamps came first; then the filament lamps were demonstrated by Swan in 1878 and Edison in 1879. Other advances have been made since then, and our modern street lighting has become almost comparable with daylight, as shown by the above photograph taken at night in London.

THE ROMANCE OF THE MAGNET

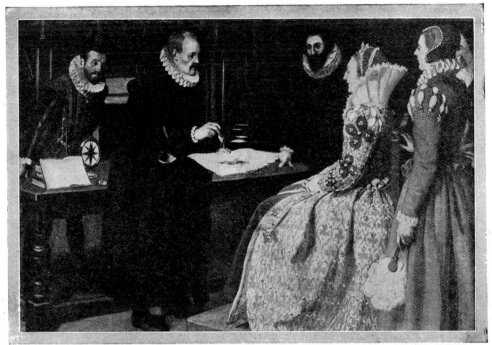

A QUEEN AND THE MAGNET

William Gilbert, court physician to Queen Elizabeth, was the first Englishman to take a scientific interest in electricity. He put forward the theory—since proved correct—that the earth itself is a huge magnet. The artist has here represented him demonstrating the properties of the magnet to his royal mistress.

THERE lived in Woolwich, about 100 years ago, a shoemaker named Sturgeon. Becoming tired of stitching shoes, he joined the Royal Garrison Artillery. In his spare time he amused himself with little experiments in electricity, and one day he tried the effect of passing an electric current through an insulated wire wrapped round and round an iron bar. To his great astonishment and delight, the bar now behaved just like an ordinary toy " permanent " magnet, clinging to any iron or steel object brought near it. This discovery raised the humble ex-shoemaker at a bound from obscurity to fame as the inventor of the *electro-magnet*.

The Magnetic Poker

You can easily copy Sturgeon's famous experiment for yourself. All you need is an iron poker—all in one piece—a few yards of bell-wire, and a pocket flash-lamp battery. (Do not be tempted to use an accumulator, if you have one, as you would probably ruin it.) Wind most of the wire round the poker near the tip and connect its ends to the battery. You will then have converted the poker into an electro-magnet which will pick up needles, screws and other small iron and steel objects.

The electro-magnet is so useful to us because it remains magnetised only as long as current passes through it. It can be made to take hold or let go at will. Immediately the current is cut off, its core becomes—well, just a piece of iron.

We shall deal with some of the applications of the electro-magnet a little later, but for the moment we are

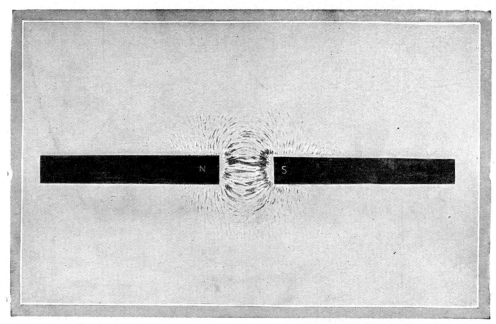

The space surrounding the poles of a magnet, throughout which the magnet's influence is felt, is called a magnetic field. Two magnets have here been laid on white paper with "unlike" poles close together, and iron dust has been scattered about. The dust arranges itself on curves running from one pole to the other.

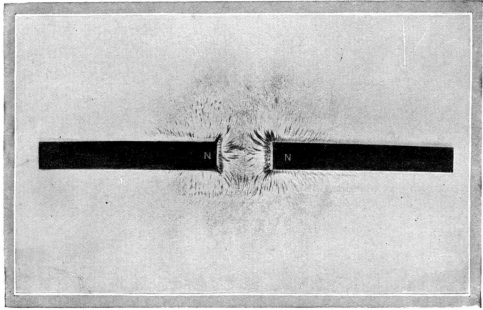

Photos: L.E.A.

The magnetic curves are called lines of force. In this second experiment the magnets present "like" poles to each other. The positions taken up by the dust show that lines of force no longer span the gap, those of one magnet repelling those of the other.

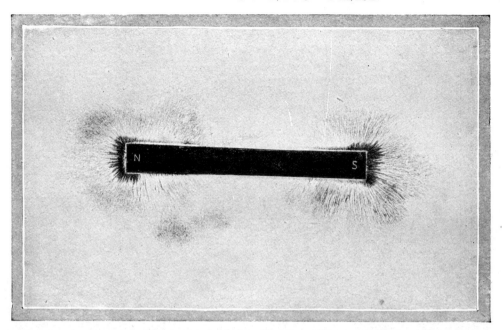

Here we are concerned with one magnet only. The lines of force are clearly visible at each pole. The dust lies along incomplete curves, each related to a curve at the other end of the magnet. The magnetic field weakens so quickly with increasing distance from the poles that the dust cannot show in full the lines running from pole to pole.

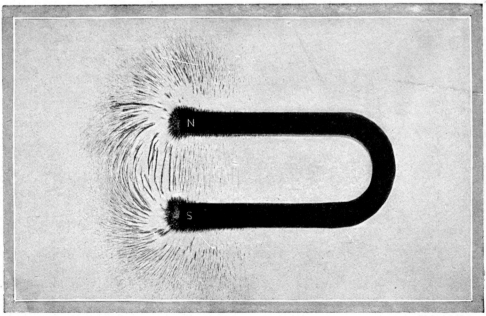

Photos: L.E.A.

The horseshoe magnet, with its poles close together, concentrates its field, and, as the iron dust reveals, the lines of force are vigorous. A metal ring moved to cut the lines of a magnetic field has a current induced in it, and to this fact we owe our ability to generate current with a dynamo.

following the story of the electric generator. Soon after Sturgeon had discovered the electro-magnet, the great Michael Faraday discovered, in 1831, a fact of the utmost importance to mankind. Experimenting in his laboratory one day he found that if he moved a loop of wire up and down close to the poles of a magnet, a current flowed through the wire. The effect was much greater if a coil of wire were used instead of a loop. By studying the picture shown on p. 159 you will be able to see the steps by which inventors, using the discovery of Michael Faraday, have given us the machine called the dynamo, or electric generator. Great coils are made to revolve, by steam power or water power, between huge electro-magnets, and pour electricity into conductors, as the pumps at a city's waterworks pump water into the mains. Almost every year sees larger generators brought into use, and over 60,000 horse-power may now be drawn from a single machine.

How Electricity is Stored

When electrical engineers had discovered electric generators which would produce very large quantities of electricity, they began to look round for some means by which they could store some of the electricity so that it would be ready for use whenever the generator had to be shut down for repairs or periodical cleaning. In 1859, a Frenchman called Gaston Planté discovered that if two sheets of lead were placed in a jar containing fairly strong sulphuric acid, the cell so formed had the property of storing electrical energy. If a battery of these cells has current passed through it from a dynamo the electricity is " stored " in the cells and will remain there for several weeks ready for use whenever it is required.

Later on, the famous inventor, Edison, experimenting in America, discovered another type of storage battery. Instead of lead plates immersed in sulphuric acid, Edison used one plate of nickel and one plate of iron in a solution of caustic potash.

To-day, electric accumulators, or storage batteries, are used for a great variety of purposes. Every motor car is provided with a storage battery, submarines run entirely on their storage batteries, and hundreds of delivery vans use as their motive power electric motors driven from storage batteries.

Small electro-magnets are used in

Igranic Co. Ltd.

A GIANT ELECTRO-MAGNET

In big engineering works electro-magnets are widely used, as no special lifting-hooks and slings are required. The electro-magnet seen above is lifting two coils of sheet steel weighing nearly 3 tons.

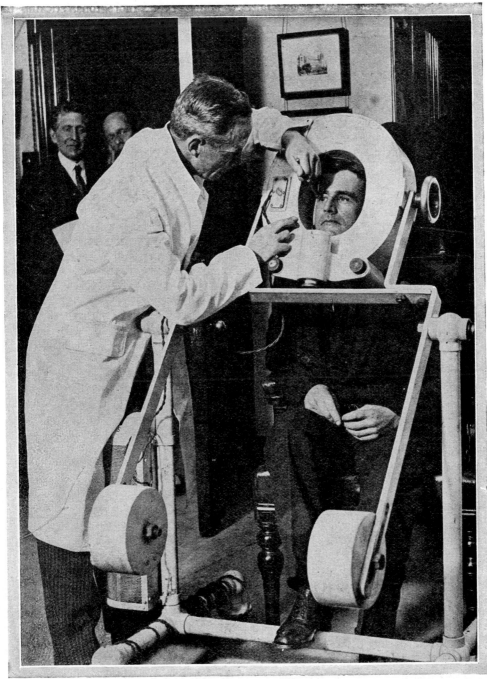

L.N.A

A surgeon is here seen extracting a steel splinter from a patient's eye with the aid of a specially-designed electro-magnet. Current passing through coils inside the circular case sets up an intense magnetic field, which converts the iron bar held by the surgeon into a very powerful magnet. In most instances the magnet performs its wonderful work quite painlessly.

many electrical instruments, including telegraphic apparatus. We will not linger over these, but pass on to magnets designed to exert a very strong pull.

We find such magnets in the magnetic brakes of a tramcar. If the driver wishes to pull up suddenly, he moves a small lever, and magnets hanging just clear of the rails at once grip the rails with such force that the car can be brought up " all standing." Many pedestrians crossing our streets have owed their lives to these brakes.

Giant Magnets

But if you wish to see the electromagnet at its best, you should visit a steelworks or shipyard where such magnets are used for handling masses or large plates of steel and iron. In one place you may find a magnet hanging from a crane, with a huge iron ball, weighing 15 or more tons, sticking to it. The craneman touches a switch, and, crash! the ball falls on to a heap of " scrap " cast iron below, smashing it into pieces of a size suitable for smelting. Presently the crane lays the ball aside and lowers the magnet on to the pile of broken metal. It picks up a ton or so of pieces, swings round, and, in obedience to the switch, drops its load into a railway wagon.

This job finished, the crane moves off to deal with a pile of 5-ton iron bars, which it raises and places where wanted with the greatest ease. Or perhaps it may be needed to unload a cargo of pig iron from a ship. The magnet and craneman between them will do in an hour as much of this work as sixty men using their hands.

Specially drawn for this work.

AN ELECTRO-MAGNETIC SEPARATOR

Material containing odds and ends of iron and steel is here depicted passing over an electro-magnetic separator. Magnetic attraction makes the intruders stick to the belt, while the other material falls clear, and they are carried on underneath to a point where the magnetic pull becomes too weak to hold them up. Among other things, wheat is cleaned of steel and iron objects in this manner.

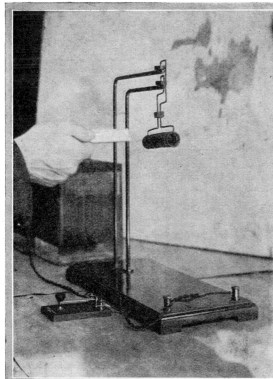

relieved of the chip, which, if left in place, might cause great pain, just as the eye-splinter might have led to blindness. Even to-day many ex-soldiers of various battlefields have pieces of shrapnel shell in their bodies, and such splinters may in many instances be extracted by electro-magnet.

In these and several other ways, such as recovering iron or steel from the bottom of a river, removing bits of iron from wheat before it goes to the grinding rolls, or separating nails and screws from workshop rubbish, the electro-magnet is a very useful servant.

COIL AND MAGNET

Here we see a coil of wire, the two ends of which dip into small cups containing mercury. A permanent magnet held near the coil fails to attract it—

Magnets as Surgeons

We now change the scene to a room in a hospital containing a very powerful electro-magnet with a projecting iron core tapering to a point. Two workmen from an engineering works near by come in. One has a splinter of steel in his eye, the other a chip of steel embedded in the back of his hand.

A surgeon brings the eye of the first patient close to the tip of the magnet and switches on the current. In a moment the magnet's force draws out the splinter painlessly. The other man is with equal quickness

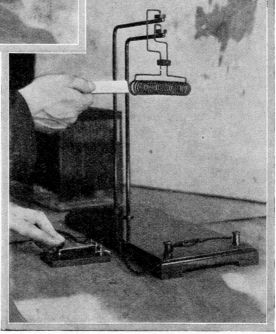

Now the tapping key has been closed so that current is flowing through the coil which swings round so that one end faces the magnet pole. The current has made the coil into a magnet. Upon this simple fact depend all the electric generators and electro-magnets in use to-day.

The Friendly and Unfriendly Magnets

Magnetise five sewing needles, holding them together by the points and drawing the north pole of a permanent magnet several times along them towards the eye. The magnet must be brought back through the air after each stroke, *not* rubbed up and down.

Five more needles are treated in the same way, but with the south pole of the magnet.

Next cut ten thin discs out of a wine cork and stick the needles through their centres. Stain the discs of the north-pole needles red to distinguish them, and dip needles and discs into thin varnish and dry them.

Drop the north-pole needles into a basin of water, eyes upwards. They at once separate, and nothing can persuade them to remain together. Then drop in the south-pole needles, also eyes upwards. They will at once take north-pole partners, for " like poles repel, unlike poles attract, one another."

There are other interesting experiments of this kind, as well as practical examples of the magnet's power. If your front door bell is of the electric kind, you have probably wondered what makes it ring. Here again the electro-magnet produces the result. The wires from the bell-push (which is only a simple device for completing the circuit) go to the bell and the battery. When the bell-push is pressed, the circuit is completed and current flows through the coils of a horse-shoe electro-magnet.

The magnet attracts the strip of metal supporting the hammer, so causing the bell to be struck. This metal strip is attached to a spring facing the poles of the magnet, and this spring pulls the strip away from a metal screw in the direct path of the circuit, thereby causing an intermittent flow of current. By this means the hammer moves rapidly off and on the surface of the bell, giving the familiar ring that we all know.

Barimar Ltd.

PLASTIC SURGERY IN AN ENGINEERING WORKS

The use of electricity in industry has increased enormously in recent years. Here we see an electric welder acting as a plastic surgeon in building up worn or damaged parts of an engine crankshaft by using a welding electrode to deposit a new skin of metal. When the worn part has been built up the shaft can be turned or ground to the correct size. Without this electrical surgery the shaft would have to be discarded and a new one provided.

HEAT AND LIGHT FROM ELECTRICITY

General Electric Co. Ltd.

SUNSHINE LIGHTING IN THE DRAWING-OFFICE

The history of human efforts to conquer darkness by means of artificial lighting showed remarkably little progress between 2,500 B.C. and A.D. 1800. Then from the age-old oil lamps and candles came the change to gas and later to electricity. An example of modern fluorescent lighting in the drawing-office of an engineering works is seen in the photograph above.

A LUMP of coal has in it a certain amount of energy; that is, the power of doing work of a particular kind, though it does not look as if it had. But burn it, and its energy is set free.

The energy at once takes another form—that of heat. The heat may be used to raise steam. The steam, say, works an engine, a large part of its heat being used to turn the shaft of the engine and its flywheel. Some heat is thus changed into a third form of energy, the energy of mechanical motion. Nor need the changing cease here; for, if the engine be set to drive a dynamo, its mechanical energy is converted into electrical energy. This in turn may produce a fifth form of energy, that which we call light.

Many Kinds of Energy

So we can have a whole string of changes; chemical energy into heat energy, into motion energy, into electrical energy, into light energy.

The changes need not always follow this order. Motion energy, for example, can be turned into heat. Rub a pencil hard with your handkerchief, and place it against your cheek. It will feel warm. Your effort as a machine has produced heat.

Now, though one kind of energy may be turned into another, there is sure to be some wastage in the form of heat, which always makes its appearance when resistance has to be overcome. Part of the work of the engine is lost through the heat of friction at the bearings and other rubbing parts. Then the change into electricity at the dynamo cannot take place without the heating-up of the magnets: more waste as heat. And when the electricity is sent through a conductor, some of its energy is again changed into heat by the resistance of the conductor to its passage.

This last wastage, though a nuisance in some ways, is useful in others. It may be encouraged and turned to account. If at any point the conductor be made smaller, or a special kind of wire be used instead of copper wire, the resistance—and the heat as well—will there become greater.

Progress in Lighting

When your grandfather went to school the class-rooms were probably illuminated by gas passing through what was called a fish-tail burner. The naked flame, yellow on the outside but with a dark centre, assumed the shape of a fish-tail and flickered a good deal. This was improved when the incandescent mantle was fitted.

You, in your days in schoolrooms in dull weather and after dark, will have the benefit of electric light coming to you through a vacuum bulb containing metal filaments. Even this is now being improved upon: many schools, and other places where a good light is of the first importance, are being equipped with fluorescent lighting, the nearest approach to day-

light and noonday sun that we have so far reached.

Fluorescent is perhaps not a very happy choice of a word. It comes from fluor, the name of a mineral; and fluorescence is a strange, blue radiation emitted by certain substances when sunshine reaches them. In a fluorescent light the material used is placed inside a long glass tube so that it glows and sends forth steady radiance when it is excited by an electrical current, though the tube itself contains no continuous wires.

Actually, the material employed is a chemical powder obtained from a curious earth called Willemite found on the continent of Europe. There is a range of these powders, each of which gives a different shade of light: but, by a careful mixture, the tone nearest to sunlight can be produced. On the other hand, with varying mixtures, the deepest reds or blues, such as are

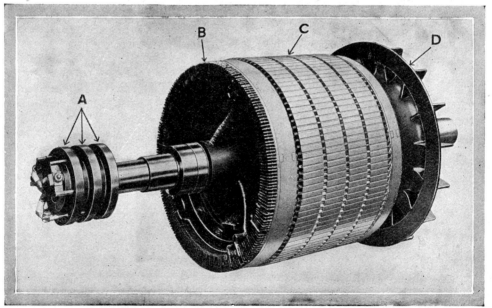

General Electric Co. Ltd.

THE PART THAT DRIVES

This is the rotor, or revolving and driving part, of an alternating current " induction " motor. The drum C is built up from a large number of steel stampings, clamped side by side and slotted right across to take the coils B of the rotor winding. The fan D forces cooling air through the rotor; and the slip-rings A connect the rotor through brushes with devices used in starting and for varying speed.

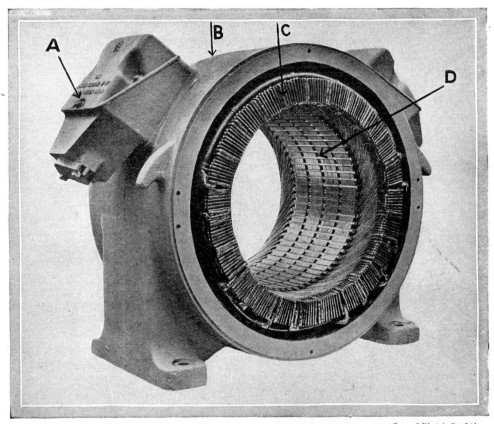

General Electric Co. Ltd.

THE PART THAT STANDS STILL

The rotor turns inside a stationary part, the stator, whereof B is the frame, and A the box through which connection is made with the electricity supply. Its winding C—the primary winding of the motor—is held in slots in steel stampings D. The stator winding is not connected in any way with the rotor winding. Current creates a " revolving field " in the stator, and the rotor derives its driving force from magnetic compulsion to follow this field.

needed in advertising signs, are obtainable.

Wireless Electricity

It may be said that this modern fluorescent system is related to Neon lighting, in which electrical current is discharged through a gas or vapour, whilst the wireless valve also has contributed to its development. We shall understand the matter far better, however, if we visit a factory where fluorescent fitments are manufactured and so see some of the processes for ourselves.

Let us imagine we have just arrived at such a factory. At the starting point of our tour we shall see first of all large numbers of tubes of thick, clear glass $1\frac{1}{2}$ inches in diameter and 5 feet in length. We learn that these tubes begin in a cauldron of molten glass, from which they are drawn through the nozzle of a machine, like lead piping, in unbroken lengths. When the glass has cooled it is cut up just as required for the lamp tubes, save that a little bit extra is allowed for the finishing process. In weight, each of the tubes would turn the scale at about 1 lb.

When we arrive, an operative is testing these tubes and smoothing off the ends before washing them in running hot water to remove dust, and standing them on their ends to drain. Meanwhile, we are shown some of the fluorescent powder, exactly as it has been ground in the mills, and we wonder how such a fine flour-like substance can ever be spread evenly round the inside of a glass tube.

In the next department, however, we see some of the tubes upright in a machine, their tops closed in and their bases fitting tightly over what is best described as a bung, or valve. Soon, under the force of compressed air, a creamy solution comes surging up the tube, to flow back again when power is cut off, and we observe that the whole interior of the tube has been coated as though with a brush. As for the solution, it has contained the powder mixed with resin and spirit, the resin being the carrier and the spirit the solvent, to help in getting rid of the resin.

With Collector Plates

We realise at once that only the powder is wanted and are interested to see carrier and solvent removed in a gas-heated appliance, the next step being to fit a coiled filament electrode at each end of the tube, both electrodes having collector plates, though they are not connected through the tube by wires. It is of the utmost interest, too, to watch some of the other processes, such as the closing, shaping and annealing of the ends of the tubes; the insertion at low pressure of a very small quantity of the gas argon to start the electrical discharge; and of a " blob " of mercury to help in producing ultra-violet rays. The air in the tubes must be exhausted to form a complete vacuum.

Metal caps must next be fitted at each end, and a thorough test made before the finished article goes on to the packing room. Even this work calls for ingenuity, each tube being protected in a sleeve of corrugated cardboard before it is placed in its box.

What happens when the tube is fitted to an electrical circuit and the current switched on must next be explained. First of all, the wires of the electrodes are coated with a material which emits electrons freely directly it is

British Thomson-Houston Co. Ltd.

MAKING ELECTRIC LAMP BULBS

Until fairly recent years electric light bulbs were hand blown, but to-day they are made automatically on complicated Westlake machines turning out up to 100,000 bulbs in 24 hours. A human hair is half as thick again as the 0.0016-inch thick filament wire of a 100-watt lamp, and not more than 2½ per cent. variation is allowed.

heated. Thus, in about two seconds the electrodes are a cherry red and the ultra-violet rays cause the fluorescent powder near the ends of the tubes to glow, and finally to light up over their entire surface as busy electrons jump from one electrode to the other.

The ordinary electric light supply is used for fluorescent tubes, leads being taken to each end of the lamp. Switching on in the usual way, there is within the mechanism a starter device with a small heater coil which cuts out when sufficient warmth has been conveyed to the electrodes. There is also a choke, because, though the lamp takes all the available current to begin with, less voltage is required directly the lamp warms up to its full lighting capacity. To allow for this, the choke automatically reduces the flow of electricity directly the electrodes are functioning freely.

The Secret of the Process

The secret of the whole process is in ultra-violet rays coming from the electrodes. They are not visible to us, but it is they that excite the powder and cause it to give out light. In the factory we have watched many fascinating features in the routine, such as the spot-welding of the cathode assembly, the insertion of the argon gas through tiny glass tubes, the soldering

Delapena Ltd.

ELECTRONIC HEATER FOR PLASTICS

Electronic heating is particularly suitable for warming certain materials thoroughly and rapidly. In this photograph we see an operator placing pellets of moulding powder (called " preforms " and used in the manufacture of plastics) between two metal plates connected with a radio valve circuit, generating very high frequency oscillations. This method distributes the heat very quickly and evenly throughout the material.

of the terminals, and other processes too technical for description. We can see the results in the test frame, and learn that an 80-watt tube produces as much light as a 200-watt lamp made with filaments, so that about one-third of the electricity gives a comparable amount of illumination. Though the fittings are more expensive to begin with, fewer of them are needed to obtain the same result and their life is longer than that of ordinary lamps.

The schoolroom is an obvious place where the most efficient lighting is essential and I daresay you can think of many others. There is the drawing office, for example; the bench at which diamonds are benig cut; hospitals; the printing works and all such places where people have to depend upon their sight and concentration. In a drapery store the natural white light of these tubes enables every object to been seen in its true colours and it is important to remember that fluorescent lighting when properly installed does not throw shadows.

Generally speaking, the tubes are arranged in reflecting troughs suspended from the ceiling at such a height that the light is evenly diffused over the work in hand. It is equally possible to have a tube as a portable fitment to be moved from place to place and used in an upright or horizontal position, with or without reflectors.

In our homes this type of lighting can be concealed behind cornices or picture rails or fixed to the ceiling or on walls in company with appropriate shades. Thus, when entering a room and operating the switch there will come almost instantaneously a flood of illumination to correspond with remarkable closeness to that of natural daylight. Apart from its pleasing appearance, there will be nothing in this form of lighting to cause glare, or to try our eyes in any way.

The principal street of New York City is Broadway, which runs north and south for thirteen miles, the whole length of Manhattan Island. It is probably the longest street in the world under one name. But it has a second claim to distinction. At night it is lit up by electric advertising signs,

General Electric Co. Ltd.

MINE LIGHTING BY FLUORESCENT LAMPS

The difficulty of safe lighting in the black underground tunnels of a coal-mine has been overcome in the past by different types of safety hand-lamps. Here we see a great step forward in this photograph of fluorescent lighting of roads and coal face at Chislet Colliery in Kent.

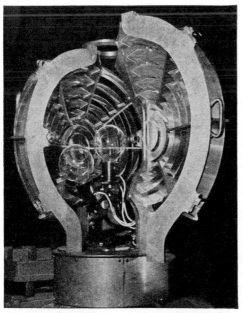

Chance Bros.

TO GUIDE THE MARINER

Here we have an inside view of the optical system and single flashing apparatus of a modern lighthouse. One of the very earliest uses of electricity for lighting was in the South Foreland Lighthouse at the end of 1858.

W. Bridge & Co.

A LIGHTHOUSE LAMP

The first electric lights were from arc lamps and then came the filament lamp, largely used in our homes to-day. In this photograph we see a large modern electric filament lamp designed for use in lighthouse projectors.

so many, imposing and brilliant, as to make people call it the "White Way."

A good many years ago now, a huge steel erection rose on the roof of one of the Broadway hotels. It measured 70 feet in height and 80 feet in width. For a long time workmen were busy on it, and then one night its 20,000 electric bulbs began to flash, and behold! a Roman chariot race, with horses galloping madly, their tails streaming in the wind, and dust rising from their hoofs ; now stumbling, now flogged into further effort by the charioteers. Ahead of the chariots, mounted men cleared the path for the racers, pressing back the crowd.

How Electric Signs Work

The illusion of motion was produced, of course, by bringing different sets of lamps into use in proper succession. In this, as in every electric sign in which the lamps are not all burning continu-

ously, every lamp is connected with an electrically-driven switching device, called a "flasher." The most important part of this, in the case of a "living" sign, is a revolving drum, which may have pins projecting from it like those of the cylinder of a musical-box. Whenever a pin touches a flexible "brush" fixed in its path, a lamp, or group of lamps, lights up for the space of just a moment.

Heat from Electricity

One of the most useful attributes of electricity is that when it is passed through a thin wire the wire becomes hot. This simple fact has enabled engineers to construct many of the useful electric appliances which you find in your home.

For instance, the heating element of an electric iron is simply a sheet of mica with a special kind of fine wire wrapped round it. When electricity is passed through this wire by switching on the iron the wire becomes red-hot and transmits its heat to the body of the iron.

The electric kettle is another example of the way in which we can make use of the heat produced when electricity flows through a very fine wire of special material. The electric kettle contains a heating element rather similar to that used in an electric iron.

In the case of the electric fire one can, of course, see the wires which are made red-hot by the passage of the electric current.

By using a large number of heating elements similar to those used in electric fires and arranging them inside a brick-lined chamber, engineers can construct an electric furnace suitable for melting iron, steel and other metals.

Food from the Air

One of the latest uses of electric heat is its application to the extraction of nitrogen from the air. We cannot live without the food which the farmer grows for us. Nor can the farmer grow good crops unless his land be kept fertile. One of the most valuable of manures is nitrogen combined with other substances in a suitable form. The nitrogen of the air is boundless in quantity, but most plants cannot make use of it. By combining their joint knowledge, chemists and electricians have found a way of capturing some of this nitrogen and making it available to the farmer.

The new process makes use of the great heat which electricity will produce if applied in the right way. It is only by using electricity that we can make this particular kind of fertilizer, so indirectly, at any rate, we owe some of our food to electricity, and may be said to feed partly on air.

The Electric Smith

The intense heat which electricity can bring to bear on a small surface is now much used for joining pieces of metal together. Let us watch a man at work doing what is called " spot " welding. His job is to join two overlapping sheets of iron. He puts these in a kind of vice, between the ends of two copper bars. When he moves a switch a great current passes from bar to bar through the two thicknesses of iron, which become soft with the heat and are welded together by the pressure. The work occupies only a few moments. Plates " spot " welded at intervals are held together as firmly as if they had been riveted.

Under the Stars and Stripes

When the Americans entered the War of 1914–18, the Germans wrecked the engines and boilers of some of their big ships lying in New York Harbour. It was impossible to make new engines quickly, so electric welders were set to work on sticking the broken parts together. They cut away the metal at the edges of a break to form a V-shaped groove when the two parts were brought together, and filled this with metal melted by an electric flame. In quite a short time the ships were in service again —this time under the American flag.

The electric smith has even been turned to welding together all the metal parts of a ship's hull—plates, beams, frames, bulkheads, etc.—and has done it well, not a single rivet being needed.

Heating Without Wires

All the different heating appliances described above depend upon one simple fact. When an electric current passes through a wire which is very thin or which offers a high resistance to the flow of a current the wire becomes very hot.

The newest form of heating by electricity does not need any red-hot wires. This new form of heating is called electronic heating. An electronic heater has a table upon which is placed the substance which has to be heated. A flat plate is then placed in position over the substance and a very high-

HOW THIS BOOK WAS BUILT

By courtesy of the Century Engraving Co.

In a work such as *Pictorial Knowledge*, where so much depends upon the many hundreds of illustrations, the printing blocks are of the highest importance. These blocks consist of a metal plate mounted on wood to the height of the type, and in this photograph we see an etcher preparing the plate for an acid bath. He is protecting with an acid-resisting varnish those parts which are not to be etched.

THE CAMERA THAT PHOTOGRAPHS PICTURES

By courtesy of the Century Engraving Co.

Here we have the camera used for taking a photograph of the illustration to be reproduced. For printing purposes the picture is reversed through a prism, but, before the exposure is made, the image has to be adjusted on a ground-glass screen to the correct size. From the negative the image is transferred to a metal plate, which, after chemical treatment, finally evolves as a printing block.

Photos: By courtesy of the Whitefriars Press, Ltd.

The letterpress in these volumes was set up on a Monotype machine. Here you see the keyboard which has 276 keys. These keys punch holes in a roll of paper ribbon.

The ribbon is transferred to this machine, known as a caster. By means of the punched holes the letters and signs are selected and the type comes forth in units ready for use.

A COMPOSITOR SETTING UP TYPE

Before the days of the Monotype and Linotype machines all type had to be set up by hand, but in these volumes only the chapter headings are done in this way. In the illustration above a compositor is seen at his work selecting the letters required for a heading. His upper-case contains the capitals, small capitals and figures, while in the lower case are found the ordinary letters and spaces.

Photos: By courtesy of the Whitefriars Press, Ltd.

When a long length of type has been set up—sufficient for about two columns—it is placed in a metal tray known as a "galley" and a proof is taken with a hand-press. William Caxton, who first brought printing to England and set up his press in Westminster in 1477, used a crude sort of hand-press for the same purpose to produce the earliest printed books in this country.

The compositor, seen in the photograph above, gathers together the type required and also the blocks which will reproduce the illustrations. He has the Editor's "make-up" in front of him and, with this as his guide, he assembles the type and the blocks in page form and another proof is then taken.

Photos: By courtesy of the Whitefriars Press, Ltd.

Here is the printer's proof-reader, whose duty it is to check proofs with the greatest care to see that the setting and "making-up" have been correctly done. Sometimes his assistant will read aloud from the original manuscript. Proof-readers have a special code of signs for marking corrections.

WHEN THE PAGES ARE "MADE READY"

Such corrections as the reader makes on his proof must be put right in the metal type. When the pages are ready, however, they are laid together and tightly wedged with quoins in a steel frame known as a chase. When the printed sheet is folded the pages will come together in the proper order.

Photos: By courtesy of the Whitefriars Press, Ltd.

This is one of the presses used for the printing of this book. The sheet of paper is fed in at the far end of the press and a revolving cylinder carries it over the inked type and pictures. Printed sheets are delivered at great speed on to the tray in the foreground.

FIRST STAGES OF BINDING

Our books are printed in large sheets, each of which bears the impression of thirty-two pages of type. When the ink is thoroughly dry the sheets are folded into 16-page sections. These sections are collated in their correct sequence and are then sewn together on this sewing machine.

Photos: By courtesy of Hazell, Watson & Viney, Ltd.

We now have a complete volume with its edges untrimmed and with many of the pages still uncut. These volumes are now brought to the machine shown in the photograph above and here the sewn books have three of their edges evenly trimmed in one operation.

ROUNDING AND BACKING THE BOOKS

The books are beginning to take their correct shape. Before entering this machine the backs of the volumes are flat but they must now be rounded and the shoulders jointed. This is known as "rounding and backing" and provides a hinge on which the case, when pasted to the book, will open easily.

Photos: By courtesy of Hazell, Watson & Viney, Ltd.

Passing on to the next stage the books are strengthened by glueing muslin and strong brown paper linings to the backs of the volumes. In this picture we see the books being fed into the machine where these operations are carried out in their proper sequence.

THE BOOKS ARE COMPLETED

In this photograph the operator is seen at work feeding the material required for the covers into a case-making machine. As it passes through the machine the material is automatically glued, fitted to the boards, and finally ejected from the machine as a cover ready for the decoration.

Photos: By courtesy of Hazell, Watson & Viney, Ltd.

We come to the last stage in which the books are pasted into their covers. This process is known as "casing in." When this work has been done the books are put into a powerful press where they are left to dry thoroughly. They are then ready to be packed for despatch.

frequency voltage is switched on between the table and the plate. A high-frequency voltage means that the electrical pressure is applied first in one direction and then in the other direction, the changes taking place perhaps a million times in a second. This has a curious effect upon any substance, such as rubber, plastic or plywood, which may be placed on the table of the electronic heater. The effect is that the whole of the substance is rapidly heated right through. Electronic heating is, therefore, very suitable for quickly warming materials such as plastic, rubber, and the sheets of wood and the cement used for forming plywood.

A picture of one of the latest types of electronic heater will be seen in these pages. This particular heater is used for warming plastic materials before they are put into the moulding press.

Compass and Magnet

A young man was once asked to explain to some ladies the working of a railway locomotive.

" Oh! " said he, " it's ever so simple. You see, the driver claps the boiler on to the fire, and the fire gets into the water, and the steam gets into the wheels, and away we go! "

Hardly a brilliant effort! We wonder what he would have made of the electric motor, if he could do no better than this with a steam engine, which at any rate has a good number of visibly moving parts. The electric motor is so much more mysterious a contrivance.

However, we will do our best to throw some light on its working, in a manner that you can understand.

By way of introduction let us suppose that we have on the table before us a small pocket compass and a horseshoe magnet. On presenting one pole of the magnet to the compass needle—which also, as you know, is a small magnet—one end of the needle will at once fly towards it. We now present the other pole, and the needle promptly swings through a half-circle. By moving the horseshoe magnet quickly to and fro sideways we can make the needle spin round and round, and we

Stewart & Lloyds Ltd.

SAWING WHITE-HOT METAL WHILE IT MOVES

Here we see an electrically-driven circular saw being used for cutting white-hot steel tube into required lengths as it comes from the tube mill. The saw with its motor is mounted on a carriage which moves to and fro as it cuts through the moving tube.

have an electric motor in its very simplest—and, we fear we must add, most useless—form. Its motion is due to alternate attraction and repulsion between the poles of the big magnet and one pole of the small one, the changes being made at just the right moments to keep the needle moving.

Another very interesting thing is this: if a current is passed through a coil of wire the coil becomes a magnet, and if it is hung so as to be able to swing easily it will turn north and south like a compass needle. If you reverse the direction of the current, the coil will swing through a semicircle, for its poles also have been reversed. An iron bar or core with a coil of wire wrapped round it becomes a magnet when electricity is sent through the coil. This is called an *electro-magnet*. The ordinary horseshoe magnet and the needle of a compass are both called *permanent magnets*.

Next we will get to grips with a practical motor. This has a fixed circular frame with two electro-magnets projecting inwards from it opposite to one another, and an iron drum-like part, mounted on a spindle, turning in the space between the curved ends of the magnets. The drum is wound from end to end with a coil of wire.

Friendship and Enmity

When current is sent through the magnets and the drum coil, the coil becomes a magnet too, and one end of it is attracted to each of the fixed magnets. Just as it comes into the position it likes best, the current through the coil is automatically reversed. Friendship is at once changed into enmity, and each fixed magnet demands the opposite end of the coil, spurning that nearer to it. So the drum makes another half-turn, the current is again reversed, and this changing is repeated so quickly that in a few moments the drum—electricians call it the armature or rotor—may be spinning a thousand or more times a minute.

The motor described, though it would work all right, would be jerky in its action, as the spindle is turned much more strongly in some positions of the coil than in others. So the drum is usually wound with a number of separate coils distributed round it, and each comes into use twice during every revolution of the spindle. Then the motor pulls equally hard all the time, and gives steady motion to whatever machine it is set to drive.

British Thomson-Houston Co. Ltd.

AGAINST THE BLACK BACKGROUND OF NIGHT

Flood-lighting of historic or important buildings at nightfall has in recent years been a feature of national and local celebrations. Here we have a view of the Horse Guards Parade, London, illuminated by Mazda Mercury Vapour Lamps in floodlight projectors.

Famous Inventions
and How They
Were Evolved

What Master Minds
Have Done for
the Good of Man

H.M. *Stationery Office.*

THE FIRST MACHINE TO REPRODUCE TALK

This is the original phonograph made by Thomas Edison in 1877. The grooved cylinder in the middle, covered with tinfoil, is revolved and moved slowly endways by turning the handle. On each side of it is a recorder with diaphragm and needle for indenting the foil, in obedience to sound-vibrations, and reproducing sounds.

HOW SOUNDS ARE WRITTEN DOWN

ONE day in the year 1877 Thomas Alva Edison, the great American scientist, took a sheet of tinfoil and wrapped it round a metal cylinder having a fine corkscrew-like groove cut in it from end to end. The cylinder was mounted on a horizontal shaft, cut at one end with a screw-thread of the same pitch as the groove on the cylinder. When the shaft was turned by a handle, the cylinder moved endways slowly, the groove being always opposite a sharp steel point pressing on the tinfoil.

The steel point was connected with a disc on the end of a mouthpiece. Edison turned the handle steadily and spoke into the mouthpiece. Every vibration of his voice drove the disc away from him and made the steel point press the foil more or less deeply down into the groove behind it. When the needle reached the end of the foil, it was lifted off, and the cylinder was run back into its original position. On the cylinder being turned forward a second time, with the needle touching it, the dents in the foil made the disc flutter exactly as it did when " talked at," and the original words were reproduced.

Thus, in the year following that of the invention of the telephone, Mr. Edison became the parent of a machine by means of which, to use the words that appeared in *The Times* soon afterwards, " the old familiar voice of one who is no longer with us on earth can be heard speaking to us in the very tones and measures to which our ears were once accustomed."

Phonograph and Dictaphone

This new invention was named the phonograph—the recorder of sounds. Its tinfoil soon gave place to a hollow wax cylinder, into which a hollow-ended sapphire cutter gouged tiny depressions, corresponding in frequency to the sound vibrations shaking the disc of the mouthpiece. A phonograph record, examined under a magnifying glass, appears as a series of scoops, varying in length, depth and spacing. To reproduce the sounds a tiny sapphire ball, as large across as the cutter, is used. This falls into the depressions, and in doing so shakes a disc in a sound-box, and sets up air vibrations in a horn.

The phonograph both records and reproduces sounds. If a record be needed no longer, the wax may be shaved away deeply enough to remove the sound waves, and the cylinder can then have another record made on it. But as a means of entertainment the phonograph has nowadays gone out of use, because wax cylinders are delicate and rather awkward to store. A special form of it, however, called the dictaphone, is employed in many business offices for taking down letters. The dictated records are transferred to reproducing machines in the typist's office.

From the phonograph was developed the instrument with which we are familiar to-day—the gramophone.

The Gramophone Co. Ltd.

YOU WILL RECOGNISE THIS

The picture " His Master's Voice " has made this dog—a real dog that really listened—world-famous as the central feature of what is probably the most successful pictorial advertisement ever produced.

Many improvements in the methods of making records have been made since the early phonograph days.

The Gramophone

This cannot make records, but only reproduces them, by following with the tip of a steel needle a spiral groove in a hard, flat disc.

The groove appears smooth enough to the eye, but really it is a series of zigzags. The needle is fixed to one end of a delicately pivoted lever, the other end of which is attached to the centre of a mica or metal disc, clamped firmly round the edges in a sound-box. The tip of the needle follows every zigzag in the groove, and in doing so vibrates from side to side. The sound-box disc necessarily vibrates with it, and creates air waves which reproduce the sounds recorded.

How a Gramophone Record is Made

Thanks to the kindness of the Gramophone Company, Limited ("His Master's Voice"), we are able to give a short description of the various operations needed in the making of a gramophone record.

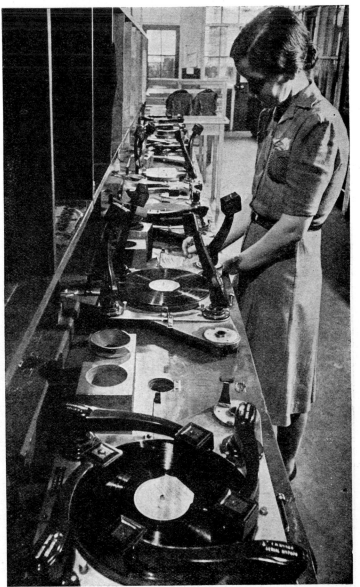

E.M.I. Sales and Service Ltd.

TESTING THE RECORDS FOR WEAR

From the original wax record a copper shell, known as the Master, is made, and then a second record, known as the Mother, or working matrix, is taken. The Master record is carefully stored away, but from the working matrix the records to be sold to the public are made. From each batch a certain number are tested and in this photograph we see sample records undergoing tests for wear.

We will assume that Madame X., the famous soprano, is to have one of her songs recorded. The singing is done in a studio specially equipped for the purpose, in front of a microphone.

Every vibration of the singer's voice makes the microphone disc flutter and send an electrical impulse to the stylus or cutting point of a recording machine. The last has a revolving table like that of an ordinary gramophone, on which is a circular slab of a special wax, about an inch thick. As the " wax "—this is the technical name given to it—revolves, the stylus, which can move sideways only, cuts in it a groove about $\frac{7}{1000}$ inch deep and $\frac{1}{400}$ inch wide. A tiny gauge-wheel, running on the top of the slab, prevents the stylus sinking in too far.

While the table revolves once, the stylus is drawn about $\frac{1}{100}$ inch towards the centre of the " wax ". The result of the revolution of the " wax " and the sideways travel of the stylus is a continuous volute or spiral groove having 100 turns or so to the inch.

While the stylus cuts it also vibrates sideways in time with the vibrations sent from the microphone. So the path which it makes for itself is a zigzag one. If, for example, it is recording a note having 3,000 vibrations a second, the stylus will zigzag at the same rate. So one need not be surprised if even a strong magnifying glass fails to reveal the individual zigzags. One has to remember, too, that the nearer the stylus gets to the centre, the smaller is the length of groove cut in a given time, and the zigzags must be crowded closer together. Nor is it a matter of simple zigzags, for each zig-zag has in it smaller zigzags, peculiar to the particular *cause* of the sound. If it were not for what we may call these secondary zigzags, which give sounds their special *timbre* or quality, it would be very difficult to tell whether a musical sound issued from the human throat or a piano, or a violin, or what not.

The " wax " on which Madame X.'s song has been recorded is so soft that it can be

Dictaphone Co. Ltd.

TYPING FROM THE DICTAPHONE

One form of the original sound-recording invention has been developed as the Dictaphone for business purposes. It enables the busy man in industry, politics, and even authorship, to dictate letters, notes and chapters just when most convenient to him. The secretary, as seen in the photograph above, afterwards types the letters or manuscripts from the record's dictation, the speed of which can be adjusted.

E.M.I. Sales and Service Ltd.

TO ENSURE THAT EACH RECORD IS PERFECT

Every detail of a new record is carefully tested to make certain that only a perfect record is sent from the factory to the distributor who sells to the public. In this photograph the final stage of these tests has been reached and the label on the record is finally checked to see that every detail is correct.

scratched with a finger-nail, and the needle of a gramophone would ruin it immediately. So it must be copied, down to its finest details, which are extraordinarily minute, in some substance hard enough to stand the wear of many reproductions.

Through Copper and Nickel

The "wax," after being cleaned, has its face dusted with fine metal (bronze) powder, which is rubbed in by a brush revolving so fast that any excess of powder is flung off by centrifugal force. It is next placed in an electro-plating bath, and a coating of copper is deposited on the metal which, unlike the wax itself, is able to conduct electricity. The copper coating, when peeled off, is, of course, a "negative" of the "wax," with ridges on it in place of grooves. This negative, known as the "master," is preserved very carefully.

Coated with Nickel

The "master's" face is first coated with nickel—a much harder metal than copper—to protect it against damage, and then with a solution which prevents sticking, and goes into the copper bath. The deposit of copper on it (peeled off when thick enough) forms a positive record, exactly similar to the "wax." This copy is named the "mother" of the record. From the "mother" are made any required number of negative nickel copies, each called a matrix, by electro-plating. These, when stiffened by a backing of thick copper, serve as the dies which mould the record finally as a positive in hard material.

So you see that a record is well guarded in manufacture. If a matrix be damaged, a new one can be taken from the " mother." If the " mother " itself suffered injury, a new mother could be made from the " master."

Moulding a Record

A record which you buy for your gramophone is composed of lamp-black, shellac, copal, and other substances. The various ingredients are ground up very finely, well mixed, and pass again and again through mills heated by steam. The heat makes the mixture plastic. It is rolled out into a continuous sheet, a yard or so wide, grooved lengthwise and crosswise so that, when cold and brittle, it easily breaks up into pieces each containing enough " biscuit " for the making of one record.

In the pressing-room of the factory are enormously powerful presses, able to give a 70-ton squeeze. A matrix of one record is fixed firmly, face upwards, to the lower plate of a press, and that of another record, face downwards, to the upper plate.

A Piece of " Biscuit "

The highly-skilled pressman lays a label face down on the lower matrix, and another label face up round a pin projecting through the top matrix. He then takes a lump of soft disc material—a piece of " biscuit " heated up—adjusts it in the centre of the lower matrix, closes the press, and turns on the power. The dough is squeezed out flat, with impressions of the matrices on its two sides, and is almost immediately cooled and hardened by water circulating through the press. The press opens, and out comes a " double-sided " record, finished except for the polishing of its edges, which is done on another machine.

Reproducing by Electricity

Every record is examined many times over for various possible defects, some of which go by the names of " drags," " dips," " pimples " and " bumps." If it gets safely through its examination, it is carried off by a conveyor to a vast store, containing many miles of shelves on which there is room for millions of records all arranged most systematically.

The Gramophone Co. Ltd.

THE STAGES OF RECORD-MAKING

A is a lump of the special material used in making an original record, a " wax," which in B is seen ready for recording. C shows the " wax " after recording; the wax shavings produced by the cutter are now removed by suction as it is cut. In D an electrically-deposited copper copy is being stripped from the " wax." E is the material, in its powder form, used for making F, a finished record. The matrices for two records are in the mould plates at G; and in H have pressed a record.

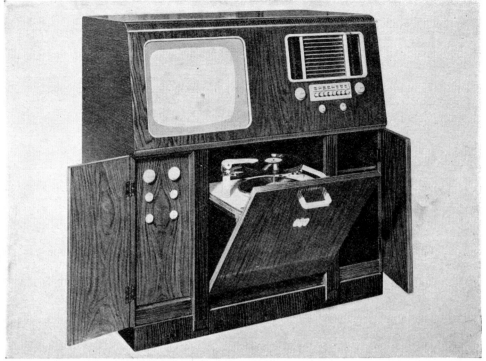

The Gramophone Co. Ltd.

A COMPLETE ENTERTAINMENT PROGRAMME FOR THE HOME

Edison, Marconi, Baird, are the names of three men whose pioneer efforts made possible the magic box shown above. The gramophone is a ten-record auto-changer, with push-button controls seen on the left. Above this control panel is the screen which brings all the Television broadcasts sent out by the B.B.C., while on the right is the 5-valve super-het radio receiver for listening to the wireless programmes from home and overseas stations.

Some gramophones make use of a device called an electrical pick-up for reproducing records. Instead of shaking a disc in a sound-box, the needle vibrates a small body of iron between the poles of an electro-magnet. The vibrations set up currents in the magnetic circuit, and these are magnified by wireless valves and converted into sounds by a loud-speaker. A gramophone of this kind can conveniently be combined with a wireless receiving set.

By moving a switch, the record pick-up circuit is cut out, and the wireless receiving circuit connected with the valves; or the other way about.

Before the end of 1939 this combination of gramophone with a wireless receiving set had become increasingly popular, but manufacture ceased during the war years. The advantages of such a set are obvious, as the sound reproduction of a good wireless receiver is as near perfection as modern science can make it. Now that television stations are being established to cover most of the country television is ceasing to be a luxury; it is regarded as a necessity.

With wireless and television programmes before them, a good selection of gramophone records at hand, and with a modern instrument designed to give the best results from any one of the three in turn, merely by changing a switch or turning a knob, the modern family need never be bored because of lack of entertainment! As our illustration shows, all three forms of entertainment are now available to them from the one cabinet.

MESSAGES AND PICTURES BY WIRE

Post Office.

IN LONDON'S CENTRAL TELEGRAPH OFFICE

Some idea of the great number of telegrams sent from a big business centre can be gained from this photograph taken in the main office of the telegraph service in London. Roughly two-thirds of all telegrams sent in this country are business messages and one-third social messages. Less than 2 per cent. contain bad news while 4 per cent. are congratulatory.

AS in every other department of Science, progress in all branches of electrical engineering has been not merely rapid but almost revolutionary in the past fifteen or twenty years. This is particularly true in the field of telegraphic communication. Instruments and methods which were described as modern less than twenty years ago are already museum pieces.

The first practical electrical telegraph was produced in 1837 when Cooke and Wheatstone in England brought out the needle telegraph while in America Morse produced his electromagnetic telegraph. From these inventions standard instruments were developed and used in different types of work.

For nearly a hundred years the Morse code was employed for the transmission of messages by telegraph. The sender at one end tapped a pivoted brass lever in front of him and so caused an electrical contact of brief or not quite so brief duration which resulted in a series of dots and dashes being recorded at the other end.

The message thus tapped out was received at the other end by an inking device recording the dots and dashes or heard on a " sounder "; this was decoded and the message written out in plain language for the person to whom the message was being sent. There were other types of apparatus which punched holes in the paper tape, which was then put into an automatic typewriter (Creed) and the message printed in clear words for all to read.

Fairly early in the history of the telegraph Professor D. E. Hughes invented an apparatus for delivering messages directly in printed type. At the sending end was a piano-like keyboard with twenty-eight keys on each of which was a letter of the

Post Office.

The Teleprinter is now established in all large Post Offices for the sending of telegrams. As will be seen from the photograph it is similar to a fairly large typewriter and the keyboard is operated in much the same way. The message can be received on an unattended machine if the operator is not there. This message is printed on paper tape or, in some machines, on a roll of paper, exactly as typed at the sender's end. It is then pasted on the official form and is ready for dispatch to the addressee.

alphabet or other character. The receiving apparatus had a typewheel with twenty-eight characters on it. If key A were pressed down, the receiver printed A on a paper strip. The chief difficulty at first was to keep things in step but this was eventually overcome.

From this machine developed the " Tape " machine, so named because it printed on a long paper tape. It has been in use for many years in stock exchange offices, business houses and clubs as well as newspaper offices for receiving the latest news.

From Morse to Teleprinter

A few years before the Second World War the telegraphic system in British Post Offices was completely reorganised. Up to the year 1935 various types of apparatus were in use in different offices from the " dot and dash " Morse sounder machines to the punching machines already described, as well as the Hughes piano-keyboard transmitter. Further reorganisation by changing from manual to automatic switching has been undertaken recently.

To-day the Teleprinter has replaced all other instruments and has been installed as a general rule in all Post Offices where 150 or more messages are handled daily. Smaller offices accept telegrams but they are immediately telephoned to the nearest Teleprinter office from which they are dispatched.

The Teleprinter, as will be seen from the photographs, is very similar in appearance to a large typewriter and has very much the same keyboard. It is slightly different in " touch " compared with a typewriter owing to the fact that the Teleprinter is electrically operated. Each time a key is depressed an electric current comes into operation and many miles away a similar Teleprinter apparatus types out the letters, figures, and spaces, as the distant operator types them.

In some of the Post Office machines the message is printed on paper tape, as in the photograph on page 187, but in others the message is typed direct on to a roll of paper. The tape can easily be torn or cut into small pieces and pasted on the official telegram form; the portion on the roll containing the message just received can also be easily torn off for similar treatment.

Signals are exchanged between the operators at each end so that one knows when a message is to be received and when it ends, while the sender learns that it has been correctly received. As the Teleprinter has a typewriter keyboard, works up to 65 words a minute, and prints the telegram ready for delivery, its advantages are obvious. It is believed, too, that operators working Teleprinters are able to retain a high degree of manipulative skill until a much later time of life than was generally possible with the morse-key working.

Under the G.P.O. " Telex " system Teleprinters can be installed in the offices of big commercial companies so that they can communicate direct with their branches or with other users of the " Telex " system, or direct with the Post Office telegraph office.

The use of private wire teleprinter circuits by commercial and other large concerns has increased rapidly during the last few years and a large number of circuits, both single and in groups with switchboard facilities, have been installed by the Post Office.

Working Without Strain

It is worth mentioning that the Post Office attach great importance to the training of their staff to make sure that those who will operate the Teleprinters acquire the right touch and correct rhythm. A well-trained staff works accurately and easily and without any sense of strain. Special telegraph training-schools are run by the G.P.O. to give newcomers thorough training before they tackle the real thing.

For special occasions the Mobile Post Office comes into use. This is really a

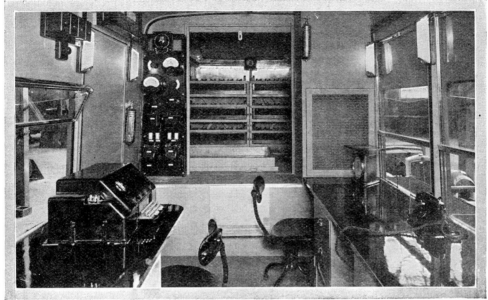

Post Office.

A MOBILE POST OFFICE

On special occasions when telegraph facilities are needed in some place where they do not exist or are too far away from the actual scene a Mobile Post Office is sent. This is really a motor-caravan fitted with Teleprinter and telephone which can be quickly connected up to the nearest lines and business carried on as in an ordinary Post Office.

motor caravan, but fitted with tele-printer and telephone apparatus which can be quickly connected up so that no delay occurs when urgent messages have to be sent from some place where normal telegraphic facilities do not exist. The adoption of teleprinter working has also enabled special events such as race meetings and big sports gatherings to be dealt with in a much more satisfactory manner than when the Morse apparatus was in use. A temporary telegraph office is quickly set up and the flood of messages is dis-patched without any unnecessary delay.

The Pen that Destroys Distance

The word telegraph comes from two Greek words: *Tele* = far off, and *grapho* = to write. To telegraph, therefore, means literally to write something at a distance. The use of the printing apparatus about which we have just been reading is real tele-graphy, if words delivered in type may be called writing; and the apparatus which we will next notice enables one to telegraph undisputedly in the full sense of the word.

What happens in this case is as follows: You pick up a pencil in, say, London, and write a message with it. As you do so, a pen in Liverpool, Manchester, or some other distant place copies every movement of your pencil so faithfully that what it writes is undoubtedly *your* handwriting, not that of anyone else. Instead of ordinary characters you may use short-hand if you like. Or, if some particular point can be explained better that way, make a simple sketch or diagram. It is all the same thing to the telewriter.

This service has not been developed very fully, partly owing to the fact that the ordinary telegraph and telephone provide all that is usually required, and partly owing to the war. Telewriters have been in use, however, on the Liverpool Cotton Exchange, Manchester Royal Exchange, and the reporters' gallery at the House of Commons.

Wireless has played a part both in the telegraph and telephone services in the sense that experiments in one direction have opened up possibilities in another. Among the discoveries affecting telegraphy and telephony is what is termed "voice frequency" working. In the beginning each pair of persons talking over a telephone or using the telegraph instrument needed a pair of wires. Nowadays by adopting a method used in wireless each pair of wires can carry several conversations or machine-sent messages.

The sounds go over the wires as a jumble but at the other end each different voice or teleprinter message is picked out by a suitable filter and the jumble is automatically and neatly sorted out. One line between London and Birmingham actually carries 320 conversations on one pair of wires. The apparatus required at each end to combine the different conversations in the beginning and then to separate them at the end is highly ingenious, and, as can be imagined, wonderfully complicated so that no easy and simple explanation of its working is possible. Those of us who lack technical knowledge in such matters can only stand and wonder.

But it is this "voice frequency" system which has revolutionised the engineer's task in both telegraph and telephone practice and still improvements are being made. The introduction of this system has resulted in a complete co-ordination and harmony between the telephone and the telegraph services. The same lines serve both services and in the case of the telegraph it means that the service is nowadays almost without distance limits. On this particular system repeater stations are situated at intervals of about fifty miles.

Cables Under the Sea

There is another branch of telegraph

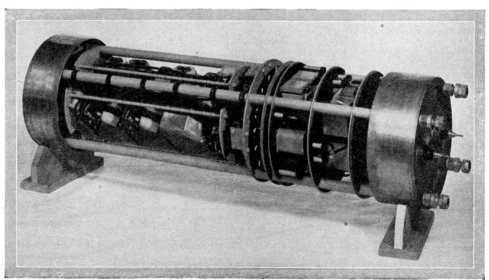

Post Office.

A POWER HOUSE UNDER THE SEA

One of the handicaps of submarine cables has been the fact that it was not possible to have amplifiers between the shore terminals. This has now been overcome by the Post Office engineers and our photograph shows the inner assembly of the "Repeater" which forms part of the cable laid in 1946 between Lowestoft and the island of Borkum off the German coast for the Continental service. This inner assembly is 4 feet long by 13 inches diameter and is enclosed in a larger chamber constructed of welded steel plates ⅝ inch thick which will withstand a pressure of 1,000 pounds to the square inch.

TELEPRINTERS AT THE DERBY

For special events such as important racing and sports meetings a staff of telegraphists with their Teleprinters are installed on the spot. The photograph above shows the scene on Derby Day, and although horses, jockeys and crowds are somewhere just beyond the camera's range the teleprinters are sending results and descriptions after each race.

Any telephone subscriber or call office user can make a call to " Telegrams " and dictate a telegram to a Post Office operator for transmission. These telegrams are known as " Phonograms," and this photograph shows the Phonogram operators at work in a big Provincial office.

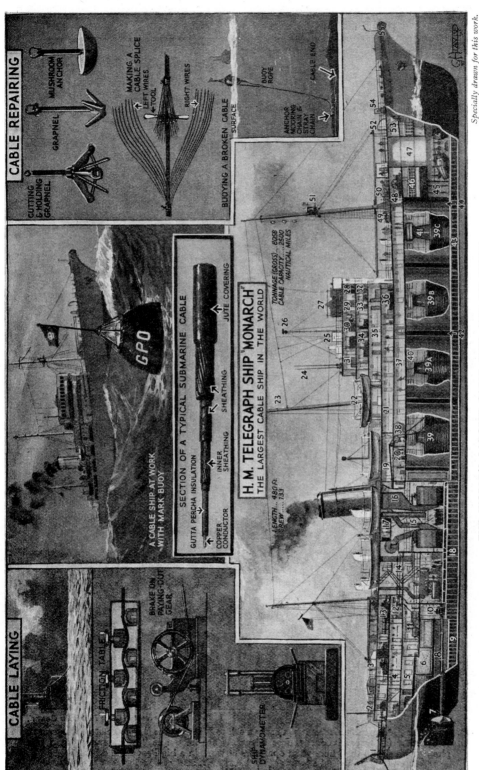

CABLE REPAIRING

CUTTING & HOLDING GRAPNEL

GRAPNEL

MUSHROOM ANCHOR

MAKING A CABLE SPLICE

LEFT WIRES

TOOL

RIGHT WIRES

BUOYING A BROKEN CABLE

SURFACE

BUOY ROPE

ANCHOR MOORING CHAIN & STRAY CHAIN

CABLE END

A CABLE SHIP AT WORK WITH MARK BUOY

GPO

SECTION OF A TYPICAL SUBMARINE CABLE

JUTE COVERING

SHEATHING

INNER SHEATHING

GUTTA PERCHA INSULATION

COPPER CONDUCTOR

H.M. TELEGRAPH SHIP "MONARCH"

THE LARGEST CABLE SHIP IN THE WORLD

LENGTH.... 480 FT.
CREW.... 133

TONNAGE (GROSS).... 8058
CABLE CAPACITY.... 2500 NAUTICAL MILES

CABLE LAYING

FRICTION TABLE

BRAKE ON PAYING-OUT GEAR

SHIP DYNAMOMETER

Specially drawn for this work.

THE WORLD'S LARGEST CABLE SHIP AND ITS WORK

There have been four vessels which have borne the name of H.M. Telegraph Ship *Monarch*; the latest of these, an 8,058 ton vessel, is fitted with every modern device and invention for cable-laying and repairing. It was launched on the Tyne in 1945 and came into service the following year. This drawing shows some of the equipment carried and the tasks carried out by the ship. The key to the numbers shown in the drawing of the *Monarch* in the lower half of the picture is given on the opposite page.

work about which a large volume could easily be written. The Post Office is responsible for 373 submarine cables, but as new cables are still being laid this figure is increasing steadily.

It was in 1850 that the first submarine cable was laid between England and France. Something went wrong very shortly after it was laid and it took a little time to discover the truth. A Boulogne fisherman had hooked up the cable with his trawl, and, puzzled by his catch, cut off a piece—and then promptly set sail for home. He believed that he had found a new and rare kind of seaweed the centre of which was filled with gold. The gold, of course, was merely copper wire and the " seaweed " had been specially made in England.

This unfortunate beginning did not deter the engineers and during the next year, 1851, the first successful cable to the Continent was laid. In 1870 the Post Office took over several cables belonging to different companies as well as the cable ship *Monarch*, a paddle-steamer of some 500 tons.

Since then there have been three other ships which have borne the name H.M. Telegraph Ship *Monarch*. The latest *Monarch* is a large cable-laying ship of 8,000 tons, fitted with every latest improvement to enable her to make use of the many scientific developments in this important branch of telecommunication between countries separated by the oceans.

Largest in the World

The *Monarch* is indeed a wonder ship, fitted with four cable tanks in which about 2,500 miles of deep sea cable can be carried, and having electrically-operated cable gear. She was launched in 1945 and is the largest cable ship in the world.

Cable-laying is almost as highly scientific as is the work of the engineers who have devised all the apparatus now in use. Even in the deepest water the cable rests on the bottom of the ocean. When laying a cable in a depth of three miles it is calculated that, with a ship's speed of eight knots, the distance from the stern sheave where the cable leaves the ship to the point where the cable actually touches the bottom is over 20 miles. It takes a particular point in the cable more than two hours to reach the bottom from the time it enters the water.

Flashed Across the Ocean

A new cable for the Continental service was laid in 1946 between Lowestoft and the Island of Borkum off the German coast. It is 200 nautical miles long and the cable has Polythene insulation instead of the old gutta-percha covering. This particular cable is fitted with a submerged repeater which is in effect a small power house on its own, renewing the current and amplifying the messages. Like other highly technical improvements in the electrical engineers' world

---

H.M. TELEGRAPH SHIP " MONARCH "
Key to numbers shown in the drawing on the opposite page.

1. After Paying-out Sheave ; 2. After Dynamometer ; 3. After Brake Control ; 4. Quarters and Corridor ; 5. Refrigerated Stores ; 6. Water Tanks ; 7. Starboard Propeller ; 8. Starboard Propeller Shaft ; 9. Feed Water Tanks ; 10. Thrust Block ; 11. Generating Machinery Room ; 12. Engineers' Workshop ; 13. After Paying-out Gear ; 14. Engine Room (Starboard) ; 15. Boiler Room ; 16. Uptakes ; 17. Galley ; 18. Fuel Tanks in Double Bottom ; 19. Ward Room ; 20. Master Gyro Compass ; 21. Officers' Accommodation and Corridor ; 22. Starboard Motor Boat ; 23. Cable Signal Lights ; 24. Whip Aerials ; 25. Radar Room ; 26. Radar Scanner ; 27. Range Finder and Compass Platform ; 28. Wheel House and Bridge ; 29. Chart Room ; 30. Radio Room ; 31. Sea Cabins and Offices ; 32. Captain's Day Cabin ; 33. Captain's Sleeping Cabin ; 34. Sea Cabins ; 35. Cabin Corridor ; 36. Cable Test Room ; 37. Gangway, cabins, offices, etc. ; 38. Cable-Leads Testing Station ; 39, 39a, 39b and 39c. Cable Stowed in Cable Tanks ; 40. Crinoline Cable Guide (on each tank) ; 41. Cones in each Tank round which the cable is turned ; 42. Pitometer Log Chamber ; 43. Double Bottom ; 44. Echo Sounder Chamber ; 45. Fore Hold Stowage of working gear, buoys, etc. ; 46. Stowage Bins ; 47. Hatch Trunk ; 48. Forward Picking Up and Paying Out Gear ; 49. Winch ; 50. Forward Jockey and Hauling-Off gear ; 51. Crow's Nest ; 52. Companion Way ; 53. Forward Crew's Space, etc. ; 54. Forward Dynamometer ; 55. Bow Sheave for picking up and paying out cable.

AS THE NEWS COMES THROUGH ON THE TAPE

This is the tape machine which is used in Stock Exchange offices, clubs, newspaper offices and other places for share quotations and news items, particularly those containing figures. It works on much the same general principles as the Teleprinter.

it is impossible to give a simple explanation of its parts or its manifold purposes. Yet it does help us to appreciate the marvels of our modern world if now and again we are given a glimpse of the ingenious inventions and devices which "make the wheels go round," or, in this case, flash our words in a twinkling across the wide oceans.

Another wonderful aspect which has developed within recent years is Picture Telegraphy. This differs from all other forms of telegraphy (with the exception to some extent of the Telewriter) in the fact that an exact reproduction of the original images or signs is received at the other end of the wires.

The history of picture telegraphy goes back as far as 1843 when Bain invented a system by which handwriting and simple line-drawings could be reproduced in facsimile. Then came the Berlin system which was used in France between certain towns from 1924 onwards. The system now used by the British Post Office is the Siemens-Karolus.

The Moving Light-Spot

In this system the picture to be transmitted is fixed round a drum by means of spring clips. When the apparatus is started the drum rotates with uniform speed, and at the same time a spot of light is thrown on to the surface of the picture. This light-spot scans the picture with a spiral movement so that all portions of the picture from one end of the drum to the other are explored. The light from the sending lamp is interrupted by a rotating shutter in the form of a toothed disc.

The light reflected from the surface

LANDING AND GRAPPLING FOR CABLES

Sport and General.

In 1926 England and America were for the first time connected by a submarine cable having its conductor wrapped from end to end in a continuous spiral of special alloy wire which greatly increases the speed of transmission and the clearness of signals. The English end of the cable is here being landed at Sennen Cove, Cornwall.

Post Office.

A cable ship is fitted with equipment for locating the cable lying on the ocean bed, raising it from the depths and carrying out tests to locate any faults. When the exact position of the fault is found the cable ship sails to the spot and again the cable is brought to the surface. Rafts may be used by the men carrying out the repairs. Our photograph shows some of the grapnels in use on H.M.T.S. *Monarch*.

13—2

of the picture actuates a photo-cell, and originates instantaneously a pulsating electric current proportional to the varying tones of the picture; the lighter the part of the picture the greater the current. The photo-cell current is extremely small and it is accordingly amplified in a valve amplifier, after which it is transmitted over a suitable telephone line.

At the receiving end the current is amplified in a valve amplifier and is applied to the terminals of a Kerr cell

L.E.A.

PAYING OUT THE CABLE

Different types of sheaves are fitted on the cable ships. The bow sheaves are used for repair work or laying short cables, while the stern sheave is used when laying long cable. Here, the cable is running over a special platform and sheave at the stern of a steamer.

or an oscillograph. The cell controls the intensity of a light spot which scans spirally as at the sending end by being projected on to a photographic film mounted on a drum rotated at exactly the same speed as that at the sending end. The film is taken from the drum in a dark room where it is developed, fixed and printed in the usual way.

Both before and after transmission the operators at both stations speak to each other over the wire by means of telephones connected to the picture apparatus. In due course the receiving station reports whether the picture has been received satisfactorily or not.

The advantages of picture telegraphy are many, some of which we have already learned to appreciate by photographs in the daily papers, taken hundreds or even thousands of miles away on the previous afternoon. Chinese characters, shorthand, fingerprints, and even delicate lace designs have been sent by this form of telegraphy.

By Wire and Wireless

At present of course it is chiefly the newspapers which make use of picture telegraphy, but it is quite likely that as time goes on and more stations are opened which cater for this kind of telegraphy there will be a big increase in its general use.

It may be, too, that a shorter and more distinctive name will be adopted in place of " picture telegraphy " as the service becomes more popular. The word " Telicon " has been suggested as

Post Office.

MILES OF SUBMARINE CABLE IN STORE

The Post Office has four cable depots at Woolwich, Dover, Dalmuir (Clyde) and Faslane in the Gairloch where submarine cables can be stored in specially-constructed tanks. Each depot has about nine of these tanks, and our photograph shows one at Woolwich with various types of cables in the same tank. Normally these tanks are kept full of water as the insulation deteriorates if cable is kept out of water for any length of time.

being in line with the well-established "telegram" and "telephone."

The Post Office controls and operates all the wireless, telegraph and telephone systems in the country and a good deal of work has been done to co-ordinate these varied services. The question of competition between them scarcely arises since one method is suitable for certain cases while for a different purpose another method is found best. In some cases one helps the other and a message may begin its journey across the world through the telephone, then go by cable across a wide stretch of ocean to be passed on finally by the radio operator on a wireless station to his colleague in the cabin of an ocean liner.

At different times the Post Office staff have sought an answer to the question: What are the reasons which decide the choice by the ordinary sender between the telegraph and the telephone message?

Certain types of messages must obviously be sent by telegram. For example, telegrams of congratulation and good wishes in connection with weddings and other social events are scarcely suitable for telephoning. Imagine the plight of bride or bridegroom at the wedding reception if a score of friends from near and afar all decided to make use of the telephone to convey their good wishes!

Then there are many business messages of which it is desirable to have a written record. Here again the telegraph scores over the telephone. In the case of short-distance messages, especially where an immediate answer is desired, the telephone is generally much more convenient.

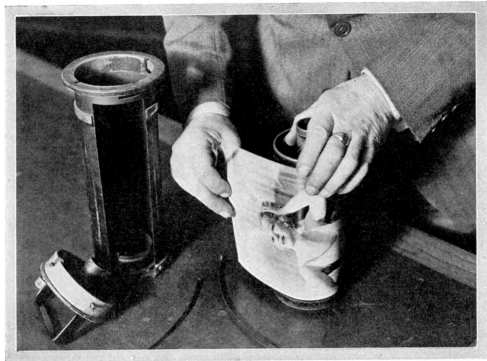

Post Office.

PREPARING THE PHOTOGRAPH FOR TELEGRAPHING

Photographs are now sent regularly by telegraphy. Our illustration shows a print which has been handed in to the Post Office for transmission being clipped on to the drum in readiness for sending through the wires by a pulsating electric current which gives every gradation of the different tones in the picture. This current operates a pencil of light at the receiving end and so produces a photographic negative from which prints can be made.

At one time it was apt to be assumed that, as far as its social side was concerned, the telegram was the bearer of bad news. That idea is dying out to-day. Actually less than two per cent. of telegrams come into this category, while about four per cent. carry congratulations.

In an analysis of trade telegrams it was found that "fish" messages amounted to nearly nine per cent. of the total, and it was clear that the telegraph service plays a big part in the buying and selling of perishable goods such as meat, fruit and vegetables.

The way in which the telephone and telegram are complementary to each other is seen in the fact that nearly three-quarters of all telegrams come from the senders to the Post Office by telephone.

In this chapter we have dealt only with messages and pictures conveyed by electric current through wires. The British Post Office have of course control of the largest network of radio communications in the world. By Act of Parliament passed in 1904 the Postmaster-General became the sole licensing authority for wireless telegraphy and telephony and all wireless apparatus installed in this country or on board British ships.

It will be seen therefore that the three services, Telegraph, Telephone and Wireless, are not working in competition with each other but can be used to supplement each other. When some new invention or revolutionary method comes along in any sphere there is a tendency at first to think that the new will oust the old system.

LANDED!

After long and patient dragging, this cable has been hooked and brought safely to the surface for repairs. Two men, lowered on " bosun's chairs," have made the cable fast on both sides of the point at which it will be cut. At the top of the chains we see parts of the bow sheaves of the ship.

telephone in making swift communication.

The telephone is in the main a short-distance service while the telegram is more generally used over longer distances. Taking an average of all telegrams sent in this country the message sent via the teleprinter travels about 150 miles. The average telephone distance is very much less.

Whatever new devices and improvements may come along it is safe to say that in the next few years the telegraph services will be able to give the British public an increasing number of advantages as old systems are improved and new ideas are brought into practice.

G.P.A.

A NICE LITTLE FISH-HOOK!
The grapnel, having done its work, is made fast over the bow sheaves, of which, you will see, there are three. Grapnels of various forms are used to cope with different conditions of dragging.

Thus the rapid advance of the telephone service in the years before the last war led many people to believe that the older telegraph system would rapidly become out of date. Radio, too, seemed likely to oust the old telegraph and cable systems when first its wonders and possibilities became apparent. The actual outcome, however, has been that radio has its own distinct field, and it is not a competitor with either the telephone or telegraph services. For inland service the telegraph has become even more important as a partner with the

Post Office.

PICTURE TELEGRAPHY
Pictures are now telegraphed many hundreds of miles. Our illustration shows the photograph of a youngster playing on the sand which was sent as a telegram from the Continent.

THE TELEPHONE AND HOW IT WORKS

Photos by courtesy of the Postmaster-General.

THE FIRST TELEPHONE AND ONE OF ITS DESCENDANTS

On the left in this photograph is seen the telephone by which the first spoken message was ever transmitted by its inventor, Dr. Alexander Graham Bell, in 1876. Millions of telephones are now in use throughout the world and the instrument on the right, familiar to all of us, is one of the modern descendants of Dr. Bell's first telephone.

HAVING dealt with the first means of sending messages electrically —the telegraph—we will discuss the second means—the telephone. In its action, if not in its working principles, the telephone is a much more delicate apparatus than the telegraph. The telegraph transmits pulses of electricity at a rate limited to thousands a minute; the telephone transmits electrical vibrations numbering thousands a second. It is therefore able to respond to the very quick vibrations of the human voice and other sounds, and makes it possible to transmit sounds, as opposed to signals, very faithfully.

The first practical telegraph, the needle instrument, was produced in 1837. The telephone did not appear till much later. On July 1st, 1875, Mr. Charles Watson, assistant to Alexander Graham Bell, a Scottish doctor who was professor of vocal physiology at Boston University, heard words, transmitted by electricity, which were spoken by Professor Bell in another room. He could not distinguish the meaning of the words but he was sure that the sounds *were* words. After a little more experimenting the day came

(March 10th, 1876) when Bell, who will always be famous as the inventor of the telephone, heard quite clearly some words uttered by his assistant, and sent back to him the first telephone message ever transmitted: " Mr. Watson, please come here; I want you." This was a memorable day in human history, for it may be regarded as the birthday of the telephone. Dr. Bell carried out his early experiments, and took out his first patents, at Brantford in Canada, when he first went to North America as a young doctor in 1870.

Bell's First Telephone

Though the instrument originally used by Bell was soon improved out of use, it deserves a short notice. At the back of its mouthpiece was a tightly stretched parchment disc, connected to a small strip of iron, one end of which was fixed and the other near the pole of an electro-magnet. The coil of wire wound on the magnet was connected at one end to earth, and at the other to a wire running to a similar instrument elsewhere with its own earth wire. When the telephone was in use it was necessary to use the same

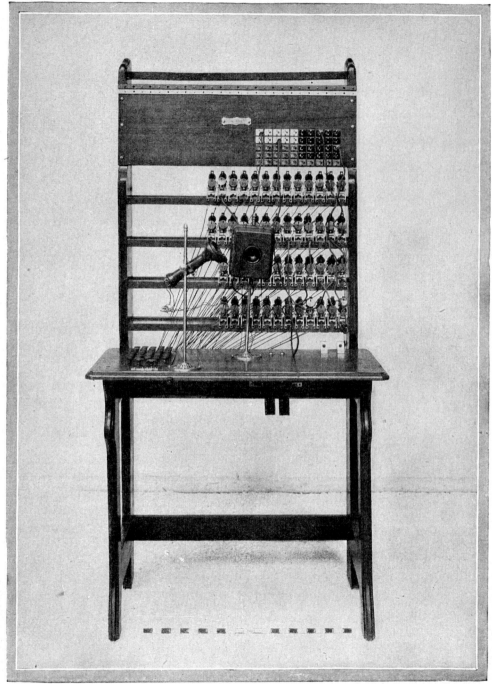

Rischgitz.

This is a telephone switchboard such as was used in telephone exchanges seventy years ago. It looks very crude beside the wonderful switchboards of to-day. But at that time telephony was only four years old, and telephone subscribers were very few, so that it was probably large enough to meet the needs of a big town. Nowadays there are over 3,000 automatic exchanges in rural areas in this country.

FOR TELEPHONE USERS TO=DAY

In your telephone directory instructions are given on how to make an Emergency Call in case of fire, or if the services of the police or the ambulance are urgently required. Many lives have been saved by this particular service. In this photograph we have a view of an Emergency Services switchboard where all " 999 " calls are dealt with immediately.

Photos by courtesy of the Postmaster-General.

Other services exist to help the telephone user when necessary. A person may wish to telephone someone outside his own area, or someone whose name does not appear in the directory. The Enquiries Branch exists to deal with this and similar difficulties. Here we have a view of the operators at work in the Directory Enquiry branch in Birmingham.

transmitter for both voice and ear. The words uttered near a mouthpiece caused the parchment disc and iron strip to vibrate. The movements of the iron strip in the " field " of the magnet disturbed what are called the " lines of force " of the magnet, and produced variations in the current flowing through the coil and line corresponding in frequency to the vibrations of the voice. These current variations altered the pulling power of the magnet in the instrument at the other end of the line, so that it moved its iron strip and the parchment attached thereto in exact time with the movements of the other parchment. Waves set up in the air by the disc of the receiving instrument reproduced the words spoken into the transmitter.

Bell soon improved his first instru-ment by using permanent magnets in place of electro-magnets in his apparatus. The new device served, like its predecessor, for both sending and receiving. Its construction was practically the same as that of any modern receiver—the thing which you lift off the instrument and hold to your ear when you ring up or answer the exchange. If we took this to pieces we should find an iron disc at the back of the earpiece, very close to the pole or pieces of the magnet. Round the disc end of the magnet is wound a coil of wire, the two ends of which are con-nected to the wires in a flexible cord entering the back end of the instrument.

Bell's second telephone outfit con-sisted, then, of two of these instruments connected by two wires. When one was spoken into, the vibrations of its

Postmaster-General.

THE INTERNATIONAL TELEPHONE EXCHANGE

Telephonic communication with practically every country in the world can be made from Britain, and all such communications pass through the International Telephone Exchange at Faraday Building, London. Here we have a view of the operators at work on one section of the big switchboards, and the names of a few of the very many distant places with which telephonic connection is made can be seen above the boards.

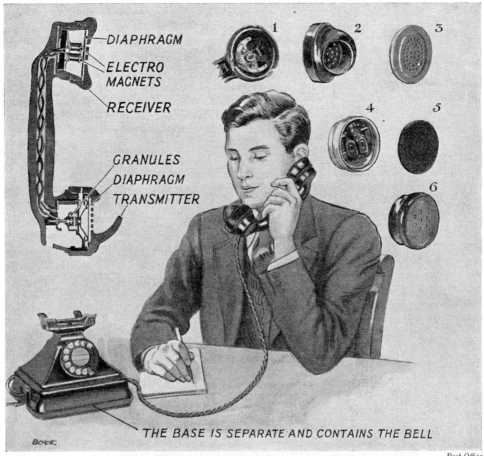

DIAPHRAGM
ELECTRO MAGNETS
RECEIVER

GRANULES
DIAPHRAGM
TRANSMITTER

1 2 3

4 5

6

THE BASE IS SEPARATE AND CONTAINS THE BELL

Post Office.

THE HAND MICROPHONE AND ITS PARTS

Our illustration shows the hand-microphone telephone instrument now in general use throughout the country. In the diagram on the top right-hand side are shown (1) the transmitter contacts, with (2) the mouthpiece into which one speaks ; (3) the transmitter, (4) the receiver electromagnets, (5) the receiver diaphragm, and (6) the receiver cap, or ear cap, which brings the voice of the speaker at the other end to the listener's ear. The position of these different parts is shown in the drawing on the left-hand side. In some instruments the bell is contained in the base or it can be a separate attachment on the wall.

iron diaphragm altered the lines of force of the magnet and caused tiny currents to be " induced " in the coil round it. These currents, passing through the line, affected the magnet in the other instrument, alternately strengthening and weakening its pull on the iron disc near it. So this disc vibrated in time with that at the transmitting end, and reproduced the sounds. In order to carry on a conversation it was only necessary to provide two instruments

at each end of the line, connected together and to the line wires. —

Modern Telephones

While the Bell permanent-magnet instrument has been retained for receiving, great improvements have been made in transmitting apparatus. At the back of the mouthpiece into which one speaks is a device called a microphone. This consists of carbon grains packed between two carbon plates, which are connected with the poles of a battery. The current flows from one pole to the other through the grains. The vibrations of the voice shake one of the plates and vary the pressure between the grains, which pass current more freely when pressed more tightly together. The receivers at each end of the line may have no direct connection with the transmitters. Currents produced in a transmitter are imparted to the circuit containing the line wires and receivers through a thing called a transformer or induction coil. This has two separate windings of insulated wire round a single iron core. One winding forms part of the microphone circuit, the other is part of the line wires and receivers circuit. So when either transmitter is spoken into and currents pass through its coil in the transformer, currents are induced, or formed by sympathy, in the line wires

and the receivers at both ends of the line. The transformer windings are so arranged that the induced currents are at a higher pressure than the microphone currents, and therefore able to travel more easily through the line.

Every telephone instrument is provided with a bell, which attracts attention to it when a distant person wishes to speak; and with a switch which puts the bell " in circuit " with the line when the receiver is hung on its hook.

So extraordinarily sensitive is the telephone that a movement of a transmitter disc at one station through a 10-millionth part of an inch will cause a corresponding vibration in the receiver of another station! This great sensitiveness of the receiver is such that it is necessary to use *two* line wires in a telephone circuit, one taking the place of the earth " return " in telegraphy, to

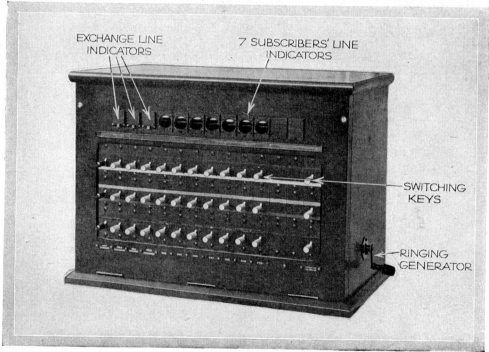

A SMALL TELEPHONE EXCHANGE

Post Office.

In many offices a private telephone exchange is installed and our photograph shows a small telephone switchboard with three lines from the main exchange by which outside subscribers can be connected with any of the different departments in the office. The operator uses an ordinary telephone instrument which will have a dial if the main exchange is automatic.

Postmaster-General.

WHERE THOUSANDS OF LINES MEET

In this photograph we have a view of the main trunk lines switchboard at Faraday Building in London. It will be noted that this is a manual switchboard as the automatic system is not always suitable for trunk calls. Some idea of the thousands of connections made from different exchanges and subscribers in London, or in other areas which can be best linked with some distant town through London, can be gathered from the long line of operators all kept fully employed during the busy hours of the day.

avoid interference from stray earth currents.

Apart from human speech, a telephone may be used in many ways for the picking up of faint sounds or electrical vibrations. One important use is the reception of wireless signals.

Telephone Exchanges

The usefulness of the telephone depends largely on the possibility of users being able to get quickly into communication with each other. The wires of every telephone in a district run to a switchboard in a building called a telephone exchange, where any pair can be connected in a moment with any other pair ending there, or, through connecting lines, with any pair ending in another exchange.

The connection is usually made by hand. But very many exchanges are automatic, and a subscriber, by working a dial at his instrument, can call up any other subscriber.

The automatic exchange, as it is called, may be compared with a motor car. It has no mind of its own, but will respond exactly to proper guidance. It rings up any number wanted, signals if the number is engaged, cuts off subscribers at the end of a talk, and records the call. Seldom, if ever, does it make a mistake.

The mechanism of an automatic exchange is so very complicated that it can only be explained in technical terms. Just to give you some idea of its complexity, we will tell you this : In an exchange with 9,999 subscribers the switching is able to make any one of 2,400,000,000 different connections.

By Night and Day

But we can at least explain something about automatic telephone working. The automatic exchange is rapidly ousting the manual exchange, and for several good reasons. It gives quicker service, and as good service by night as by day; and it is quite secret.

In the London area we can say that it has been almost completely adopted. And a sign of this is that in the London Telephone Directory, and in many provincial directories, the first three letters of every exchange are printed in heavy capital letters: GERrard, HOLborn, VICtoria, CHAncery, WIMbledon, and so on. In using a dial instrument one has merely to dial the first three letters of the Exchange required, followed by the number.

Let us look at a telephone used by a subscriber connected with an automatic exchange in a " Director " exchange area. At the base of it is a dial with ten holes in its face near the edge. Behind the holes we see the numbers 1, 2, 3, 4, 5, 6, 7, 8, 9, 0, in this order. We see also letters of the alphabet, except behind hole No. 1, in this fashion:

ABC   DEF   GHI, and so on.

2   3   4

Suppose that a subscriber wishes to ring up someone on the—well, let us call it the HAMpstead—exchange. He lifts off his receiver, puts a finger in the H hole, and turns the dial clockwise till

Postmaster-General.

IN AN AUTOMATIC EXCHANGE

This is some of the very wonderful apparatus which connects subscribers in an automatic telephone exchange. When a subscriber " rings up " the exchange, one of the many " selectors " seen in the racks will at once begin hunting for the number for which he has asked by working the dial on his instrument.

WHERE MACHINERY REPLACES FINGERS

In another part of an automatic exchange will be found the extraordinarily ingenious devices called " directors," which enable a subscriber to put through a call to any exchange in his area. Even if his call has to pass through two or three intermediate exchanges to reach the subscriber wanted, the directors clear the path for him in obedience to the three " code " exchange letters which he dials before giving the number.

his finger comes up against a stop. Then he withdraws his finger and the dial turns back into its original position. The letters " A " and " M " are dialled in the same way. When the dial has returned to normal for the third time he is " through " to the Hampstead exchange.

He may have to go through two, or even three, exchanges to get Hampstead. It doesn't matter, the code will perform the task thoroughly, for things are so arranged that no two exchanges have the same first three letters in the same order or of the same value. Our subscriber then dials the number wanted immediately after dialling the letters of the exchange.

As in telegraphy, experiments are continually being made to improve and extend the uses of the telephone. Not only the Post Office technical staff but the communications engineers on our railways are carrying out development work which will combine the ordinary telephone system of the country with radio telephony.

It is possible that in the near future a business man travelling from London to Newcastle by train will be able to ring up his office in the City and talk over the telephone with a member of the staff just as easily as he could make the call from a town office.

Another application of this system is designed to equip all railway breakdown trains with apparatus which will enable them to communicate with headquarters through the nearest signal box, the operator in the box switching the conversations on to the normal railway telephone system.

The invention of the telephone was due to what might be called the hobby of a medical man who specialised in vocal physiology and was interested in sound and phonetics. He experimented in transmitting sound by electricity and by light. The outcome was the first telephone instrument seen on page 201.

Graham Bell lived until 1922, long enough to see the telephone become an essential part of business and family communication throughout the world. The centenary of his birth was celebrated in 1947 by engineers in many countries, and there are many thousands of people to-day who owe a debt of gratitude to the Scottish-American doctor whose pioneer efforts produced the first telephone.

Postmaster-General.

THE CALLING DIAL IN A DIRECTOR AREA

To signal any letter or figure, the subscriber places the tip of a finger into the hole through which it shows, and revolves the dial in the direction taken by a clock's hands, until his finger strikes the stop at the bottom. As the dial flies back after being released the signal is sent.

RADIO TELEPHONY

Photo by courtesy of the Postmaster-General.

THE INTERNATIONAL RADIO TELEPHONE EXCHANGE

Early in the present century the first long-distance radio telegraph message in Morse code was sent. The development of radio-telephone communication was a natural outcome after the invention of the triode valve. In this photograph a section of the International Radio Telephone Exchange in London is seen.

IN 1901 Marconi startled the world when he succeeded in sending a message across the Atlantic Ocean by means of radio waves. Since that date the science of radio-communication has made amazing strides, and to-day wireless waves are used for a host of purposes ranging from sound and television broadcasting to measurements of the height of the moon!

Marconi sent his message by radio telegraphy, that is, he broke up the radio wave into a series of short or long trains to represent the dots and dashes of the Morse code—a method incidentally which is still in use to-day. Naturally experiments were soon begun with the idea of transmitting the human voice by radio, and after the invention of the triode valve in 1907 comparatively rapid progress was made. Developments were interrupted by the 1914–18 war, but transatlantic radio telephony was successfully demonstrated in 1923, and a regular service between Great Britain and America was inaugurated in 1927.

In order to understand how radio telephony works we must briefly examine the nature of sound and radio waves.

Wave Frequencies

Sound waves consist of alternating changes in air pressure produced, in the case of speech, by the larynx in the speaker's throat. The compressions and rarefactions comprising the wave travel through the air at about 1,130 feet per second, and the numbers of them occurring in one second is known as the frequency of the wave. A low note, such as the hum audible in many broadcast receivers, has a frequency of 100 cycles per second compared with, say, 5,000 for a high-pitched whistle. It is

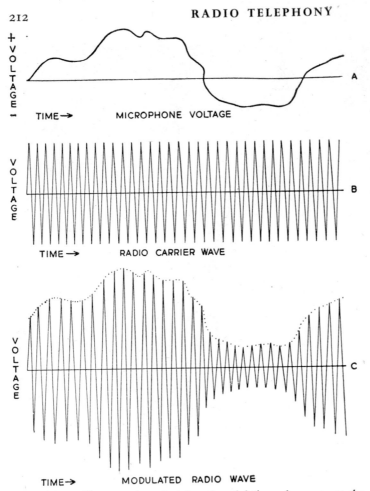

This diagram illustrates the principles of modulation: A represents the voltage due to the microphone; B the radio carrier wave; and in C the dotted line shows how the sound wave-form is " carried " by the radio wave.

megacycles per second are used for radar and other applications.

A simple analogy which helps to explain the process of radiation is that of a stone dropped into a still pond. Ripples will spread outwards in all directions from the point where the stone enters the water, and if a leaf or twig is floating at the edge of the pond it will bob up and down when the ripples reach it. Now the motion of the leaf is due to the stone, but no water as such has passed between them. What has happened is that a series of *disturbances in the water* (i.e. the ripples) has conveyed a fraction of the stone's energy of motion to the leaf. In a similar manner a radio wave, which is a series of electrical disturbances in space, is able to convey energy from the transmitting to the receiving aerial.

The first step in conveying speech by radio is to obtain an electrical equivalent of the sound waves. This is done by a microphone, which is able to convert the changes in air pressure due to the speaker's voice into a varying electric current. This current after suitable amplification is used to control the amplitude (or strength) of a radio carrier wave. This process, which is called modulation, is illustrated diagrammatically above, where A represents the voltage due to the microphone, B represents the radio carrier wave

interesting to note that, as the wave is a disturbance in the air, sound cannot travel through a vacuum.

A radio wave may be simply described as a series of electrical trains in space which travel with the speed of light, i.e. at 186,000 miles per second. The radio wave is also alternating in nature, but the frequencies used are enormously higher than those of sound. For example, the long-wave B.B.C. transmitter at Droitwich has a frequency of 200,000 cycles per second, the B.B.C. television transmitter in London uses a frequency of 45 megacycles (millions of cycles) per second, and frequencies as high as 4,000

MASTS AND MOBILE RADIO

The masts at the Rugby Radio Station are 820 feet high. This photograph gives some idea of the constructional work in each of these twelve giant masts.

Here is the base of one of these masts. From the platform a tiny lift inside the mast itself enables the summit to be reached. Each mast weighs some 200 tons.

Photos by courtesy of the Postmaster-General.

Another picture taken at the Rugby Radio Station shows the aerial leads. The term "wireless" seems out of place in view of the network of wires at the station itself.

Apart from long-distance communication, radio telephony is used on short-distance services, as in this case where a Thames tug is in touch with shore headquarters.

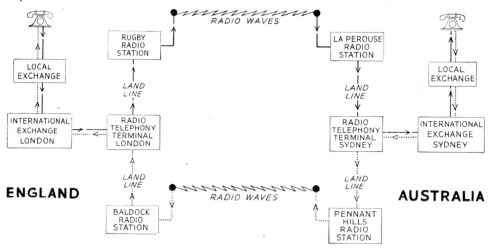

BETWEEN ENGLAND AND AUSTRALIA

In this diagram the different links are shown whereby a telephone subscriber in Britain is able to speak to another telephone user in Australia. From Rugby radio waves carry the speaker's voice to La Perouse Station in Australia.

and C the modulated radio wave which results from the combination of the two. It should be realised that, due to the very high frequency of the radio wave, the sketch only shows those waves occurring in a very small fraction of a second. It is the strength of the wave *from instant to instant* which is controlled by the speech, and this should not be confused with slow changes in strength such as fading.

The modulated radio wave travels outwards in all directions from the transmitting aerial and induces in any receiving aerial it encounters a voltage which is a minute replica of that present in the transmitting aerial. This voltage is amplified many thousands of times by the valves in the receiver and is then applied to the detector. Broadly speaking, this is a device which is able to respond to the instantaneous strength of the radio wave, thereby producing a replica of the voltage originally due to the microphone. After further amplification this voltage is applied to a loud-speaker or telephone receiver, where it controls the movements of a diaphragm. This alternately compresses and rarefies the air in a similar manner to the larynx in the distant speaker's throat.

Calling Australia

Now that we have examined the way in which speech is carried by a radio wave we can see how this knowledge is used to enable a person in Great Britain to speak to a friend in Australia. The general arrangement for a typical circuit between the two countries is shown in the sketch above.

You will see that the caller in Britain is connected via the inland telephone network to the radio telephony terminal which is located at Brent in north London. Here the circuit divides and here is located the technical operator who controls and monitors the radio part of the circuit in co-operation with his opposite number in Australia.

Once the circuit has been established the operation is as follows: speech currents from the caller in Britain travel to the radio terminal by land-line, and thence, again by land-line, to the giant Post Office radio station at Rugby. Here they are used to modulate the output of a 30,000-watt transmitter. The modulated radio wave carries the speech round the world to the Australian receiving station at La Perouse. After detection in the receiver the speech currents pass by land-line to the radio

FOR LONG AND SHORT RANGE

At the great Post Office Radio Station at Rugby enormous electrical power is required for the sending of radio messages to many distant parts of the world. This photograph gives a view inside the Power Room in the Short-wave Building.

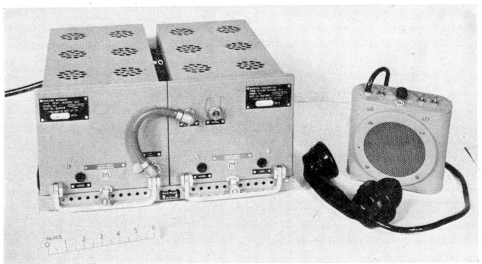

Photos by courtesy of the Postmaster-General.

Short-range radio-telephones are used in great numbers to-day by the police, fire services, defence forces and by many large commercial establishments. Here we see the typical radio equipment for a mobile station such as one operating on a River Thames tug.

terminal in Sydney, and thence via the telephone network to the distant party. When the latter replies his speech is carried to his friend in England in a similar manner, except that it comes via the Australian transmitting station at Pennant Hills and the Post Office receiving station at Baldock in Hertfordshire.

Technical Problems

Many of the technical difficulties in the operation of such a link have been omitted in the simplified outline given above. For example, the radio waves, which must travel half-way round the world, do so in a number of hops by reflection between the earth and electrified layers which exist in the upper atmosphere. The condition and position of these layers change with the time of day, the season of the year, activity on the sun's surface and other factors. The result is that at any given time there is a particular wavelength which will give the best results, depending on how much of the radio path is in darkness and the other factors mentioned above.

Highly directional aerials are used at both receiving and transmitting stations in order to improve the strength of the received signals. The Post Office station at Cooling, in Kent, uses an arrangement of aerials known as the M.U.S.A. System for the reception of traffic from America. Here a line of huge aerials some two miles in length is used to feed a receiver employing over 1,000 valves!

Another problem which has to be solved is that of privacy. Clearly, subscribers will not wish to have their conversations overheard by anyone using a short-wave broadcast receiver, and hence the speech has to be scrambled before it is transmitted and unscrambled again at the distant end. This is done at the radio terminals, so that even the personnel in the various radio stations in the circuit cannot understand the conversations, which sound rather as though they were being carried on in Chinese.

It has been possible to describe only some of the difficulties and complications involved in the operation of these long-distance services, but enough has been said to explain why a typical call costs £1 per minute.

In addition to the fixed radio-telephone circuits to many countries overseas the Post Office also operates a service to all the larger liners at sea. The *Queen Elizabeth*, for example, is in constant telephonic communication with London and New York on her transatlantic trips and on the average handles over 4,000 radio-telephone calls a year.

Compact and Mobile

Short-range radio-telephone circuits are used in great numbers to-day by the Government, by public and municipal authorities and by many commercial concerns. The frequencies used are higher than those of the long-distance circuits and generally lie in the V.H.F. (very high frequency) band. At these frequencies the radio waves travel in straight lines in a similar manner to light. They are not reflected by the electrified layers in the upper atmosphere, and as a result the service area is limited to something under fifty miles by the curvature of the earth. This means that stations on the same wavelength will not interfere with one another provided they are separated geographically. At these short distances low-power transmitters can be employed, so that the apparatus can be compact and highly mobile.

Well-known uses of radio telephony include the control of police cars, motor cycles and launches by Scotland Yard; its use by all the fighting services for communication between tanks, aircraft, troops, etc.; and its employment by radio taxi firms for the control of their vehicles. Not quite so well known perhaps is the use of radio by the fire services. A mobile control centre is set up at the scene of the fire and is able

IN THE TRANSMITTER HALL

Rugby is one of the most important Radio Stations in Europe, and its equipment represents the results of a half-century of continuous experiment and development. This photograph shows the Transmitter Hall in the Short-wave Building.

to keep in touch both with headquarters and with the individual fire fighters, each of whom is equipped with a pack set, or walkie-talkie as they are often called. Walkie-talkies are also used in railway yards and docks, by film and construction companies and by mine rescue squads.

A short-range public radio-telephone service recently introduced by the Post Office is that to shipping in the Thames Estuary. Known as the Thames Radio Service, this enables any tugs and other vessels suitably equipped with radio apparatus to be connected to the London telephone network. The fixed radio station for this service is at Shooter's Hill, in London, and the operating position is in the International Exchange in Wood Street.

Recently the Post Office has developed V.H.F. radio-telephone links to provide communications with various isolated communities in the United Kingdom. These include remote hill farms in the Yorkshire dales and many of the small islands around our coasts. In these circumstances the radio link is a better

proposition than a conventional telephone circuit, since the provision of the latter may entail blasting pole holes in rocky terrain or the provision and maintenance of a submarine cable link to an island surrounded by a rocky sea-bed and swift-flowing currents.

The equipment developed is of two types. The first, which is used where the calling rate is low and there is no public electricity supply, is battery operated and provides one speech channel only. So cleverly has the apparatus been designed that it will operate completely unattended for three or four months on end. Battery economy is achieved by arranging for the receiver to be energised for only two seconds in each half minute. If the distant transmitter is calling, the receiver automatically locks on and switches on its own transmitter to return a " Go ahead " signal to the caller and to complete the circuit. With a radiated power of only one-twentieth of a watt these links will operate over distances of up to twenty miles.

The second type of equipment, which

can provide up to twenty speech channels, is generally used for links to the larger islands. The equipment is operated from the public electricity supply or a diesel generator set in the event of mains failure.

Vest Pocket Radio

It is probably true to say that the invention of the valve in 1904 was mainly responsible for the wonderful progress made in the science of radio-communication in the last half century. It is fitting therefore that we should conclude with a brief reference to the transistor, a device which will certainly replace the valve in many applications and may well lead to a revolution in radio techniques.

The transistor is essentially a tiny crystal of the rare metal germanium, containing traces of controlled impurities and having electrodes bearing on it rather like the cat's whisker and crystal of early radio days. The advantages of the transistor are its robustness, small size and weight, almost unlimited life and, above all, the fact that unlike a valve it does not require any heater power.

This latter fact results in considerable saving since most of the power consumed in a normal radio is wasted—much of it in heating the valves. Already a battery operated television receiver employing only transistors (with the exception of the cathode-ray tube) has been successfully demonstrated in America.

Bearing in mind the savings in weight, size and batteries due to transistors and the modern trend towards making smaller and smaller components, it may well be that the two-way vest-pocket radio of science and detective fiction will prove to be a practical possibility in the not too distant future.

Photo by courtesy of the Postmaster-General.

RADIO TELEPHONES FOR REMOTE PLACES

Short-range radio-telephone circuits now provide means of swift communication with various isolated communities in the United Kingdom, such as the hill farms in Yorkshire or the islands around Britain's coasts. The V.H.F. (very high frequency) Radio Station at Kirkwall, in the Orkney Isles, is seen above.

THE MARVEL OF RADIO

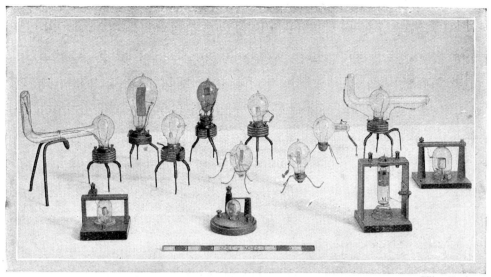

VALVES USED BY EARLY EXPERIMENTERS

The invention of valves for wireless came about in 1904, marking one of the greatest advances in the reception of sounds and signals through space. A valve is not only a receiver, but an amplifier also. We see in the above print some types of early valves. Wireless telegraphy is now a little over fifty years old, and wireless telephony was invented more recently.

TURNING on the radio to-day is just as easy as turning on a tap to obtain water, but it is much more exciting. A water tap will give hot water if it is a hot water tap, or cold water if it is a cold water tap. But we all know that by turning the right switch on a modern radio set, we can listen to any of a dozen or more different programmes.

There is a great romance behind this. It all began in this country in the year 1867. In that year a great British scientist named James Clerk-Maxwell suggested that it might be possible to create waves of electricity which would travel through space at the same speed as light. These waves were not discovered until 1887, when Heinrich Hertz, a German professor of physics, made his famous discoveries, on which " wireless," as we familiarly call it, is based.

Passing Through Space

Hertz used an induction coil to make sparks jump across the space between two brass balls, just as the magneto of a motor car makes sparks jump gaps in the cylinder sparking plugs. He found that, if an almost complete ring of wire were held near the apparatus, sparks appeared in the gap between its ends. Waves of some kind had passed through space from the one thing to the other, setting up currents in the second.

Once scientists had discovered that electrical waves could be passed through space they began to experiment on finding better and better means of generating these waves at the transmitting end, and better and better means of picking up the waves at the receiving end. One of the most important further discoveries was made by Sir Oliver Lodge, a Birmingham scientist. In 1897, Sir Oliver, who was then Mr. Lodge, found that if the sending circuits and receiving circuits were tuned with each other the reception of wireless signals was very greatly improved.

What is Meant by Tuning?

The easiest way to understand what is meant by " tuning " a radio receiver

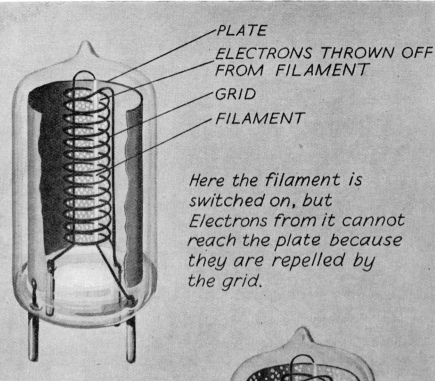

PLATE
ELECTRONS THROWN OFF
FROM FILAMENT
GRID
FILAMENT

Here the filament is switched on, but Electrons from it cannot reach the plate because they are repelled by the grid.

Here the aerial currents are reaching the grid, making it release the imprisoned Electrons in a varying stream. The variations in the Electron stream correspond to the oscillations received on the aerial but are greatly magnified.

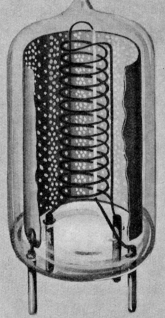

Specially drawn for this work.

At first sight a wireless valve might be mistaken for an electric lighting bulb, but the resemblance is really only superficial. The device is called a valve because it allows current to pass through it in one direction only. The electrons forming the current jump from the glowing filament to a small plate, on their way traversing the coils of a " grid," which varies their flow.

HOW CURRENT GOES THROUGH VALVES

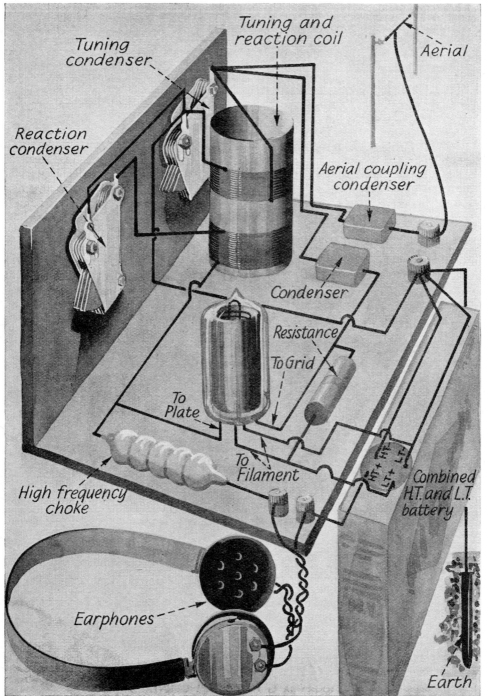

Specially drawn for this work.

This pictorial diagram explains how the tiny currents set up by wireless waves in the aerial reach the regulating grid of the valve through a grid leak and condenser. The low-tension battery is connected with the filament of the valve to make it glow and supply electrons which are sucked in gusts through the grid to the plate and headphones or loudspeaker by the pull of the high-tension battery.

is to think first of all of an ordinary tuning fork pitched, or tuned, to a particular note, say, the middle C. If this tuning fork is set in vibration and another tuning fork of a different pitch is brought near it, the second fork will not respond very much to the vibrations of the first tuning fork, because its natural period of vibration is different. If we now bring a third tuning fork which is tuned to exactly the same note as the first one and placed at some distance away from the vibrating fork it will immediately respond to the C note, because the sound pulses from the first tuning fork reach it at just the right intervals.

In other words, if we wish to make any tuning fork give out its note, this is easily done by striking it against some hard object, but if we wish to keep the fork sounding continuously we must supply it with a series of very rapid impulses which correspond to the frequency or note to which it is tuned. In the example mentioned above, the first tuning fork was sending out sound waves at just the right frequency to start the similarly tuned fork vibrating in sympathy.

Now, it so happens that the electrical circuits used in radio transmitters and receivers behave rather like tuning forks, but instead of the vibrations being mechanical vibrations which we hear as a musical note these circuits vibrate or oscillate electrically. These circuits have another convenient property, namely, that by the turning of a condenser knob they can be tuned to respond to different electrical notes or frequencies.

Sir Oliver Lodge discovered that if the receiving circuit is tuned to the same frequency as the transmitting circuit the radiations or waves sent out from a transmitter would be picked up by

B.B.C.

PROGRAMMES FOR OTHER COUNTRIES

One branch of the B.B.C., known as the Transcription Service, records selected programmes on light-weight discs, and these are supplied to Broadcasting stations all over the world, particularly in Commonwealth countries. They can then be broadcast by the stations on their own wavelengths and are free from atmospheric interference. This photograph shows a disc recording channel. Two machines are used, which allows programmes to be recorded without any break.

the receiver through its aerial very much more easily than would be the case if the circuits were not tuned.

To-day when we tune our radio receiver to any particular broadcasting station we are making use of this important discovery.

One of the first men to apply these discoveries on a commercial scale was an Italian, Guglielmo Marconi.

Across the Atlantic

In December, 1901, wireless signals were sent across the Atlantic for the first time, and really long-distance wireless telegraphy began. The current needed to emit signals was now supplied by electric generators giving out hundreds of kilowatts. For receiving signals the crystal detector, which was later used in the first domestic wireless sets, came into use, for it was discovered in 1906 that if the currents from the aerial were made to pass through a crystal touching a piece of metal —or through two crystals pressing on each other—and a telephone headpiece, the signals could be heard even if too weak for other kinds of detectors to pick them up.

At that time all radio signalling was done by the dots and dashes of the well-known Morse code invented by an American, Mr. S. F. B. Morse. The next important step forward was the discovery of the radio valve. Professor J. A. Fleming, who later became Sir Ambrose Fleming, took the first step towards this discovery. He made

B.B.C.

ON THE LIGHT PROGRAMME

In this photograph the Continuity Engineer is at the control position, selecting the various programme items, time signals, etc., in their proper turn. The programme is " faded up " and adjusted to the proper volume, while the exact times of all programmes, with technical details, are entered in the log book.

a very simple form of valve known as the Fleming Valve. This was improved by an American, Mr. Lee de Forrest. In its improved form the valve enabled speech and music to be broadcast and received at great distances with surprising clearness.

This rapid progress in the technical development of Radio was accompanied by a very great public interest. Experiments by private individuals and large manufacturers had shown that it was now quite possible for every one to have an inexpensive home radio receiver, which could be tuned to pick up radio programmes from a large number of different stations. Six

" HERE IS THE NEWS " *B.B.C.*

Most important of all regular items broadcast by the B.B.C. are the news bulletins. Our photograph shows one of the members of the team of news-readers and announcers, Alan Skempton, about to read the news in the Home Service.

of the largest electrical manufacturers combined together to form the British Broadcasting Company. These were: The Marconi Co., The General Electric Co. Ltd., The British Thomson-Houston Co. Ltd., The Metropolitan Vickers Electrical Co. Ltd., Siemens Bros. & Co. Ltd., Edison Swan Electric Co. Ltd.

For a period of two years the B.B. Coy. transmitted broadcast programmes which were available to any one possessing a radio receiver. At the end of this period the Company received a charter of incorporation from the Government and became The British Broadcasting Corporation. This occurred in the year 1925, and the Corporation still functions as a national concern under a Government charter.

How Radio is Broadcast

What happens when you tune in the radio to a particular broadcasting station ?

In order to answer this question let

REHEARSING A SYMPHONY ORCHESTRA BROADCAST *B.B.C.*

In this photograph we have the scene in the B.B.C.'s large Orchestral Studio at Maida Vale when a famous Continental orchestra, under its own conductor, Hans Schmidt-Isserstedt, rehearsed for the concert to be given from the Royal Festival Hall in London. This concert and another from the B.B.C. studios were broadcast in the B.B.C. Third Programme.

us pay a visit to Broadcasting House and enter the studio from where the next item on the Home Service programme is being broadcast.

We should find that the studio is like a moderately sized concert hall with platform for the artists, orchestra and audience. The walls and ceilings of the studio are acoustically treated to produce the correct atmosphere. At one end of the room will be seen a large clock face with the second hand revolving steadily, so that the programme announcer is able to begin and finish to the second.

Whilst the audience have been entering the studio the microphone has been disconnected from the broadcasting system. As the time approaches for the broadcast to begin a red light flashes on to tell the announcer that the studio is due " on the air." The announcer presses a buzzer when the studio is quiet and the red light becomes steady.

After the opening announcement the

B.B.C.

THE HOME OF BROADCASTING

Broadcasting House, Portland Place, London, W.1, is the main headquarters of the B.B.C. There are regional headquarters in the provinces.

B.B.C.

IN THE CONTROL ROOM

The task of the engineers is of paramount importance, and in this photograph we see some of the operators on duty in the Control Room at the B.B.C. headquarters.

Sounds made in the studios, whether by the human voice or musical instruments, are first caught by the microphone, but before these sounds can reach your set they have to be sent into the air and given the power to travel through space. This work is known as transmitting, and here we see the Control Desk of a high-power transmitter.

B.B.C.

This photograph shows the Control Desk of the medium-wave transmitter at Stagshaw, near Newcastle-on-Tyne. This station radiates on a wavelength of 261 metres in the Home Service, while the one at Daventry in the upper picture is used in the B.B.C.'s Overseas Service transmissions.

"CALLING ALL CARS!"

Marconi's Wireless Telegraph Co.

Scotland Yard and other police headquarters make considerable use of radio in these days when the law-breaker also has at his disposal scientific devices and rapid transport. Here we see an up-to-date police car fitted with Marconi wireless equipment for communicating with Headquarters or with other police cars.

Marconi's Wireless Telegraph Co.

All sorts and all sizes of wireless receivers can be obtained nowadays, but a wireless transmitter presents more difficult problems. Here we see a Marconi portable field equipment for communication on short-wave (transmitter, receiver and pedal generator) in actual use.

artists come up to the microphone and go through their performance; the orchestra which strikes up at the appropriate moments and the sound-effects man with his special apparatus have their respective microphones, the outputs of which are blended to form the composite programme. The opening and closing of a door, the dropping of crockery, the withdrawal of corks from bottles and similar sounds are generally made in the studio, but almost any desired sound can be supplied from the B.B.C.'s library of records.

An Artificial Ear

The audience in the studio may consist of, perhaps, 200 people listening with all ears. There is, in addition, one artificial ear which listens for the millions of people who have just tuned in their sets to hear the broadcast from this particular studio. This artificial ear is what we all know so well as the microphone. The jokes, the music, the sounds of opening and closing doors and the other sounds incidental to a broadcast cause a thin aluminium ribbon in the microphone to vibrate in sympathy with the sound waves which are set up by the speech or music. This thin ribbon of aluminium foil is suspended between the poles of a powerful magnet.

Many years ago it was discovered that if a wire was moved to and fro between the poles of the magnet, small electric currents were generated in the wire, the strength of these currents depending upon the amount of the to-and-fro movement. This is exactly what happens to the microphone ribbon whilst the broadcast is going on. The tiny currents which are set up in the coil, corresponding to the various sounds reaching the microphone, pass through an electric cable into the control room at the Studio Centre. They are then sent out over special G.P.O. lines to the transmitters throughout the country. From the transmitter wireless waves are being radiated from the aerial. These waves are tuned to a certain wavelength, i.e.,

for the London Home Service programme 330 metres.

By an ingenious arrangement of valves, the programme current received from the studio centre is first amplified and then fed on to the control grid of the large transmitter valve. The sounds from the studio are in this way radiated into space from the aerial, or "put on the air," riding as it were on the back of the main carrier wave which is being transmitted.

When you tune your set to the Home Service wavelength of 330 metres your set becomes responsive to this particular carrier wave which, as we have already seen, is now carrying on its back the sound current as produced in the studio microphone. The circuits and valves inside your receiving set reverse the process which has taken place in the transmitting station. They separate from the main carrier wave the sound current which was originally superimposed on it, and they deliver this sound current to the speech coil of your loudspeaker.

Now the loudspeaker is very much like the microphone : it contains a powerful magnet with a coil of fine wire poised between the poles. Attached to the coil is the diaphragm of the loudspeaker.

When the sound current passes through the speech coil of your loudspeaker the coil begins to move to and fro, or vibrate, exactly in sympathy with the moving ribbon in the studio microphone. This moves the large diaphragm of the loudspeaker so that it gives out sounds similar to those which are being heard in the studio by the microphone.

Sight and Sound

Most of us at some time have heard or read the fairy tale about the Princess who possessed a magic mirror. By looking into this mirror she was able to see what was happening at places far distant. The modern television receiver has brought the Magic Mirror of

IN A SHORT=WAVE TRANSMITTER

Marconi's Wireless Telegraph Co.

Some idea of the equipment used in a modern broadcasting transmitter can be gained from the above photograph, which shows a pre-tuned circuit truck being wheeled into place in a Marconi 100 kw. short-wave transmitter. A separate truck is used for each frequency to which it is desired to tune the transmitter so that frequency changing is simply a matter of removing one truck and replacing it with another.

the Princess into actual existence. The development of the present-day television set would make a long and highly technical story. Some brief details of this development will be found in a later chapter "The Magic Mirror." Here we will just say that in the Television studio a camera, fitted with an electric eye, looks at or "scans" the scene which is to be televised. Tiny electric currents are set up in a wire connected with the electric eye and these currents are amplified and broadcast. In the television receiver a wonderful device known as a cathode ray tube is used for reproducing the scene which is being observed by the electric eye camera in the studio.

From Radio to Radar

Long before the 1939 war began British scientists had been working in secret upon a most exciting discovery. It had been found that wireless waves sent out from a transmitting station were sometimes reflected back to the station when they met any obstruction, such as an aeroplane in the sky or a ship at sea. By using a cathode ray tube and connecting it to the transmitter it was found that the tube would show a picture of a pulse sent out. It was also found that if the broadcast wave was reflected back a similar pulse would appear on the screen of the cathode ray tube a little distance away from the transmitted pulse.

B.B.C.

BROADCASTS FOR CHILDREN AT SCHOOL

Some 15,000 schools listen to one or more of the series broadcast by the B.B.C. in their Schools programme, and this number is steadily growing. About fifty broadcasts are given each week, covering a wide variety both of subjects and of age. One of the most valued services over a long period has been "Music and Movement" for the younger children, by Ann Driver, and in the picture above we see the class learning a new song.

By working on, and perfecting this discovery, British scientists were able to set up round our coasts a number of Radar stations which enabled watchers to see on the Radar screen any aircraft approaching the coasts when they were many miles distant. It will be appreciated that this was of immense importance to us during the war. Modern aircraft can fly at more than ten miles a minute. Without Radar, aircraft could only have been spotted, even in the last war, when they were about five miles away from the coast and then only in a cloudless sky. These enemy aircraft might be flying at great heights.

Our swiftest fighter aircraft required several minutes to climb to such heights and without Radar our only way of intercepting bombers would have been to keep many squadrons of fighter planes continually in the air. Now a swift fighter can remain aloft for only an hour or so before it has to return to its base for refuelling, and while it is flying it uses up petrol at an alarming rate, i.e., from 300–600 gallons per hour.

It is no exaggeration to say that without Radar our air defences would have been thrown into chaos if several groups of enemy raiders had attacked at different points simultaneously. Radar enabled our observers to keep a constant check on the German bomber planes, very often from the time they left their aerodromes in France. This advance information was invaluable in enabling us to use our limited supplies of fighter planes to the very best advantage. Without Radar the Battle of Britain would have been lost.

The early work of developing the use of radio for giving warning of approaching aircraft was carried out in secrecy in this country before the war.

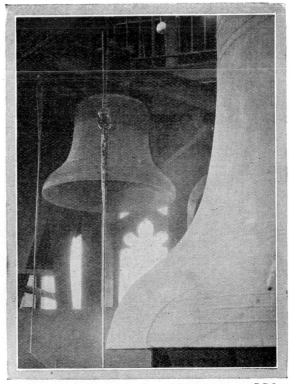

B.B.C.

BIG BEN AND " MIKE "

Many a time you must have set your watch by the deep sonorous notes of Big Ben, which reached your ears from Westminster by means of wireless. Here is the monster bell, with the rubber-covered microphone in position up above.

No doubt, in other countries, particularly the United States of America, research scientists were working on the same problem, but it is true to say that the British equipment in 1940 was far in advance of anything which had been developed elsewhere.

When America entered the war all the results of British discoveries and development were placed at their disposal and there was a free interchange of scientific ideas between the two countries.

Radar and the Submarines

The submarines which were used in an attempt to isolate Britain from other countries during the war had to remain submerged during the daytime. At night, however, they came up to the

WIRELESS IN HOSPITAL AND SCHOOL

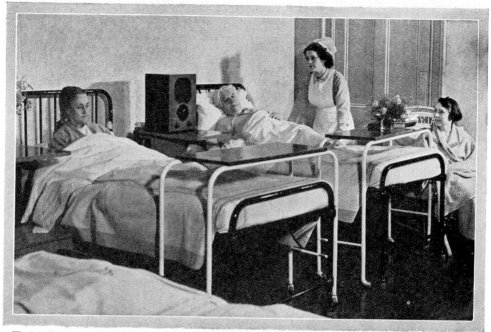

To few listeners can wireless be a greater boon than to invalids slowly recovering from illness in the wards of our hospitals. This photograph shows a corner of a hospital ward with nurse and patients listening-in to the broadcast programme.

B.B.C.

Older scholars as well as the younger children listen-in to their own programmes in the Schools broadcasts. The lecturer at the microphone and the school audience co-operate in these senior lessons. Our photograph illustrates a class following a lecture on " Current Affairs," and the schoolmaster is assisting his pupils as the speaker refers to the map.

FROM STUDIO TO PICNIC PARTY

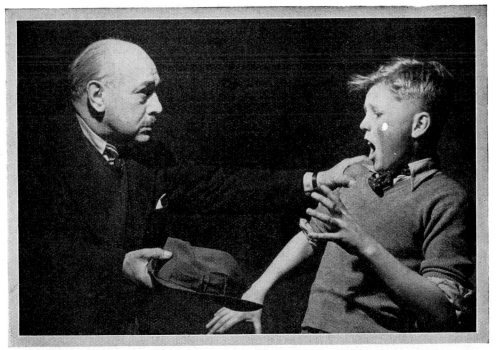

Here we have a photograph of the actual scene in the studio during a broadcast of one of the famous
"Just William" stories.   William's good intentions have once again gone astray and his father is
confronting William with definite evidence of the damage he has done.

B.B.C.

To the younger generation the miracle of modern radio is not so astounding as to those old enough
to remember the first efforts of the London Broadcasting Station (2LO) which began in May, 1922.
To-day a portable radio receiver is among the normal luxuries about which it is unnecessary to say
much beyond the warning " Don't annoy others ! "

surface, so that they could run their engines to recharge their batteries and also replenish their air supply for the next day. The Germans for a time were very mystified at the number of sinkings of submarines which usually occurred during the night while they were surfaced. The reason was that we were using Radar to detect the submarines.

To-day Radar equipment is being installed for peacetime purposes in ships and in aircraft. By its use ships can steam full speed ahead through the thick fog, because the Captain can be certain that any other vessels in the vicinity will be shown on his Radar Screen when they are several miles away. Aircraft pilots can use their Radar at night or in fog to obtain an outline of the country over which they are flying and to make sure that they are sufficiently high to avoid any mountains which may lie on their route.

It was through the discoveries made by the wireless pioneers that television and Radar became possible. But radio still remains the great marvel of the present century. The transmission of speech and music by wireless was unknown except to a comparatively few enthusiasts who were able to listen-in during the years 1920-1922.

Then, in 1922, London (2LO) began to broadcast programmes and radio went swiftly ahead. To-day there are over 10 million listeners' licences and nearly 3 million television licences issued in Britain.

B.B.C.

THE SEA LION MAKES A RECORD

The libraries at Broadcasting House are concerned with many other items besides books. There is, for instance, the Effects Library where special gramophone records giving different sound effects are kept. Here we see one of the sea lions at Regent's Park Zoo kindly recording its vocal efforts in front of the microphone held by the man from the B.B.C.

TELEVISION—THE MAGIC MIRROR

The General Electric Co. Ltd.

THE MAGIC MIRROR AT WORK

The modern television receiver provides an almost unlimited variety of entertainment, which can be enjoyed in the comfort of one's home. The picture being received is clearly visible in the frame at the top of the receiver.

MORE than twenty-five years ago John L. Baird, who was then working in an attic in Soho, London, constructed the first apparatus to demonstrate that television was practicable.

Television means being able to sit in a cinema or your own room at home and to see on a screen what is taking place in a studio, or at a Test Match, *whilst it is actually happening.*

In Mr. Baird's early apparatus, lenses and, later on, mirrors were used for "picking up" the scenes to be televised, but to-day special kinds of cameras, one of which is called an Emitron camera, are used. A photograph of another type of camera now in use appears on another page.

An electric cable connects the camera to the associated amplifiers and to other necessary apparatus. Inside the camera a stream of tiny particles, called electrons, is moving rapidly over the view which is thrown on to a special kind of plate. This stream of electrons passes across every portion of the plate fifty times per second, so you will realise it moves to and fro and up and down at an enormously high speed. When it comes to parts of the plate which are very bright, a comparatively strong current comes out through the cable leading from the camera. When the ray, or stream, is on darker portions of the plate, the current coming out of the camera is less.

The Cathode Ray

Now let us stop for a moment and imagine what happens whilst the camera is in use. The powerful lens throws on to the sensitive plate a perfect image of the scene towards which the camera is pointing. In the meantime the beam of electrons, or

The first home of high-definition Television in Britain was at Alexandra Palace, and from here the first high-definition Television service began in November, 1936, but had to be discontinued 1939–46. Besides Alexandra Palace there are now other stations at Sutton Coldfield, Holme Moss, Wenvoe and Kirk o' Shotts.

B.B.C.

Here we have a scene in the Lime Grove Studio Centre at Shepherd's Bush, London. A rehearsal of the " Billy Bunter " school stories is in progress. Other scenes which have a place in the stories can be seen on the left. Two C.P.S. Emitron cameras and a cardioid type microphone are in use.

SPORTING EVENTS BY TELEVISION

Two shore-based cameras and two on the launch *Everest* (seen above) were used to televise the Oxford and Cambridge Boat Race, which was followed by the cameras from start to finish. The two cameras are on the cabin roof, while in the stern are the aerials for the sound and vision transmitters, as well as the inter-communication radio-telephone installation and the radio-vision monitors.

B.B.C.

As the B.B.C. Television Service extended, its use in broadcasting pictures with running commentaries of big sporting events became one of its most popular attractions. In this picture the Television camera is in operation on a balcony at the Oval during a Test Match.

B.B.C.

CORONATION TELEVISION CONTROL ROOM

This gives a view of the interior of the Westminster Abbey Television Control Room. The outputs of the television cameras were selected and controlled from this point. On the six lower screens the producer could view the camera outputs continuously while the two above showed the picture leaving the Abbey and the picture received from the Alexandra Palace transmitter. On the left is the sound mixer's position ; centre, the producer's desk ; right, vision mixer's control desk.

cathode ray, as it is called, is sweeping rapidly across the plate exploring, or scanning, every part of it in orderly sequence. Tiny electrical currents, of a strength which varies according to the position of the cathode ray at any moment, are flowing out of the camera through the electric cable. These currents are led to the television sending station, which is very similar to that used for ordinary broadcasts, and so, whilst the camera is in action, wireless waves are being sent out from the television transmitter, and these waves are varied (or, as experts call it, " modulated ") according to the brightness of each little bit of the picture on the camera plate as the cathode ray passes over it.

From Waves to Pictures

Now let us look at the receiving end and find out how these wireless waves are turned into a picture on the screen of the television receiver.

The photograph at the beginning of this section will show what a television receiver looks like, though most of you will have seen similar television sets in operation. It is similar to a large radio receiver, and it has an oblong opening through which can be seen a greyish screen.

When the receiver is properly adjusted, a picture appears on this screen which is a faithful copy of the scene towards which the television camera is pointing. This is brought about in a way which you will have no difficulty in following, if you have understood the explanation already given of the manner in which the camera picks up the picture.

You will remember that the final result of pointing the camera at the picture to be televised was that a rapidly varying electric current came out of the cable connecting the camera with the television transmitting station. You must now imagine that this current has been transmitted " over the air " and has reached the television receiver.

Inside the receiver is a very ingenious device, which is known as a cathode ray tube. A picture of one of these tubes will be seen on another page, and it is the front end of the tube which forms the screen in the television receiver. You will remember that in the case of the camera, the cathode ray was made to sweep over the *picture* very rapidly. Now, inside the cathode ray tube in the receiver, a similar cathode ray sweeps over the *screen*, keeping exactly in time with the cathode ray inside the camera.

Wherever the ray strikes the screen, the special coating becomes lighted up. Now, whilst the ray is moving over the end of the tube, its strength can be turned up or down. If the strength is turned down, the screen will not light up where the ray strikes it. If the strength of the ray is increased, the screen will become very bright wherever the ray touches it. And now we can see the use of the electric currents which are coming into the receiving set from the aerial.

Through a suitable arrangement of valves the incoming current is used to strengthen or weaken the cathode ray as it sweeps over the surface of the screen. And so, when the cathode ray in the camera is passing over a dark part of the plate, the cathode ray in the receiver is turned down and the corresponding part of the screen appears dark. Similarly, when the exploring ray in the camera is passing over a bright spot, the cathode ray in the receiver is turned on at nearly full

B.B.C.

CLOSE-UP OF A TELEVISION CAMERA

This gives a front view of the Pye Image Orthicon, one of the cameras used for Television Outside Broadcasts. It is smaller and lighter than previous models and has a motor-operated four-lens turret which enables the lenses to be changed either from the camera itself or from the control position. The large knob on the side controls the focus.

strength, and the screen glows brightly at the corresponding spot.

If you remember that all this is happening so fast that the cathode ray travels over the screen fifty times per second, you will understand how it is able to build up on the screen a picture which moves and shows all the details which are being viewed by the television camera.

Television as a public service had only just passed its experimental stage when the war broke out in 1939, and for the next seven years the screens of those who had become early owners of television sets were dead and useless.

The Second Beginning

Then, in June, 1946, the Alexandra Palace studios opened again and the first studio programme was sent out over the air. In less than twenty hours after this studio performance the television cameras were mounted in The Mall and viewers in their own homes saw the complete Victory Parade as viewed from a position opposite the Royal saluting base.

It was a complete success and since then, despite the handicaps imposed by the austerity conditions of the times, the B.B.C. television cameras have transmitted a large number of "O.B.'s"—outside broadcasts—from sports grounds and other open-air scenes, besides shows from theatres, dance halls and other places of amusement, as well as studio performances.

At the end of 1949 a new television station was opened at Sutton Coldfield, near Birmingham, to serve the Midlands. Other stations have now been opened at Holme Moss, Wenvoe (Cardiff) and Kirk o' Shotts (Scotland). Within a few years it is probable that the television receiver will be as commonplace in our homes as the ordinary radio set.

The General Electric Co. Ltd.

THE CATHODE RAY TUBE

The tube illustrated is an experimental one, but its appearance is similar to those used for television receivers. The white portion at the end is the screen on which the picture appears, and the cage-like objects in the stem of the tube are used to control the movement of the ray.

THE TELEVISION MEN IN ACTION

B.B.C.

In this photograph is seen the motorised camera dolly for television. It is powered by a half-horse-power mains-driven motor and is steered by the pillar at the back on which the controls for forward and backward motion are mounted. The camera-man can raise or lower himself and the camera by means of the pedals.

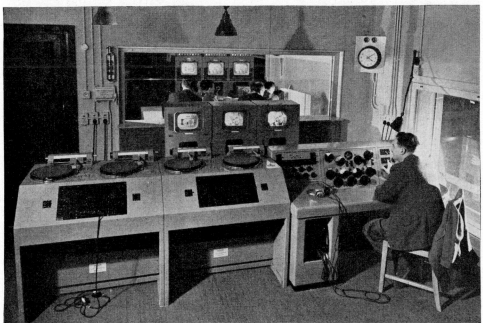

B.B.C.

This is a view in one of the largest control rooms at Lime Grove, Shepherd's Bush, London. In the foreground are gramophone reproducers for sound effects and the sound mixer's desk. Facing the engineer are three picture monitors. Beyond the glass partition are other members of the production team who can see into the studio through the window on the right.

Television and Radar

In the sections on " Radio " and " Modern Inventions and Discoveries " the subject of Radar is dealt with more fully, but it may be mentioned here as television has considerable connection with Radar. The cathode ray tube, as we have seen, plays a big part in television, and it is also of the utmost importance in Radar.

The mountaineer who stands on the top of a cliff and shouts across the space to the wall of another cliff so that he receives back an echo, is using the simplest kind of Radar. His voice takes a certain time to travel to the opposite cliff and back again, and by noting the time between the shout and the echo he can calculate the distance.

Radar does exactly the same thing, using wireless waves instead of sound waves. As wireless waves travel with the speed of light, that is, 186,000 miles every second, some very sensitive means

had to be found to measure the tiny interval of time between the wireless " shout " and its echo. The cathode ray tube provides this.

In the simplest form of Radar receiver, the screen of the cathode ray tube shows a single bright line. When the transmitter sends out a wireless beam a large kink, like an inverted " V," appears on the line. When the echo is received back from the target a smaller kink appears on the line. The distance between these two depends on the distance of the target. If the target is close at hand the two pips are close together on the screen. If the target is a considerable distance away, the two pips are widely spaced on the screen. The screen is graduated in miles or yards, so that the distance can be read off immediately. The direction from which the target is approaching is determined by using directional aerials for transmitter and receiver.

B.B.C.

IN THE TRANSMITTING STATION AT SUTTON COLDFIELD

The Television Station at Sutton Coldfield, near Birmingham, covers the Midlands area, and in this photograph the vision transmitter is seen. Beyond this is the sound transmitter, while on the left, through the curved window, is the control room from which both transmitters are operated.

THE WONDERS OF X-RAYS

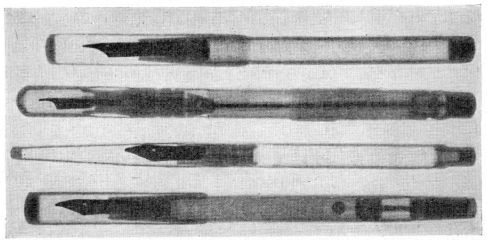

Ellison Hawks.

PENS UNDER X-RAYS

An X-ray "shadowgraph" made through a tray of fountain pens. Externally the pens look much alike, but the revealing rays show plainly enough that they differ considerably inside. The bodies of two are empty; one contains a vacuum piston on the end of a thin rod; and the record of the fourth proves it to have a metal lever used in filling the reservoir.

IN November, 1895, an announcement of high importance to scientists all over the world was made by Professor W. K. Röntgen, of Würzburg, in Germany. He had discovered a mysterious kind of ray which enabled him to obtain photographs of the internal parts of living creatures.

As Röntgen himself did not recognise the nature of these new rays he named them "X" rays. We know now that these X-rays or Röntgen-rays, as they are often called after their discoverer, are waves in the ether and of the same nature as waves of light, but are very much shorter.

We have already seen in earlier sections that electricity is a flow of electrons through a wire or other metal conductor. Electrons can, however, be made to pass through a space where there is no wire or metal "bridge" for them to cross. If an electric wire is cut the electricity immediately stops flowing because the electrons cannot get across the space between the two ends of the wire. This is because the air is an insulator, that is, it stops the flow of electric current. If, however, these two ends were sealed into a glass tube and nearly all the air extracted from the tube, the electrons would begin to pass across the space, providing a sufficiently high electrical pressure or voltage were applied to the wires.

Probing A Mystery

Scientists discovered this fact many years ago and constructed various kinds of vacuum tubes so that they could study the flow of electrons through empty space. It was in the course of experiments of this nature that Röntgen found that if he applied a very high voltage to the two wires entering the opposite ends of the vacuum tube the electrons shot across the intervening space at a very high speed.

Röntgen arranged at the receiving end a target to catch the electrons. This target was made of tungsten. He found that when the electron beam struck the tungsten target some mysterious rays were given off. He further discovered that these "X" rays would pass easily through many substances which are opaque to light. There were certain substances, however, such as flesh and wood, which they penetrated much better than others, while substances which conduct electricity well, especially metals, resisted the rays. Bone, too, had considerable resistance to the new rays.

By using an X-ray tube and allowing the rays to pass through his hand on to a photographic plate, Röntgen found that he could obtain a photograph showing clearly the bones of the hand. No camera or lens was required, the plate being merely encased in a light-proof envelope and placed on the further side of the object being photographed.

The importance of these new rays was recognised almost immediately, and they have been of incalculable value in surgery, for they practically endow the surgeon with a pair of matter-piercing eyes. If a limb be broken, a photograph is taken through the fracture. On the developed plate the bones appear white, surrounded by darker flesh, while in the positive print made from the negative the tones are, of course, reversed, the bones now appearing almost black and the flesh much lighter. Having the print before him, the surgeon knows exactly what he should do.

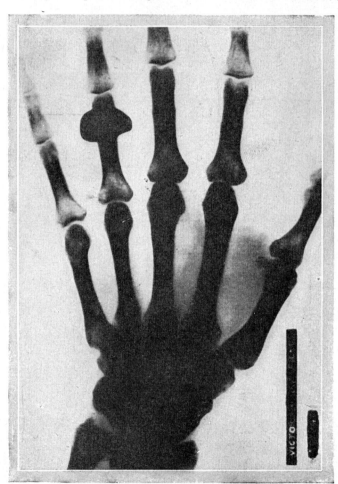

International Western Electric Co. Ltd.

THE FOUNDATIONS OF THE HAND

This photograph, which was printed from a negative " telegraphed " over 931 miles of telephone wires from an original X-ray negative, shows very clearly most of the bones in a human hand. Only those of the little finger are here complete— the long metacarpal bone between the wrist and the finger proper, and the three phalanges of the finger itself. The strange-looking lump on the third finger is a metal ring.

Saved from Death

Or, again, instead of probing about for a bullet buried in the flesh, he takes two or three X-ray photographs in different directions, and by comparing them can fix the exact position of the intruder. Should a person be suffering from an internal complaint, the X-rays are often of great service, for they can show whether the heart, lungs, or other parts are affected. It is not going beyond the

RAYS THAT PENETRATE MATTER

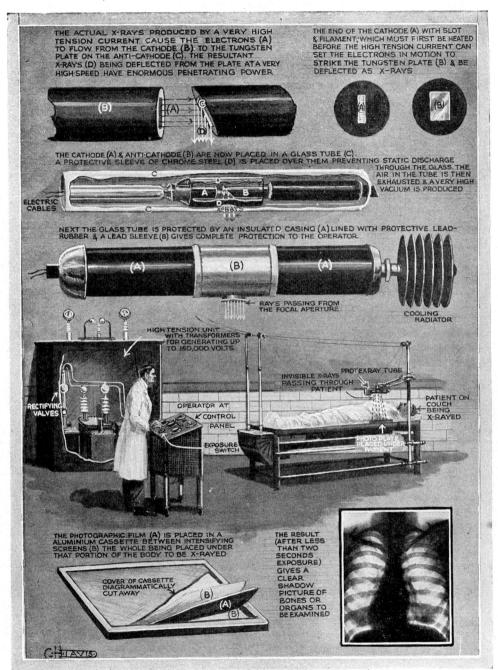

THE ACTUAL X-RAYS PRODUCED BY A VERY HIGH TENSION CURRENT CAUSE THE ELECTRONS (A) TO FLOW FROM THE CATHODE (B) TO THE TUNGSTEN PLATE ON THE ANTI-CATHODE (C). THE RESULTANT X-RAYS (D) BEING DEFLECTED FROM THE PLATE AT A VERY HIGH SPEED HAVE ENORMOUS PENETRATING POWER

THE END OF THE CATHODE (A) WITH SLOT & FILAMENT, WHICH MUST FIRST BE HEATED BEFORE THE HIGH TENSION CURRENT CAN SET THE ELECTRONS IN MOTION TO STRIKE THE TUNGSTEN PLATE (B) & BE DEFLECTED AS X-RAYS

THE CATHODE (A) & ANTI-CATHODE (B) ARE NOW PLACED IN A GLASS TUBE (C). A PROTECTIVE SLEEVE OF CHROME STEEL (D) IS PLACED OVER THEM PREVENTING STATIC DISCHARGE THROUGH THE GLASS. THE AIR IN THE TUBE IS THEN EXHAUSTED & A VERY HIGH VACUUM IS PRODUCED

ELECTRIC CABLES

NEXT THE GLASS TUBE IS PROTECTED BY AN INSULATED CASING (A) LINED WITH PROTECTIVE LEAD-RUBBER & A LEAD SLEEVE (B) GIVES COMPLETE PROTECTION TO THE OPERATOR.

RAYS PASSING FROM THE FOCAL APERTURE

COOLING RADIATOR

HIGH TENSION UNIT WITH TRANSFORMERS FOR GENERATING UP TO 150,000 VOLTS

RECTIFYING VALVES

OPERATOR AT CONTROL PANEL

EXPOSURE SWITCH

INVISIBLE X-RAYS PASSING THROUGH PATIENT

PROTEXRAY TUBE

PATIENT ON COUCH BEING X-RAYED

PHOTO PLATE PLACED UNDER PATIENT

THE PHOTOGRAPHIC FILM (A) IS PLACED IN A ALUMINIUM CASSETTE BETWEEN INTENSIFYING SCREENS (B) THE WHOLE BEING PLACED UNDER THAT PORTION OF THE BODY TO BE X-RAYED

COVER OF CASSETTE DIAGRAMMATICALLY CUT AWAY

THE RESULT (AFTER LESS THAN TWO SECONDS EXPOSURE) GIVES A CLEAR SHADOW PICTURE OF BONES OR ORGANS TO BE EXAMINED

Specially drawn for this work.

The upper part of this illustration describes the construction of the special form of vacuum tube used for projecting X-rays, which are of the same nature as light, but have a vastly shorter wave-length, of about one 250,000,000th of an inch. The rays are created by the " bombardment " of an anti-cathode plate by electrons shot off from a heated cathode plate, which corresponds to the filament of a wireless valve. Their very high frequency enables them to penetrate many forms of solid matter. Metals stop them and that is why the tube is encased in lead, to protect the user.

picture a genuine " Hals." Others persisted that it was a modern forgery.

The X-rays were called in, and they revealed the fact that the parts of the wooden panel on which the picture was painted were held together with wire nails. As this kind of nail was not made till at least two centuries had elapsed after Hals' death, the matter was definitely cleared up.

In a further case, examination by X-rays proved that a valuable old picture

A PEEP INTO A PENGUIN

The bones of a bird's neck are so jointed that they allow a bird to twist its neck about in a manner impossible for human beings. This X-ray picture shows us the vertebræ or neck-bones of a penguin.

truth to say that tens of thousands of people every year owe to these rays an escape from much suffering, and even from death.

X-rays are helpful in many other ways. Let us take an example: Expert judges of old pictures were recently much perplexed by a painting said to be the work of the famous Dutch painter, Frans Hals, who died in 1666. One great authority pronounced the

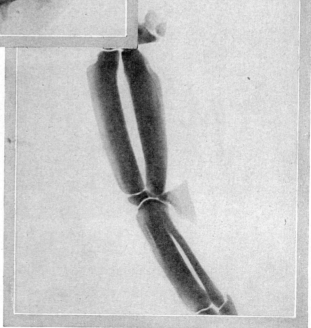

Photos: Central Press.

FLIPPER BONES

And here we see the bones of one of a penguin's flippers or undeveloped wings, useless in the air, but very useful to the bird when swimming under water.

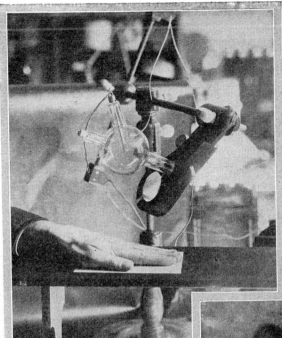

trouble. Nor are the rays useful only in finding broken bones and misplaced parts of the body. In certain cases of illness the patient is given bismuth or similar salts to swallow. These salts are not soluble and it is possible by means of X-rays to take photographs of the digestive passages and so find out for certain the seat of any local trouble.

Not only does this save time in bringing relief, but it may prove an operation to be unnecessary.

The X-ray analysis of solid substances proved of the

AN X-RAY TUBE—
Here is a simple form of X-ray tube. The stream of electrons from the right-hand side strikes the tungsten target in the centre of the bulb and X-rays are given off.

had another and much more modern one painted on top of it.

In the Workshop

The maker of sham jewels has a foe in the rays, for they treat the real and the fraudulent article differently. The maker of electric cables, on the other hand, has a friend in them, since a cable passed between an X-ray tube and a screen at once betrays any metal bodies lurking in its insulating cover. This is a great boon, as even a piece of thin wire in the wrong place may cause

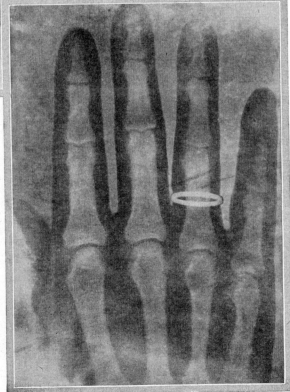

AND ITS RESULT
These rays pass through the hand and on to a sheet of photographic paper which has been placed downwards on the bench. The result of this is seen above : the bones and the metal ring are not penetrated and are shown up clearly.

utmost value to doctors, chemists, industrialists and others. Röntgen's discovery also turned the attention of scientists to further investigation of rays and marked the beginning of a new era of wonderful discovery.

It was from these further experiments that what has been called X-radiation was discovered. In 1896 Professor Henri Becquerel found that a certain compound of uranium emitted a stream of radiation continuously and of its own account.

This led to experiments in other directions. Among them were those carried out by Professor and Madame Curie, who searched for other substances having this " radio-activity," as the new property was called.

The result was the discovery of radium. Going a stage further, Lord Rutherford made considerable advances in his experiments on the structure of the atom. To-day the tremendous power of atomic energy has been demonstrated and our hopes for the future rest on its wise use.

The British Atomic Research station at Harwell is already supplying medical men with radio-active substances for the treatment of certain diseases.

Here again we see how the discoveries in one field of science are linked with those in another. Experiments in splitting the atom led to the most terrible weapon of destruction the world has ever known. But they have also opened up great possibilities in the field of medical science.

X-rays have long proved useful to the surgeon, and in recent years their use in industry has developed considerably. Special X-ray units are employed in big workshops to ensure that important parts of machinery, which will be subject to heavy strain, are entirely flawless.

Newton Victor Ltd.

X-RAYS IN INDUSTRY

In this photograph is seen a million-volt Industrial X-ray unit in use in a modern workshop. The operator is placing a heavy casting on the light-proof envelope containing a photographic film. The resulting X-ray photograph will reveal whether the casting is perfect or whether there are any internal flaws which might render it unsafe.

INVISIBLE RAYS

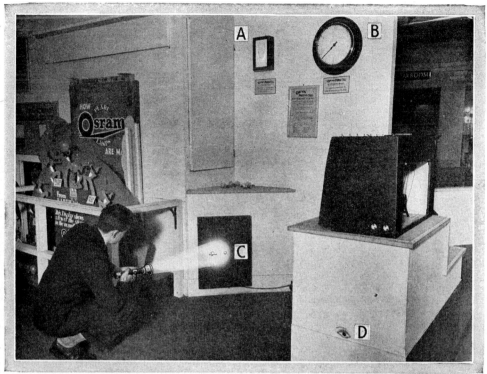

General Electric Co. Ltd.

TWO USES FOR PHOTO-ELECTRIC CELLS

The extraordinary sensitiveness of a photo-electric cell to light, as shown by variations in a current passing through it, is now utilised in many ways. If, for example, a light were thrown on to safe C at night, a burglar alarm A would be brought into operation by such a cell. On the right is seen an " electric eye " D that can be placed at the entrance to, say, an exhibition. Every one passing between it and the light causes the pointer on the counting dial B to move on a step.

AFTER long plotting and planning, a cracksman, who is badly wanted by the police for his many successful raids on other people's property, is about to bring off his most daring coup. Midnight struck two hours ago, and here he is in the treasure-house of the great store of Midas, Ltd. All round him are thousands of pounds' worth of jewels, fenced off only by the flimsy protection of glass sheets. His diamond will make short work of *them*.

Not a sound is to be heard. The stillness of death broods over the great chamber. The watchmen are about somewhere, but for the moment, at any rate, the coast is clear. Our burglar gets out his tools and, after a careful search for possible tell-tale electric wires, sets skilfully to work.

The Burglar Foiled

Suddenly a slight rustle makes him look up, and, to his horror, he sees several men cutting off his retreat in all directions. The game is up. He will do no more safe-breaking or case-robbing for some years to come.

Our burglar is clever; but science and invention are cleverer still. He did not know that at one place he crossed a band of invisible rays, sent out by a hidden apparatus on one side of the chamber towards a concealed selenium " electric eye " on the other. The moment at which he interrupted the beam with his body was fatal to him. In a distant room a small red lamp on an indicator board suddenly lit up, informing the watchman on duty there that an intruder had entered the jewellery department. A few words were spoken into a telephone, and arrest followed. Science is making life *very* hard for folk anxious to take a short cut to wealth.

Escorted by Warships

Another picture: A great merchant ship is ploughing her way across the Atlantic, bringing much-needed supplies to England during the stress of war-time needs. She is one of a fleet of similar ships being shepherded through a submarine-infested area of the ocean by an escort of warships. An officer on the bridge is peering into a kind of telescope, watching the blinking of a tiny screen inside. The sudden short glows of greenish light are signals from the flagship of the escort. Not a sign of light pierces the darkness of the night, yet light is being used to send a message, and it is a message which the commander of an enemy submarine can read neither with his eyes nor with his wireless apparatus.

A mile or two away, on the flagship, there is an electric lamp encased in a special kind of glass, which cuts off all rays that the eye can see. But the infra-red rays find their way through, and on reaching the screen on the telescope they make it glow with fluorescence, as phosphorus glows in the dark, and so the beam radiated becomes visible to the person in charge of the apparatus.

There are several kinds of Electric Eye but they all have one thing in common. When light falls upon them electric current begins to flow, or flows in a greater quantity, in a suitable electric circuit connected with the "eye."

This electric current can be used to open doors, to operate a counting mechanism, to switch lights on or off (as in some forms of traffic control), or to stop an electric motor driving a large machine.

So by selecting the right type of "electric eye" or photo-electric cell and connecting it in a suitable circuit engineers can make doors which open as if by magic when anyone approaches. They can also use a ray of light to guard a safe or to protect a machine operator from accidental injury.

Radiovisor Parent Ltd.

AN AUTOMATIC LAMPLIGHTER

This is the upper part of a street lamp standard at Maidstone, Kent. Below the "swan-neck" supporting the bulbs is a casing containing a selenium "bridge." When dusk comes on, the selenium "feels" the lack of light and automatically switches on the lamps. At dawn it switches them off again.

MORE USES FOR "ELECTRIC EYES"

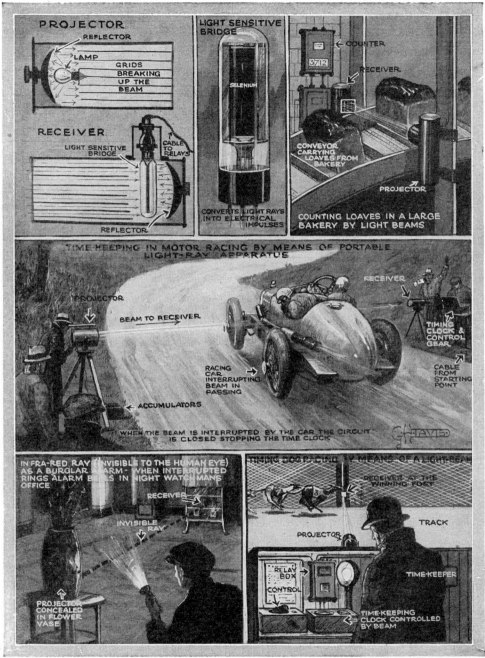

Specially drawn for this work.

At the top are—reading from left to right—an electric lamp specially designed to cast a concentrated beam of light, and a receiver for focusing the beam on to a selenium electric eye; the electric eye, enlarged ; and the two being used to count loaves passing between them. In the centre is a race-timing apparatus, working on the same principle. At the bottom are shown a similar outfit adapted for greyhound racing, and one for checkmating burglars. In the last case rays are used which are invisible to the human eye, but can affect an electric eye.

Services
We Maintain
for the
Common Good

The Work
They Do
and How it
is Carried Out

Metropolitan Water Board.

THE WATER PIPES OF OLDEN DAYS

Even in the long ago a water supply had to be ensured for people who lived in towns, since water plays so very important a part in our lives. The earliest water mains were not made of iron or steel, or even of earthenware, but consisted of short lengths of tree trunks hollowed out and made to fit into one another telescope fashion. Two such pipes are illustrated above.

THE WATER WE DRINK

IN an emergency we can live without many things that are regarded as necessities in our ordinary everyday life, but there are certain needs that must be supplied. We cannot exist without water, for instance. Water is essential to life. Our very bodies are largely composed of water and they demand a continual supply of it. Water is necessary, too, for cleanliness and health.

Every kind of industry requires water, and a good many industries cannot be carried on without a considerable quantity and a continual supply. In the beginning of human history it was to a large extent the question of an adequate water supply which decided the place where the wandering tribes eventually settled. It was the waters of the Nile which led to the beginning of the earliest civilisation.

In the Days of the Romans

For drinking and the cleansing of food we must have, not merely water, but *good* water, free from the tiny germs or chemical impurities harmful to the body. Wherever human beings collect in large numbers it becomes difficult to supply them with good water from sources close at hand. Streams in the near neighbourhood become dirty, and the wells, even if

IN SAMPLES AND IN BULK

Here we see a sample being taken from the filtered water well of a filter bed. All the utensils have been sterilised and expert analyses will be made of the samples taken.

Houses near the summit of a hill are often supplied from a water tower on the top of the hill. The water tower seen in this photograph has a capacity of 202,000 gallons.

Metropolitan Water Board.

This aerial view shows one of the large storage reservoirs into which water is pumped from the river. Its main purpose is to hold a reserve supply of water to tide over a shortage during periods of drought or low river flow. The purpose of the baffle bank seen in the reservoir is to divert the flow of water in a direct line between inlet and outlet and to minimise the waves caused by strong winds.

they yield pure water, become insufficient. Either an abundant supply of local water must be made fit for drinking, or good water must be brought to the people from a distance.

Two thousand years ago the Romans adopted the second course. They led water into Rome and other great cities by constructing artificial channels, called aqueducts, along which the water flowed on a slight slope from some unpolluted source. In order to maintain the gradual fall they bored tunnels through mountains and carried the channels across valleys on wonderful lines of arches.

Some of these Roman aqueducts still stand to-day as a monument to the wonderful engineering talents of the great nation that built them. At Nîmes, in Southern France, is the Pont du Gard, with three tiers of arches spanning a valley 850 feet wide. This

Metropolitan Water Board.
IN PLACE OF POLISHED TAPS
The above picture, taken from an old print, shows us a water-carrier of London in olden days, who hawked the precious fluid through the streets. His place is now taken by storage tanks, pipes and taps.

remarkable example of building skill was erected without the use of mortar. At Segovia, in Spain, is another Roman aqueduct, half-a-mile of two-storey arches, standing some 94 feet high. Some of these bridge-aqueducts had two or three water channels one above the other, just as in these days we lay two or three pipe-lines to bring the water from a distant lake to supply the needs of a big city.

During the four centuries ending A.D. 100, some 350 miles of aqueducts were made to supply Rome. The aqueducts entered the city at different levels, and the amount of water led in during the days of the Empire is calculated at over 200 gallons a day for each of the million and a half inhabitants of the capital. From large reservoirs in Rome the water was distributed through lead or earthenware pipes to houses, fountains, public baths, and even to the Colosseum, where a great lake could be formed to stage a mimic sea-fight. Few cities even in our own times have a better water supply than that enjoyed by the inhabitants of ancient Rome.

Modern Aqueducts

The engineer of to-day has some big advantages over his Roman predecessors. He can make use of iron and steel pipes able to stand great pressures, while his drills and explosives enable him to bore tunnels much more easily. In addition, modern pumping machinery does away with some of the difficulties the Romans had to overcome in order to ensure that the flow of water should be steadily maintained from the source of the supply to the place where it was needed.

If a piece of lead pipe is bent into horseshoe form, with one " leg " rather longer than the other, and water is then poured into the longer leg, this water will presently flow out of the top of the shorter leg. For enclosed water always finds its own level. So when a modern engineer has to take an aqueduct

Metropolitan Water Board.

INTAKE FROM THE RIVER THAMES

At several places on the River Thames there are intakes through which the water is abstracted from the river. Behind this intake, screens are fixed to remove any floating debris, and the water then passes through meters to record the quantity taken. After this it flows to the pumping station, and so to the storage reservoir.

across a valley he does not build a bridge from side to side, as the Romans did, but carries a pipe down one slope, across the low ground, and up the other slope to a rather lower elevation. The pipes are buried in the ground, or covered up in some way and kept out of sight. Should a river be in the way, the pipe is taken under it, or, possibly, carried across a specially-constructed bridge.

An aqueduct may be of pipes throughout, but generally there is some tunnelling to save distance, as well as some " cut and cover " work. The last means digging a trench, forming in this a masonry or concrete channel, closed in at the top, and then covering it with the earth taken out. Here and there, at high points, there will probably be what are called " balancing reservoirs." The water flows into them at one point and out at another. They break up the aqueduct into sections and prevent the pressure becoming too great anywhere; and they are sometimes used to supply towns near the route.

London's Rivers and Wells

There is little doubt that when the

Romans came to Britain they appreciated the fact that Londinium, because of its ford and converging trackways, was the right place to build a walled city. The natural water supply was evidently adequate and there was no need for them to construct an aqueduct. The Thames, with its tributary streams, together with shallow wells sunk in the gravel near the river, supplied all the water that was required.

Nor was there any anxiety about London's water supply when the Normans came. Thomas à Becket's secretary wrote of London in the reign of Henry II : " On the north are pasture lands and a pleasant space of flat meadows, intersected by running waters which turn revolving mill-wheels with merry din. There are also round about London in the suburbs most excellent wells whose waters are sweet, wholesome and clear, and whose runnels ripple amid pebbles bright."

As long as the sources of supply remained within easy reach, distribution was effected by water bearers or carriers. These water carriers became quite an important guild in the fifteenth century, having the title, " Rulers, Wardens and Fellowship of the Brotherhood of St. Christopher of the Water Bearers of London.'' Right down to the seventeenth century they carried on their work, using buckets and sometimes tankards rather like a milk churn. The buckets were carried in pairs, as seen in the picture of one of the craft, while the tankards, holding about five gallons, were carried on the back.

All the time London was growing, and conduits, or trenches, had to be constructed to lead the water to the more densely-inhabited districts. Various schemes for ensuring a communal supply were put forward before a wealthy merchant, Hugh Myddelton, put a plan before the City Corporation in 1609 for making a river to supply the city with water from Ware. This New River Scheme was successfully accomplished, though Myddelton was nearly ruined by the undertaking.

However, it is worth recording that Myddelton did not die in poverty but tackled other ventures and restored his fortunes. His services were recognised by King James I, who created him a baronet and excused him from paying the heavy fine, or fees, usually imposed when this honour was conferred.

This New River Scheme, from the point of view which Myddelton had in mind—the supply of water to the community—was a great success. It still plays a part in helping London's water supply but is now fed with water from the River Lee at New Gauge Intake, Hertfordshire, by Chadwell Spring (when flowing) and by water from a number of wells along its course.

Mainly from the Thames

Other Water Companies were formed in London as the city grew. Most of these companies, as well as many of the devices and inventions they introduced,

Metropolitan Water Board.

OUTLET FROM A STORAGE RESERVOIR

In this photograph is seen the outlet shaft which is approached by a bridge from the bank. A large conduit under the embankment from the bottom of the outlet shaft conducts the water from the reservoir to the aqueduct which conveys it to the distant filtration plant. The concrete lining of the inside slope of the embankment is to prevent erosion by wave action.

contributed some-
thing towards the im-
provement of the city's
supply. Eventually all
companies were taken
over by the Metro-
politan Water Board
which was established
in 1902 and began work
in 1904.

To-day, London gets
some two-thirds of its
water from the Thames,
and the supply of the
remaining third is
about equally divided
between the River Lea
(or Lee as it is some-
times spelt) and from
wells. The River Lea
really supplies the New
River, and one of the
reservoirs in the Lea
Valley, the King
George's reservoir,
covers some 424
acres.

Thames water is
stored in three
enormous reservoirs at
Staines, covering over
a square mile, as well
as in the Queen Mary
reservoir at Littleton,
which is even larger,
and twenty-one other

Metropolitan Water Board.

INSIDE A SERVICE RESERVOIR

Service reservoirs receive the water pumped in excess of demands,
and supply water to consumers when requirements exceed the
pumping. Here we see one before being filled. Such reservoirs
can be emptied for inspection, cleaned and sterilised, and then put
into use again.

reservoirs of varying size. The Metropolitan Water Board supplies daily
an average of some 324 million gallons,
including 7 million gallons in bulk to
neighbouring water undertakings. The
area directly supplied covers about 573
square miles with a population of 6½
million people and includes the whole
county of London as well as some neighbouring districts. It would require a
tank 3½ times the size of Trafalgar
Square and about the height of Nelson's
column to hold one day's supply of
water to London.

Every gallon of water used in London
has to be pumped at least two or three

times, and all the water taken from the
Thames and the Lea must be purified
before it is fit for human consumption.
There are some 290 engines at work and
they use over 155,000 tons of coal a year,
as well as 1¼ million gallons of oil and
over 36 million units of electricity.
Some of the engines each pump over 27
million gallons of water every day.

The reservoirs in which the water is
stored have been made on level ground
by excavating material on the site and
piling it up all round to form a continuous bank. Altogether these reservoirs
hold over 22 thousand million gallons
of water. The site for a reservoir must

ENSURING A PURE WATER SUPPLY

Before the water reaches the consumer it passes through various processes to ensure its purity. After leaving the storage reservoir it passes through the Primary Filter House, seen in the photograph above.   In this stage the larger suspended matter in the water is removed at a fairly rapid rate before the water passes on to the secondary filter beds.

Metropolitan Water Board.

Here we see something of the construction of the secondary or slow sand filter bed.   The water enters through the inlet which can be seen at the far end of the bed, then percolates through the sand and shingle into the tiled drains and is led to the main channel under the floor when it passes to the well at the end opposite to the inlet and is sterilised.

FROM RIVER AND WELL

In this photograph are seen the steam turbine units at one of the large pumping stations. This supplies water to a number of zones in the London area. The water dealt with here has been chlorinated and filtered and is then pumped through large diameter mains to service reservoirs, situated on high ground, and from these many thousands of consumers receive their supply.

Metropolitan Water Board.

The Thames supplies about two-thirds of London's water requirements, but quite a considerable amount is obtained also from deep wells or boreholes. Our photograph shows a well pumping-station capable of pumping 12 million gallons of water a day. A certain amount of water derived from the river is delivered to this station to supplement the quantity obtained from the well.

THE OLD FALL WELL

At the beginning of the eighteenth century the only sources of water supply in Liverpool were springs and shallow wells. The principal supply was obtained from a public well known as Fall Well. Women carried the water from this well in tin cans borne on their shoulders. Later, carts were used for carrying the water, but the cans were still employed to distribute it.

have a thick stratum of London clay underlying it. A trench is excavated on the centre line of the bank down to the clay and keyed into it. It is then filled with puddle clay which is afterwards continued upwards with the bank, thus forming a clay puddle wall, and so a watertight basin is formed.

While the water is in these storage reservoirs it deposits much of the solid matter it contains and is to a certain extent purified by the reduction of disease-producing bacteria. After circulation in the reservoirs, water is passed to the filtration plant. At one time slow sand filters were employed by themselves, but to-day the water for London goes through a system of double filtration, consisting of roughing filter beds in the first place and secondary or slow sand beds afterwards. The primary or roughing filter beds supply partly filtered water to the slow

sand beds, the output of which is in consequence considerably increased. Photographs of these primary and secondary filters are seen on page 258.

The water percolates slowly downwards through the sand and gravel of the secondary filter beds, and leaves on the surface any suspended matter which may have been in it. The water now receives a small dose of chlorine, the dose varying according to several conditions. Large tanks, known as contact tanks, hold this chlorinated water for a period up to two hours, thus enabling the chlorine to do its work before the water leaves the works. After this the water is pumped through an intricate network of underground mains and does not see daylight again until it is turned on at the tap.

The mains through which the water is distributed are made of cast-iron or steel. The pipes range from 4 inches to

FROM LAKE VYRNWY TO LIVERPOOL

Stewart Bale.

Between 1890–1905 the upper valley of the River Vyrnwy in Montgomeryshire, Wales, was converted into a lake by the construction of the dam seen in the photograph above. When it was completed it was for a time the largest artificial reservoir in Europe, and the first in Great Britain in which a high masonry dam was employed. The length of the lake is nearly 5 miles and it holds more than 12,000 million gallons.

Altigraph Ltd.

It was not until 1847 that Liverpool Corporation became responsible for supplying the city and environs with water. From that time onwards it became a difficult problem to keep the supply adequate for the ever-growing demands. Among the schemes carried out has been the construction of Lake Vyrnwy and the pipe-lines necessary to convey the water from the Welsh lake to the great storage reservoirs at Prescot, near Liverpool, seen in the photograph above.

48 inches across inside. The largest distribution mains throw off smaller branch mains, and these still smaller branches and so on. There are also a number of service reservoirs on high ground in various parts of London and these ensure a regular supply of water at all times.

At different points along the mains are valves for cutting off the supply, as well as standpipes and connections for use in case of fire. A street main supplies all the houses in the street, each house having its separate turn-off valve. The length of the mains used in London is over 8,000 miles.

Taking Away the Waste

There is another aspect of the water question which in the years gone by has been just as great a problem as the water supply, and that is the disposal of the surplus and used water. When you have had your bath, out comes the plug and away goes the water. Where ? Or again, there is a heavy rainstorm and for a brief space the streets become almost a river. An inch of rain is equal to 101 tons, or 22,635 gallons of water per acre of surface land on which it falls.

The original sewers of London were designed to carry off rain-water only and it was not until 1874 that a really comprehensive scheme was planned and tackled in a scientific way. It has since been enlarged and the area drained has been increased, but the principles remain the same. A great part of the sewage and rainwater has to be pumped from one point to another. The largest

Stewart Bale.

BENEATH THE MANCHESTER SHIP CANAL

Throughout the whole length of the 68-mile aqueduct which brings the water from Lake Vyrnwy to the city of Liverpool there are many crossings over or under rivers, railways and canals. In the above photograph the pipe-lines under the Manchester Ship Canal are seen in their brickwork tunnel, 12 feet in diameter and at a depth of 63 feet below the surface.

TWO AUSTRALIAN WEIRS

The waters of the 1,600-mile long Murray River have been harnessed by river works which cost £12,000,000. Our photograph shows No. 3 Weir, one of six similar installations on this great South Australian river. These reservoirs supply the water for the irrigation schemes in the States of Victoria and South Australia.

Photos: Australian News and Information Bureau.

One of the problems which has at times demanded urgent action in Australia has been the supply of water to the goldfields. The photograph above shows Mundaring Weir, near Perth, Western Australia. From this weir a pipe-line takes water to the Kalgoorlie and Boulder goldfields, in the Coolgardie district, 350 miles away.

Abrahams Ltd.

BEFORE THE LAKE WAS RAISED

When first the proposal was made to use the water of one of the English Lakes to supply the needs of Manchester, there was strong opposition, but eventually Thirlmere was supplying an average of 50 million gallons per day. Later, Haweswater was linked up as an additional source of supply. Our photograph shows the countryside before the lake was raised by the construction of a dam across Haweswater Beck.

pumping stations are at Abbey Mills where there are pumps capable of dealing with 2,000 tons a minute. At Hammersmith is a station which can raise a thousand tons of rain-water from storm-relief sewers and pour it into the Thames.

Every city, town and village in Britain has in comparatively recent times been compelled to tackle this problem of water supply. In Liverpool, for instance, at the beginning of the eighteenth century the only sources of water supply were springs and shallow wells. The principal supply in the town was obtained from a public well known as Fall Well, not very far from where St. George's Hall now stands. The water was carried from the well by women who bore the water-filled tin cans on their shoulders.

Later, as the population increased, carts were used for carrying the water, but the cans were still used for distributing it from the carts. Other plans were put forward but nothing was done until 1786 when an Act of Parliament was passed which enabled the Town Council to supply the district with fresh water. Then companies were formed but the supply they gave was very inadequate. The water was turned on in the mains only two or three times a week and then for but two or three hours. If a fire broke out, it probably meant waiting for an hour or more before any quantity of water could be obtained.

A real beginning was made in 1847 when the Corporation became solely responsible for supplying the city with water. In 1880 they obtained authority to take water from the River Vyrnwy in North Wales and in July 1891 water from the artificial lake which had been constructed was first sent through a temporary line of 12-inch steel pipes for a journey of 68 miles right through to the city of Liverpool. At this time Lake Vyrnwy was the largest artificial reservoir in Europe and the first in Great Britain in which a high masonry dam was employed.

Removing a Village

While this new lake was being constructed, a whole village had to be destroyed. Houses, school and church were all pulled down and rebuilt below the great dam which was erected. Since it was first made, Lake Vyrnwy has gradually increased its supply to the city, and the construction of a fourth pipeline was begun in 1947.

Another city which has had to go a long way for its water supply is Manchester. It first sought for water in the Longdendale Valley in the Pennine Range, some 18 miles to the east of Manchester. The first instalment of water from this source was delivered in 1851, but the construction of the whole works extended over a period of 40 years.

Long before it was completed Manchester realised that with a rapidly increasing population the plans they had in hand were likely to fall far short of what was necessary. They went as

Abrahams Ltd.

AFTER THE DAM HAD BEEN CONSTRUCTED

In this photograph we have the same view of Mardale Head and Harter Fell taken after the construction of the dam across Haweswater Beck. This new source of supply was completed in 1941. Water for Manchester and some of the towns through which the pipe-line passes can now be drawn from either Haweswater or Thirlmere. The water surface area of the lake was increased from 346 to 974 acres.

HAWESWATER DAM JUST AFTER COMPLETION

This photograph, taken just after construction had been completed, shows the great dam at the north-east end of Haweswater. It is 1,550 feet long and its maximum height is 120 feet. The length of the lake was increased from 2½ miles to 4 miles as the waters gradually rose and spread over a wider area to form a reservoir holding 18,662 million gallons of water to supply the needs of a city 80 miles away.

far afield as the Lake District and at the time there were strong protests on the ground that if their plans were carried out they would ruin the beauty of the surroundings.

From Thirlmere and Haweswater

They were carried out, however, and even the objectors agreed later that the beauty of the district was in no way impaired. The aqueduct which brings the water from the Lake to the thirsty citizens of Manchester is 96 miles long. Eventually even Thirlmere could not meet all the requirements of the still growing city and in 1919 a Bill was passed enabling the city of Manchester to purchase Haweswater, the highest of the English lakes.

Some idea of the work involved can be gathered from the fact that the first supply from Haweswater through the Sprint Siphon and Thirlmere Aqueduct did not reach Manchester until October 1941. Haweswater is 80 miles from Manchester. By the construction of the dam across Haweswater Beck the water level of the lake has been raised 95 feet and holds a supply of over 18 thousand million gallons.

When eventually the full scheme is complete Haweswater will supply about 72 million gallons per day for Manchester and other towns near the route taken by the great aqueduct. For not only is Manchester itself drinking Lake District water; in the Act which gave the city the right to do so it is laid down that certain other towns also shall be entitled to obtain their supply from the same source. Broadly speaking, the towns permitted to do this are those which lie within five miles of the Thirlmere or Haweswater aqueducts.

The fears which, not unnaturally, many people have had in the past that the construction of mighty dams and the schemes for impounding the waters of a pleasant lake or river will destroy the beauty of the district have actually been falsified by the results. In no case, perhaps, is this more evident than in that of the Elan Valley, from which source the city of Birmingham draws its water supply by means of an aqueduct 74 miles long.

The Elan rises in Cardiganshire and then flows southeast through Radnorshire and Brecknockshire until it enters the Wye. The watersheds of the Elan and its tributary, the Claerwen, were acquired by the Birmingham Corporation and three reservoirs have been constructed on the Elan to impound its pleasant waters for the benefit of Birmingham residents.

This supply was greatly increased by the opening of the Claerwen Dam, the highest in the British Isles, by H.M. Queen Elizabeth II. on October 23rd, 1952.

Water for New York

When it comes to a question of quantity New York can claim to use more water than any other city. The aqueducts which bring water to this, the second largest city of the world, are the biggest ever constructed. The first of New York's sources of supply is the Croton Reservoir, thirty-five miles north of America's chief city. From this reservoir well over 300 million gallons of water are brought daily.

This reservoir was formed by blocking the course of a river with a dam that ranks with the Pyramids of Egypt as one of the world's greatest masonry structures.

Fox Photos.

A RESERVOIR IN THE ELAN VALLEY

Here we have a view of the source of Birmingham's water supply from Mid-Wales. This shows the bridge over the Elan with the Caban Goch reservoir and dam some little distance beyond the bridge. The city's water supply from this area has been doubled by the Claerwen dam.

Nearly half-a-mile long, 300 feet high above its base, and 200 feet thick at the bottom, it holds back 32 thousand million gallons of water.

Even this enormous quantity did not prove enough for the ever-increasing demands of the city and a still bigger scheme was carried through. An artificial lake, 12 miles long and one mile wide, was created 100 miles to the north of New York. This lake holds four times as much water as the Croton reservoir, and supplies 600 million gallons daily. The Catskill aqueduct which leads the water to the city from this mighty reservoir is 17 feet high and 14 feet wide for a great part of the distance. It passes under Croton Lake and later under the East River to Staten Island after traversing 125 miles.

Australia's Long Aqueduct

For one of the longest aqueducts yet constructed we must go to Western Australia. In 1892 gold was discovered at Coolgardie in an almost waterless desert, many miles west of Perth, the capital. People flocked to Coolgardie and before very long the shortage of water became acute. This lack of water, and the impurity of the small quantity that was obtainable, led to disease, and this became a major problem. In addition, the railway to the goldfield could not be worked owing to this same difficulty over the water supply.

The Government had to take the matter in hand. A big reservoir was formed near the coast by damming the Helena River and a 350-mile line of steel pipe, 30 inches in diameter, was laid from the reservoir to the goldfield. As the reservoir was much nearer sea-level than the goldfield, eight pumping stations had to be built to pass the water along in stages.

Planet.

CLAERWEN DAM, HIGHEST IN THE BRITISH ISLES

Birmingham is the second largest city in Britain and the centre of a great manufacturing area. A large and constant supply of good water is essential for health and industry, and in October, 1952, the Claerwen Dam was opened by H.M. Queen Elizabeth II. The dam is 184 ft. high and a roadway runs along its 1,100-ft. top. The opening of this dam marked the completion of a great scheme inaugurated in 1902 by King Edward VII.

WITH THE FIRE FIGHTERS

WHEN THE FIRE BRIGADES FACE HEAVY ODDS

Fire under control is one of our most useful servants, but in its destructive forms it is still one of man's most formidable enemies. Properly organised fire-fighting services were first undertaken in this country by insurance companies, but they have long been a public service. Our picture shows something of the task that confronted the brigade summoned to an outbreak at a great rubber dump near London.

FIRE is one of the greatest of the natural forces which have helped man in the upward climb from his earliest savage state, but it still remains one of his greatest enemies when beyond his control.

The discovery of how to make fire at will and use it for his own purposes was the first big step forward made by primitive man. Yet in recent times fire has destroyed great cities, and takes its toll of life and property every year in all countries throughout the world. Man is still, as in his earliest days, faced with the problem and peril of fire in its destructive aspect.

Even to-day, despite the precautions taken to avoid risk of an outbreak of fire, the loss caused in Great Britain amounts to about £12,000,000 each year. During the war years it was of course very considerably more, and never before was the importance of efficient fighting services against this peril made so clear. The lessons learned during those years when this country lived through its ordeal by fire have not been forgotten. To-day our fire-fighting services are highly-trained and splendidly-equipped forces, ready for instant action when the call comes.

Methods of fighting outbreaks of fire have existed almost ever since civilisation began. There is evidence that the Egyptians had fire brigades in 2,000 B.C. Hero of Alexandria, about whom we read in Volume VII, described what he called a " siphon " which was used to put out fires in the year 150 B.C. About the year 40 B.C. the Romans had a well-organised fire brigade service ready to go into action in any part of their city when outbreaks occurred. Hose pipes for conveying water to help in putting out fires were in use quite early in the Christian era.

In England nothing very much in the way of organised fire-fighting appears to have been undertaken until the early insurance companies began to form fire brigades of their own to protect any property they had insured. This was in the eighteenth century, and an Act of Parliament was passed in 1744 which ordered the church-wardens of all parishes in London to keep a proper engine to deal with any fires that broke out in their own districts.

When Danger was Foreseen

The insurance companies still led the way, however, and in 1833 they combined to form the London Fire Engine Establishment. Their first commander, James Braidwood, was himself killed while fighting a fire near London Bridge in 1861.

Five years later the fire brigades in London became the responsibility of the Metropolitan Board of Works, which was replaced in 1888 by the London County Council. In other parts of the country fire brigades were organised by the local councils and in all the important cities and towns a fairly efficient fire-fighting service was gradually developed.

When the Second World War broke out in 1939 it was realised that the risks of fire had been enormously increased. The authorities had fore-seen the danger in advance and an Auxiliary Fire Service had been formed to assist the regular brigades. Large numbers of trailer pumps, quantities of hose and other equipment had been distributed by the Government to fire brigades throughout the country.

There were some 1450 brigades in England and 200 in Scotland, and in 1941 these brigades were united to form the National Fire Service.

The number of firemen was very considerably increased and, as in the fighting forces, women were enrolled and did valuable work in control rooms, as drivers, wireless operators, motor-cyclists, cooks, and in running mobile kitchens and canteens to help in sustaining the firemen during their arduous tasks. In addition, of course, many clerical posts in the Fire Service were filled by women.

Some part of the story of the magnificent work done by these men and women of the National Fire Service and the Women's Auxiliary Fire Service during those strenuous years is told in "Their Finest Hour" in Volume II. In one period of twenty-two days and nights in London the fire fighters were in action at nearly 10,000 fires, and in other great cities many similar stories of courage and endurance can be told.

The National Fire Service was, however, formed only as an emergency measure, and with the end of the war there came a desire for the Brigades to return to some semblance of their old independence. Local patriotism counts for a good deal, and many of our Fire Brigades have their proud records and traditions of service in the same way that many of the famous regiments in the Army cherish their traditions of the past. The Fire Services Act of 1947 provided that for the future the responsibility for fire-fighting should be with County Councils and certain other authorities in England and Wales; in Scotland with the Councils of Counties and the large Burghs.

Training of firemen in the methods used to combat outbreaks remains similar throughout the country. Many invaluable lessons were learned during the testing years of 1939–45. In London the would-be fireman has 8–9 weeks' intensive training at the Training Headquarters in Southwark Bridge Road.

The prospective fire fighter must be not less than 21 or more than 31 years of age and preferably under 25. He has to pass various tests as well as a written examination before being accepted for training. That these tests are not very easy can be judged

WITH THE FIREMEN IN TRAINING

Fox Photos.

Training to be an efficient fireman is strenuous work and only the strongest and most resourceful men can take up this calling. Above we are shown a team at practice, the tower having been built specially for this purpose. From different floors in the building firemen are attacking a fire with their hoses, and we see on the left exactly how a fire fighter operates from the top of a telescopic escape ladder.

from the fact that on an average only a hundred men out of every thousand are finally passed—and the majority of applicants to-day are those who have served in one of the branches of the fighting services.

There used to be a preference for ex-seamen because in the old days the sailor was accustomed to climbing aloft and did not worry about being perched high above deck while he got on with a strenuous job. That point scarcely counts so much in these days when sailing-ships are few and the sailor who has climbed the rigging to trim sail is a rarity. Even so a man who might feel a trifle nervous when handling a hose at the top of a 90-feet turntable ladder, with flames in front of him and smoke swirling around him, would be happier in some less strenuous service than fire-fighting.

For the man in training it is a strenuous day from 8.30 a.m. to 6 p.m.

A COOL HEAD FOR HOT WORK

Often, where there are towering buildings in narrow streets, our fire fighters have to work from the tops of tall ladders, as here shown.

during these eight to nine weeks before he takes his final tests. These tests are not only practical and technical, but there are written papers and an oral examination as well before he is finally passed as qualified for the Service.

Teams in Training

Take a brief look at the Training Headquarters on any normal working day. In one yard a squad of men are practising with extensible ladders of which there are various types. On this occasion the ladder is touching the wall of the building beside an open window.

A fireman goes up, clambers through the window, and in a few moments is climbing back on to the escape again. But now he has one of his fellow recruits across his shoulders and brings him down the escape to lay him gently on the ground. True, he does not rest there very long, but practice in careful handling of rescued persons is as important as practice in seeing that every safety device on the escape ladder is in its proper position.

Later the team take turns at this rescue act from the roof. Every man has his full share of practice in carrying down a human burden—and in playing the part of the burden as well! It is not merely practice in rescuing and in learning self-confidence, but in knowing just what it feels like to be rescued. In the early stages of their training most men prefer to be the carriers rather than the carried!

Other ladder practice in another part of the training-school is with the type of ladder which is so made that it can be readily attached to a top-storey window. These ladders are fitted with a saw-like steel bar, with a hook at the end, to enable them to take a firm hold on the window-sill. First, the fireman climbs to the first storey on one ladder then a similar ladder is handed to him by a comrade and this is fixed to the next storey window. A quick test

TRANSPORT IN MANY LANDS

From animal transport to the steam locomotive was the first and most spectacular advance in transport. Electricity and the internal combustion engine have brought new marvels. Even mountains may be scaled in comfort by the method shown in the photograph above. This is a view of the aerial funicular which conveys passengers from the Rio Llabregat, below the town of Monistrol in the Pyrenees, to the summit of the "sacred mountain of the Catalans," which, according to tradition, is the site of the Castle of the Holy Grail.

IN MADEIRA'S SUN-KISSED HIGHWAYS

Keystone

The island of Madeira which belongs to Portugal is in normal times a popular holiday resort owing to its mild and salubrious climate. It is a mountainous island, with steep twisting roads and narrow streets, often paved with pebbles. Covered conveyances, known as *carros*, running on sledges and drawn by oxen, are still used, and our photograph shows this type of island transport.

H. Armstrong Roberts

A 'ricksha man plies for hire in the city of Kobe, Japan. The jinricksha, to give the vehicle its full name, was invented by a missionary about 1870. It was first used in Japan, though it soon became common in other parts of the world. Today, it competes with the modern taxicab service; it is not quite so fast, but it is comfortable and less expensive.

Will F. Taylor

Motor-cars are as popular in India as elsewhere, but away from the cities and the well-kept roads animal-drawn vehicles still have pride of place. This photograph was taken not very far from Delhi. The travellers sit cross-legged on cushions, with a shell-like canopy as protection from the sun, while the carriage is brightly decorated, and the animals' tinkling bells provide musical accompaniment.

BY CAMEL CARAVAN TO CHINA

Mondiale

Our photograph shows a camel caravan on the road from Turkestan through the Kun Lun Mountains with goods for Hanchung and thence by river to Hankow. The bonnet of a car on the left suggests that modern methods of transport are not unknown on this ancient road, over which men and animals have travelled for centuries past.

Fox Photos

Egypt is the oldest civilisation in the world and in Alexandria, second city and chief port, founded in 332 B.C., East meets West and old and new mingle, with the modern motor-car alongside a slow-moving animal-drawn cart. Here in this photograph an Arab stands in charge of a well-laden Yak, while in the background can be seen some of the modern buildings in Egypt's ancient city.

CONTRASTS FROM THE EAST

In many Eastern countries Western civilisation has introduced its modern inventions and utility attire. But the old methods are not disappearing too rapidly, nor has Western dress altogether ousted national costumes. In this photograph, taken outside an hotel in Japan, two guests are ready for an outing, one in a travelling chair while the other prefers a kago or palanquin.

We have seen a photograph taken near Delhi in a previous picture, and here in contrast we have a scene in the city itself. Electric trams have become one of the chief methods of transport through the streets of the Union of India's capital. The process of modernising the big cities has been going on for many years but there are still big areas where the bullock carts are the only means of conveyance.

Fox Photos

At first sight one would imagine that this photograph had been taken in one of the ancient lands of the East. Actually it was taken in Australia where there are great tracts of land across which the railways have still to be laid. Journeys over these sandy wastes must be made, however, and the camel still holds its reputation as the "ship of the desert."

Canada is another vast country where problems of transport are not easily solved. The task of bringing down great loads of timber from the big forests far removed from the railways is accomplished in various ways. In this photograph, taken at Hudson, in Ontario, can be seen the long line of heavily laden trucks hauled by a tractor over snow and ice-bound roads to the distant rail-head.

BY CAMEL AND BY DOG CART

Fox Photos

In those lands where the heat of the sun presents its own problems the camel is still supreme. Here we have a photograph taken at Aden, near the entrance to the sun-drenched Red Sea, showing a camel cart which has been the means of transport in this part of the world through many centuries. A native trader drives into the port to collect his load of salt and cigarettes.

E.N.A.

In Belgium and Holland dogs have been used for long years past to take round the morning milk carts in country districts. Despite more modern methods this form of transport still holds its own in many districts and has its peculiar advantages for fairly light loads and short distances with many stops on the round. Nor is the cost of upkeep a serious problem for the dog-owner.

CONTRASTS IN WATER TRANSPORT

Flower-decked boats gliding through the waterways of the Mexican Venice—the Floating Gardens of Xochimilco, a favourite spot for Sunday outings from Mexico City. The gardens are formed on the shallow lake by masses of water plants fixed by tree stakes which have taken root. The town of Xochimilco, which means field of flowers, is on the west shore of the lake.

On the far western side of the United States of America is Washington State, not to be confused with Washington, the capital, in the East. Puget Sound, which communicates with the Pacific, is a great inlet running into Washington State, and the simplest way of travelling between the big ports such as Tacoma and Seattle is by water. Seen here is a ferryboat for passengers and goods on the Sound.

A SELF-PROPELLED PUMP WITH LADDERS

The engine seen above is one of our latest fire-fighting appliances, speedy, reliable and equipped with every device science can create for the work entailed. Contrast this with the horse-drawn engines and escapes which once dashed through London's streets. To-day there is one unit, and in many cases the self-propelled pumps carry their own escapes.

assures the fireman that the ladder has gripped the sill properly.

Up the ladder the fireman goes and the performance is repeated until the top storey is reached, when the process is reversed. Watching a fairly advanced class on this particular exercise gives the impression that it is comparatively easy to young, fit men and just a matter of routine; fixing, testing, climbing, clambering from the ladder through the window, then drawing up the ladder to repeat the process again does not look a very difficult task.

But watch a fairly new class of recruits practising the early stages of this same very necessary exercise and the onlooker has a wonderful lesson on the difference which experience and practice make.

In a lecture-room another class is being shown by an instructor the simple equipment employed to put the overhead live wires used for trolley-

buses and trams out of action when they are likely to be dangerous during rescue work. There is a good deal to be learnt about equipment and its proper use. A fireman's job is one in which the motto " Be Prepared for any Emergency " is highly necessary.

Ready For Accidents

What is a fireman doing when he is not actually fighting fires? Looking after the apparatus and equipment? That is one task, of course, since everything must be instantly ready when the call comes. But fires are not the only calamities to which the firemen are called. A train smash or an aeroplane crash are just as urgent calls to action as a fire. When floods occur the most desperately-needed help is that given by the firemen with their pumps, in addition to any rescue work that may be necessary.

Then there are minor accidents such

as lifts sticking half-way between two floors, imprisoning the unfortunate passengers. The firemen know just how to handle this problem. Or a small boy finds it comparatively easy to push his head between iron railings so that he can get a better view of what is going on down below. It is only when he tries to bring his head back again that panic comes. His head obstinately refuses to come back though it went through the railings easily enough.

Caring for Animals

It is generally the fireman's job in the end. Usually special expanders are used which force the railings far enough apart for the small imprisoned head to be withdrawn and accompany its owner to the home to which his legs have been so anxious to carry him ever since the tragedy happened.

Animals, too, provide work for the firemen. The venturesome kitten climbs a tree, and, like the small boy, gets stuck in some impossible position from which it cannot escape by its own efforts. It can and does proclaim its trouble to all the world within hearing. Usually it is the fireman with his ladder who is called to the scene and carries out the rescue work quickly and efficiently.

An affectionate regard for animals is among the traditions of the Fire Service. There is a memorial stone at Southwark Bridge Road recording the virtues of Bill, the station cat for eighteen years, who was evidently a prince among cats, and yet, like all other cats, loved warmth—and a good fire!

Animal stories are numerous. There was a horse that went up the steps to a house, through the front door and the hall and up the narrow stairway without causing any traffic jam. It was only when it was in one of the

THE FLOATING FIRE ENGINE

For use against ships burning in dock or mid-stream and for fighting fires in docks and warehouses specially-equipped fire-floats are used. In this photograph one of these fire-floats is in action, her side illuminated by a blaze on the river bank. Fire-floats can often draw much nearer to conflagrations than could a vehicle ashore and they are never short of water because this element is all around them.

HOW THE FIREMEN LEARN AND WORK

Fox Photos.

In this picture is a scale model of a ware-house and offices. Smoke is pumped into the model to give realism and the firemen are then instructed in their work.

Fox Photos.

The photograph above, taken during a display given by London firemen, demonstrates how a person is rescued from a burning building merely by the use of lines.

Central Press.

For work in some classes of fire, when the smoke is very dense or charged with gas or acid, it is necessary for firemen to wear breathing apparatus.

Central Press.

In this picture the rescuer is wearing a self-contained oxygen breathing apparatus and carrying his human burden by the method known as the " Fireman's Lift."

upstairs rooms that the trouble really began. Getting into the room had been simple; getting back into the road again was a vastly different proposition. It was another job for the firemen and they did it all right.

Traditions of a Great Service

But fighting fires and rescuing those in peril remains the great task. Over the entrance to one of the buildings at the Training School is the advice given many years ago by Sir Eyre Massey Shaw, chief of the London Fire Service from 1861 to 1891. Every recruit to the Service is shown this notice written out in large letters:

" A fireman to be successful must enter buildings; he must get in below, above, on every side, through panels of doors, through windows, through loop holes, through skylights, through holes cut by himself in the gates, the walls, the roof; he must know how to reach the attic from the basement by ladders placed on half-burned stairs, and the basement from the attic by rope made fast on a chimney. His whole success depends on his getting in and remaining there and he must always carry his appliances with him as without them he is of no use."

For service in our great ports special equipment is often necessary, and fire-floats will take the place of the road-engines normally used. Again, a different technique is required at big airports, where the danger of an aeroplane making a crash-landing and bursting into flames is always a possibility.

There have been changes in equipment and in methods, but the spirit, traditions, and the discipline of this great fire-fighting service remain as they were when this advice was first penned nearly ninety years ago. Among the many and varied services which have been built up in this country for the common good, our fire fighters hold a highly important place.

Mirrorpic.

FOR FIGHTING FIRES AT OUR AIRPORTS

The most modern and most efficient fire engine in the world is this new type which has recently been installed at London Airport. It is seen here in action as it sends forth streams of CO_2 gas. The top fountain will go round and round in a circle when necessary. The engine is driven right into the centre of any aircraft fire and the clouds of white gas immediately extinguish the flames.

HOW WE GET OUR GAS

DRIVING THE GAS HOME

This is the view of the plant used for pumping gas into the great mains which interconnect gas-making and gas-distributing stations in London, and enable any one to draw supplies from elsewhere. The pressure in these mains from the " booster house " is considerably higher than that in the ordinary distributing mains of a district.

IN the year 1810 there was formed in London a company called the Gas Light and Coke Company, to supply gas and coke to the public. The idea of doing such a thing was novel, and many people regarded it as quite impracticable. The company, however, was granted a royal charter in 1812.

Gas Nationalisation

In its early days it had many difficulties to fight against, and experience in gas-making was bought at heavy cost, which made the shareholders very downhearted at times. But after it had got over what we may call its teething troubles, the Gas Light and Coke Company began to grow lustily, and gradually new gas companies came into existence throughout the country.

Then on May 1st, 1949, the 1,037 undertakings in the British gas industry, some of which were independent companies while others were owned by local authorities, were all taken over by the Government and became State-owned. The nationalised industry is now controlled by the Gas Council and by twelve area Gas Boards. The total number of consumers served by the industry in 1951 was 11,981,107, of whom 11,230,607 were domestic consumers.

Altogether the industry supplies some 2,460 million therms (equal roughly to 500,000 million cubic feet) of gas to its consumers in a year, and about 143,000 workers are employed. Nearly $26\frac{1}{2}$ million tons of coal are carbonised in a year.

Gas is not by any means the only product of the gas-works. The coke which is left behind in the retorts is used in millions of homes for water heating and as a smokeless fuel for fires. About $11\frac{3}{4}$ million tons of coke are sold every year, and the demand for coke still exceeds the supply. Tar is another

HOW COAL GAS TRAVELS—

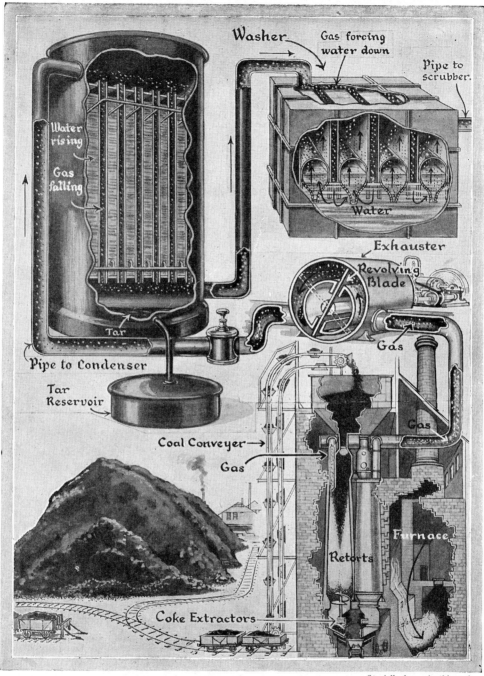

Washer

Gas forcing water down

Pipe to scrubber.

Water rising

Gas falling

Water

Exhauster

Revolving Blade

Tar

Gas

Pipe to Condenser

Gas

Tar Reservoir

Coal Conveyer →

Gas

Furnace

Retorts

Coke Extractors

Specially drawn for this work.

The life-history of coal gas begins in the retorts—the latest form of vertical retort is here shown—where the gas is separated by heat from the solid coke of the coal. The gas is pulled out of the retorts by a blower, which drives it forward through the many parts of the plant which free it of various impurities. These, if allowed to remain in it, would cause troubles of different kinds, whereas when extracted they can be turned to useful account. In the condenser the hot gas is chilled and releases the tar, which falls to the bottom and is drawn off into a reservoir.

FROM RETORT TO CONSUMER

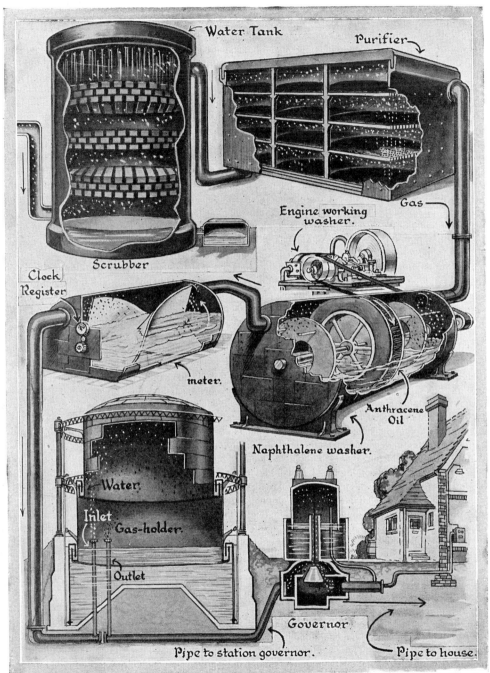

Water Tank

Purifier

Engine working washer.

Gas

Scrubber

Clock Register

meter.

Anthracene Oil

Naphthalene washer.

Water

Inlet

Gas-holder.

Outlet

Governor

Pipe to station governor.

Pipe to house.

Specially drawn for this work.

The gas next passes through water in a " washer " and rises among falling water in a " scrubber," to be deprived of ammonia gas, which the water absorbs greedily. In the " purifier," next encountered, the gas moves over trays of iron oxide. The oxide robs it of sulphuretted hydrogen, a very evil-smelling gas. Further apparatus extracts anthracene oil, naphthalene, and benzole, the last of which is used as a motor-car fuel. Between the gasholder and the distributing mains is a governor which automatically regulates the pressure in the mains.

valuable by-product of the gas-works, and nearly 1½ million tons are supplied each year. Over 2,000 different chemicals can be made from tar alone. Other products of the gas-works are dealt with elsewhere in this volume, but it is necessary to stress this aspect of gas manufacture since so many industries rely upon the by-products obtained when coal is carbonised.

A good deal of research work has been carried out to ensure that the gas supplied to the domestic consumer is not wasted. Modern gas appliances are designed to work most efficiently at a certain pressure and for a certain quality of gas. Cooking uses more gas than anything else, and the demand at certain hours of the day is particularly heavy. Now that the industry is nationalised it is possible to increase the already considerable amount of interconnection between the works in different areas so that there will be a steady supply of gas to all users, no matter how heavy the demand may be.

What Gas Means to Us

The replacement of gas by electricity for lighting may give rise to the belief that gas is of less importance than formerly. Such a belief would be a mistaken one, however, for the use of gas has increased almost as much during the last five years as during the preceding twenty years.

The fact is that people are depending more and more on gas for cooking and heating, and less on raw coal, because of the greater cleanliness and convenience of the first. Its use for lighting purposes, with which it first began, has now become considerably less, but in other directions gas consumption is increasing steadily and this is especially true so far as its use in industry is concerned.

Many houses are supplied with gas through slot meters. The consumer drops in a shilling, and when the amount of gas to the value of the coin has passed through the meter the supply stops, and another coin must be contributed. But domestic heating is only one of many applications of gas, for coal gas is used as a fuel in over 3,000 trades, and on the average for more than seven processes in each. The gas industry in this country therefore fulfils a highly important purpose.

North Thames Gas Board.

A GIANT STOKER

This great machine, moving on rails behind the rear ends of the retorts in a retort house, performs two duties. It thrusts into each retort in turn a rammer, which pushes the exhausted coke out through a front end, and at the same time introduces a fresh charge of coal, supplied from the hopper which brings it at regular intervals.

North Thames Gas Board.

INSIDE A HORIZONTAL RETORT HOUSE

This picture shows us the cast-iron ends of hundreds of retorts, which extend right through a huge block 20 or more feet thick. In twelve hours or so about 13 cwt. of coal is baked in each retort till it has given up all its gas, which passes out through one of the many upright pipes.

A Tour of a Gas-works

Let us pay a visit to one of London's largest gas-works at Fulham. These are now more than 100 years old, and probably the oldest in London. But in spite of their age, they have, so to speak, always kept young in the sense of being up to date. A tour of the 35 acres which they cover serves to dispel any belief we may have entertained that gas-works are uninteresting, even though very necessary, parts of our civilisation.

Our conductor leads us down to a wharf on the northern bank of the Thames, where we find a large sea-going ship, one of the colliers that has brought 1,750 tons of coal direct by water from the Tyne. How it passed under sixteen road and railway bridges seems a bit of a mystery until we learn that its funnel " dips," and that the ship is designed specially for up-river work.

On the wharf are three large cranes, each carrying what is called a grab. This has two great jaws which, when closed together, form a large semicircular bucket. One of them is being lowered into the hold with its jaws spread wide open. It settles on the coal below, and as it is raised bites deeply into it till its jaws meet. Then up it comes with 4 tons of " run of mine " coal; that is, un-screened coal of all sizes, from good-sized lumps to dust. The crane swings it round over a great concrete hopper, and opens it. Back it goes again for another dip. Between them the three grabs will unload the ship in five hours. Pretty quick work this—and quick work is needed, since the station always demands 1,500 tons of coal a day.

Through the bottom of the hoppers, which hold 2,000 tons, the coal falls on to an endless rubber belt, 30 inches wide, which runs over sets of rollers placed a few feet apart. The rollers give the belt a trough shape, and this prevents the coal spilling.

Carried by Belt

The belt rises on an inclined framework to a height of 20 feet or so above the ground, and passes the coal on to another belt, from which it is transferred to another and another till it reaches a crushing station, where it goes through machinery that breaks up all the large lumps. Thence it is carried by belts to storage hoppers at the top of the retort houses. Before reaching the breaking station, by the way, it travels over a yard, where any not needed for immediate use can be thrown off on to a great long pile. This pile has a railway track on either side of it for a travelling crane and grab, which transfers coal from it to two other parallel piles, or trims the piles as needed, or picks up coal from the piles and puts it on to the belts again.

The storage piles are a very important feature of the works, for in them can be collected up to 40,000 tons of coal as a reserve. One notices many iron bars and pipes sticking out of the piles. They go right through them, and warm up if the coal becomes hot underneath. Thermometers can be let down inside the pipes to find out what temperature is registered.

Where the Gas is Made

We presently find ourselves in one of the four retort houses in which gas is driven out of the coal by heat. This one has horizontal retorts. Imagine a very large chamber with a block which is 20 feet thick, and as many high, running down the middle of it.

On each side of this mass of brickwork are five tiers of iron doors, shaped like a D turned flat side downwards, forty in a tier—200 in all. The doors are the ends of retorts, which are ovens of silica brick built through the thickness of the block. The retorts are grouped in sets of ten— five pairs one above the other.

Under each set is a furnace of coke, through which air is drawn to form a combustible gas. This burns as it passes up and down on each side of the retorts, raising them to a temperature thirteen and a half times that of boiling water. After doing their duty in heating the retorts the gases are carried away through huge pipes to boilers, where steam is raised for generating electricity and other purposes. The use of the waste heat in this way means a saving of thousands of tons of fuel every year.

On one side of the wall are rails for a great machine which does the double duty of pushing the coke out of a retort that has been " cooking " its charge for twelve hours, and putting in a fresh charge of 13 hundredweight of coal. A retort door is opened and flames pour out for a moment. Then the machine comes opposite to it. Inside the machine is a great eight-sided drum with a jointed rammer lapped round it. The drum revolves, and the rammer is forced into the retort. Meanwhile, its trough-like links receive coal from a bin in the machine fed from overhead hoppers and carry it into the retort. Presently the rammer is withdrawn and wound up again on the drum.

" Drawing " the Retorts

We now go through one of the tunnels in the wall to watch the effect of the operation from the other side when the next retort is " drawn." The heat drives us back as a torrent of red-hot coke issues from an open door and falls

DRYING THE GAS

This plant removes most of the moisture from the gas by means of a concentrated solution of calcium which flows down a packed tower. The gas streams upwards through the packing, and the moisture is absorbed by the solution. The diluted liquor is reconcentrated on another part of the works and used again. This photograph was taken at the Southall works of the North Thames Gas Board.

North Thames Gas Board.

COOLING THE GAS

The hot gas from the retorts is sent through condensers, which chill it and make it part with most of the tar that it carries. This picture shows a group of condensers, containing many pipes through which cold water circulates. During its passage among the pipes the gas gives up much of its heat to the water.

on to a conveyor running at floor level along the front of the wall.

The retorts are drawn in rotation, a " round " being made in twelve hours. So there is a steady supply of gas coming away from year's end to year's end. Before troubling ourselves about what becomes of the gas after it leaves the retorts we inspect another building in which the retorts are upright. The advantage of this kind of retort is that it takes up less floor space and works continuously, coal being fed in at the top at short intervals and drawn off steadily at the bottom. Also, the coke is delivered cold instead of in a red-hot condition.

An electric lift takes us to the top of a vertical retort house, from which we get a very fine view of London for many miles round. After admiring this we turn our eyes indoors to a belt conveyor which is feeding a number of hoppers. The bottom of each hopper slopes in all directions towards four outlets, through which coal is drawn off for two retorts below.

On the Charging Floor

Descending a staircase, we find ourselves on the charging floor, below the hoppers. Our feet are now level with the tops of the retorts. By moving a lever, coal is let into a box, from which it can be released into the retort under it without admitting air.

Our guide selects a retort not in use, and lifts a cover. We peer down into a shaft nearly 27 feet deep, and measuring 100 inches by 10 inches at the top. The last two dimensions increase gradually downwards to 104 and 18 inches at the base, in order that the coal may not jam as it is coked during its descent.

There are seventy-two of these re-

North Thames Gas Board.

A LABYRINTH OF PIPES

This is an atmospheric condenser. In this case the gas has to travel from one of the great cross-pipes to the other through the many zig-zags of smaller pipes connecting them, which are cooled outside by the air. You will see that all the pipes of a zig-zag slope gently downwards, so that condensed tar or water shall drain out of them.

torts, and they can deal with about 650 tons of coal, yielding 10,000,000 cubic feet of gas, in twenty-four hours. The retorts are heated by flaming gas rising between them and an outer jacket of brickwork. Now we go downstairs to the discharging floor. Here we see hoppers in which the exhausted coke is caught. The movement of a lever empties some of the coke on to a conveyor belt, which takes it out of the retort house.

Gas from Coke, Water and Oil

" I must now show you our water-gas plant," says the obliging guide. So we pass on to another building in which air and steam are blown alternately through glowing coke. The heat separates the hydrogen from the oxygen of the steam, and this oxygen combines with the carbon of the coke.

In this manner a mixture of two com-bustible gases—hydrogen and carbon monoxide—comes away. This is " enriched," that is, made of greater heating value, by being mixed in a chamber, named a carburetter, with the vapour of a heavy oil obtained from petroleum. This water-gas plant, we are told, can convert 70 tons of coke and 5,000 gallons of oil daily into 4,000,000 cubic feet of gas, and is very useful for meeting any sudden demand on the works. Plant of a capacity of 6 million cubic feet per day has been added and the sequence of valve changes formerly carried out by hand is now arranged automatically by a mechanical operator. In the same way the heavy work of clinker removal has been eliminated by continuous extraction through a rotary grate. The water-gas, it should be added, is mixed in due proportion with the ordinary coal gas before reaching the gasholders.

Cleaning the Gas

The gas would not leave the retorts and travel through pipes of itself, so it is sucked out by engines called exhausters in another part of the works. These draw it through water in a trough called a hydraulic main, in which much of the tar it contains is deposited, and through a condenser which cools it. The condenser is a number of great zig-zags of pipes in the open air. As it flows through these the gas gives up most of the rest of its tar, which trickles down the pipes and is collected.

It is then *pushed* by the exhausters through another condenser, and an apparatus which dissolves the ammonia gas in it in water, and at the next stage it is entirely freed of tar. Then it passes to another plant in which it meets oxide of iron spread on trays, and has the sulphuretted hydrogen taken out.

The liquid containing the ammonia—called ammoniacal liquor—is sent to the Beckton works, where it is used in making sulphate of ammonia, while the oxide of iron, loaded with the sulphur it has picked up, is employed in the manufacture of sulphuric acid.

The now purified gas has a final washing in oil to remove any naphthalene, and goes through meters which can measure 1,650,000 cubic feet an hour between them, to one or other of six great gasholders.

All the coal gas may be passed through lofty towers down which oil is trickled and this dissolves from the gas the benzole and the toluol vapours. This oil at the base of the towers is sent to a still where the benzole, etc., is distilled off.

Like Great Cakes

Gasholders are prominent features of any gas-works. The container, which may be likened in shape to a huge nicely-risen cake, is a framework covered by iron plates $\frac{1}{8}$ inch thick. At the bottom it is open, and dips into a water-tight tank rather larger than itself.

The gas enters through a pipe rising in the centre of the tank and by its buoyancy raises the great weight of the container, which, when fully lifted, is still deep enough in the water to prevent the gas escaping under its bottom edge. The container is in some cases kept steady by wheels running on guides on cast-iron columns surrounding the gasholder and braced together; but in others steadiness is given by spiral rails on the outside of the container engaging with guides in the

North Thames Gas Board.

MEASURING THE HEAT UNITS

Nowadays gas is sold mainly for heating purposes, and its price depends on its efficiency as a fuel. Consumption is recorded by meters, but the customer pays for the number of "heat units" in the gas consumed. At the works the heating value of the gas supplied is accurately measured by these instruments in the calorimeter room.

tank. In the second instance the container revolves as it rises.

Then, again, very large gas-holders are made in two, three, four, five and even six storeys or lifts, telescoping into one another. Only the uppermost one has a top to it. The sides of the others are like a very narrow N in section. Two of the legs form a narrow trough for the lift above, and the third leg dips into the trough of the lift below it.

The centre lift rises first, and when it is fully up it begins to raise the next lift, and so on.

The pressure put on the gas by the weight of the gasholder is usually sufficient to drive the gas through the mains supplying the district.

Now that certain additions to the Fulham plant have been completed, it is able to make 35,000,000 or more cubic feet of gas daily, when working at full capacity.

We must not overlook the coke, which is a very important item in the output of a gas-works, since from every ton of coal used between 14 and 15 hundred-weight of coke is produced. Of this, 10 to 11 hundredweight is sold to the public for use in boilers, stoves, forges and open fires. The rest is needed for heating the retorts, making water-gas, raising steam in boilers, and other purposes in the works.

From Benzole and Tar

As already mentioned in the chapter on "What We Owe To Coal" the list of products derived from coal carbonisation as carried out at our gas-works is seemingly endless, and the discoveries made in this direction in recent years are amazing. Continual research and experiment goes on and further advances are certain.

North Thames Gas Board.

A WATERLESS GASHOLDER

This many-sided steel structure is 180 feet high. It is in effect a gigantic cylinder, containing a closely-fitting piston which is forced upwards by gas entering at the bottom.

Every ton of coal yields about 3 gallons of benzole. This benzole is treated by the chemist and separated into its constituents: benzene, toluene, xylene, etc. The separation is done by distillation which simply means boiling and then cooling, but at different temperatures, since each constituent is given off at a different boiling-point.

On page 21 you will find a diagram which shows some of the different substances which are obtained from coal while it is being carbonised to produce gas. From these substances in turn is produced a long list of valuable things we use in everyday life.

While some of the tar, for instance, is used on our roads, some of it is distilled and different kinds of oil are obtained. From these tar oils the chemists obtain the dyes which have built up another big industry in this country. Antiseptics and disinfectants as well as creosote are produced also.

It is from these oils, too, that the valuable drugs known as sulphonamides are derived. Through experiments with these drugs M & B 693 was evolved, and, as a result, many thousands of lives have been saved. Medical authorities calculated that in 1942, one of the first years in which it was used on a reasonably large scale, " the lives saved by the sulphonamides ran well into five figures."

Another fairly recent discovery due to experiments with benzole was D.D.T., the insecticide which has proved such a tremendous help in fighting malaria, bushfever, typhus and other insect-borne diseases in tropical climates as well as in the struggle to conquer the insects which work havoc among our crops. D.D.T. is the most potent single insecticide ever discovered.

Perfumes and Plastics

It is extraordinary to reflect that benzole, the by-product of the gas-works, is to-day an essential of the perfume and cosmetic industry. Until about sixty years ago the perfume-maker depended entirely on substances of vegetable or animal origin for his raw materials. To-day he is supplied by the gas-works with all that he needs and can produce a far greater variety of exotic perfumes than ever before.

Plastics, too, are largely indebted for their very great development to the usefulness of phenol, derived from coal-tar, and styrene which is chemically produced from benzole. These styrene resins are proving particularly valuable in the electrical industry. From phenol, by other chemical means, nylon is produced and from this new material stockings and parachutes, toothbrushes and aeroplane tyres are now being manufactured.

Modern aviation owes a great deal to benzole. The high octane fuels which are essential for the high speeds now attained are due to cumene, which is derived from phenol. During 1940–45, millions of pounds' worth of benzole products were sent to America for use in the manufacture of high octane aviation fuel. Even in the ordinary motor fuel benzole is used as a blending agent to increase the efficiency of the oil.

Large amounts of sulphur are recovered during the process of purifying the gas, and sulphuric acid is an important raw material of industry. At least 100,000 tons of sulphur are recovered by the gas-works each year, and 95,000 tons are used to make sulphuric acid.

Fertilisers from Coal

Ammonia, too, is one of the products obtained during the carbonisation of coal to make gas. Farmers and gardeners know sulphate of ammonia in these days as a highly important fertiliser. Its use on land newly ploughed or dug for cultivation is especially useful in ensuring good crops. Some 260,000 tons of sulphate of ammonia are produced annually by the gas industry, and this is no more than is needed to meet the growing demand from the country's agricultural industry.

Beginning of a Big Industry

We have mentioned a few of the products of our age which come to us from coal by way of the gas-works. To go back for a moment to the story of William Murdoch and the lamp he made to light him on his way, as told in earlier pages, it will be seen that the history of the gas industry comes into the category of real-life romances. First, coal was burned to produce coke and the gas went off as the smoke still does from our open fires. Then Murdoch discovered the use of gas and may be regarded as the real inventor of gas-lighting.

Instead of coke alone being the main

A CARBURETTED WATER=GAS PLANT

North Thames Gas Board.

Gas suitable for mingling with coal gas is made in the apparatus seen in this illustration. Waste gases from the furnaces of the retort house are used to raise steam in the boiler on the left. The steam, mixed with air, is blown through glowing coke, and water-gas is formed. This is enriched, that is, given greater heating value, by having added to it, in one of the other chambers, called a carburetter, the vapour of a heavy oil. A water-gas plant is very useful in a gas-works for enlarging output quickly to meet a sudden increase in demand.

product of coal-burning it became only a by-product and the gas itself took first place. A big industry was built up and the very name of the Gas Light and Coke Company tells its own story. Then the gas-light was threatened with extinction by the advent of electric light. Gas held its own and even led the way for a brief time, but the new electric light eventually gained the victory so far as the battle of lighting was concerned. By that time, however, other virtues had been discovered in coal and, instead of dying, the gas industry became the pioneer again in the treatment of coal. As a member of the Government put it not so long ago:

"The gas industry has passed through a very complicated history from the time when it produced only light to the present time when it produces fuel, benzole, tar, sulphuric acid, and so forth. Even if it is an old industry it is not very old as we judge things in these days, but I would prefer to regard it as a young industry in the sense that it is just entering on a new sphere of activity. Some of the possibilities that lie before it are only beginning to be seen."

Coal has been a great factor in Britain's prosperity in the past, and to-day every branch of chemical industry looks to coal to supply it with many of its raw materials. Dyestuffs and chemicals, plastics, synthetic rubber, soaps, lubricants, all need the by-products from the carbonisation of coal which produces the gas now becoming increasingly important to industry as a refined fuel capable of exact control.

Gas in Industry

That is the field in which the gas engineers are concentrating their energies to-day: there are gas-burners capable of giving a small pin-point of flame for the jeweller's or glass-maker's art up to those producing large-volume flame or highly-concentrated heat treatment for the steel industry. Gas-fired radiant heat installations are being used for stoving and enamelling. The use of gas-fired kilns and furnaces in such industries as pottery and glass manufacture, as well as in the metal trades, is rapidly increasing. All this means an economy in the use of coal and more exact control of the heating or firing process, while the smoke nuisance will ultimately cease to exist.

Our life as an industrial nation depends upon keeping up supplies of energy and of raw materials for our great manufacturing processes. Owing to our climate we have to use big quantities of fuel to keep our homes and offices, our factories and public buildings, warm and comfortable. But because of the value of all the chemicals in coal, it is obvious we must ensure that its valuable properties are not wasted and coal as a fuel must be used in the most economical way possible.

It will probably mean the gradual disappearance of our old open fires, in which coal is burnt wastefully without any of its valuable by-products being recovered. Gradually, too, gas-fired furnaces are replacing those in which coal is consumed. Only the gas from the coal will be used and other industries will benefit by receiving the raw materials which they require.

At present the gas-works produce 25,000,000 gallons of benzole each year and every gallon is of value in other industries. Nearly $1\frac{1}{2}$ million tons of tar is produced yearly, and tar has been described as the chemist's treasure house.

As the diagram on the following page will show, the chemist can produce from Coal-Tar the essential raw materials for hundreds of different manufactured goods. Coal has become more valuable than gold, and it is through the gas-works and the research

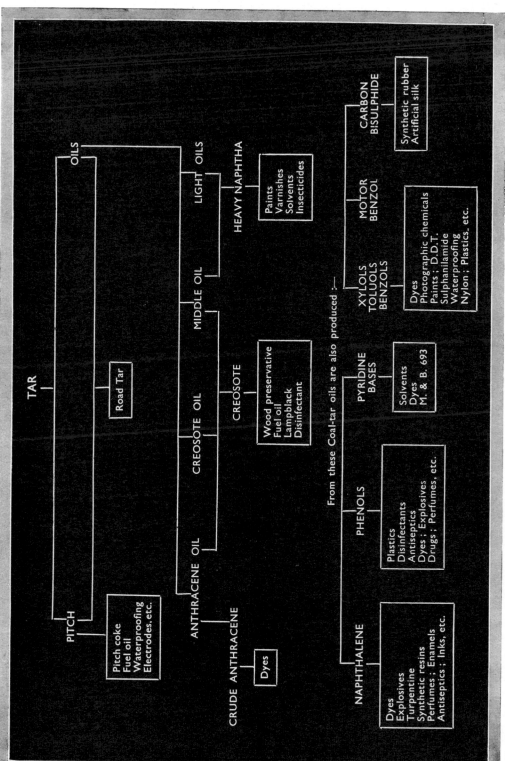

During the process of gas-making by coal-carbonisation at the gas-works 10 gallons of Tar are produced from each ton of coal. Our diagram shows some of the products in which the chemist makes use of the oils derived from this coal-tar.

chemist that all the treasures coal contains are now being revealed.

Extending the Grid System

Since the gas industry was nationalised, one of the biggest advances has been in the connecting up of supplies by means of a grid system. In the London area, and in certain other industrial districts, there was already a considerable amount of interconnection, enabling supplies from any of a number of works to be sent through the same mains. Now the whole of the area of the North Thames Gas Board has been linked in this way from Southend to Maidenhead, and large schemes are being developed in South Wales and Scotland, in the Lancashire-Cheshire area, the East Midlands and West Yorkshire.

As a result of these grid systems it is possible to cease production at many of the small isolated gas-works, which cannot be operated as economically as larger works, and to provide gas in areas previously without supplies. The grid system also ensures that exceptional local demands are met without throwing an undue load upon a single works.

This grid system is the latest development in the history of the gas industry, which began when William Murdoch lighted up his house and offices in Redruth, Cornwall, with gas. Ten years later the first public exhibition was held at Boulton & Watts' works, and enquiries began to come in from business men. The first to use gas apparatus made by Murdoch was a Manchester cotton spinner, Mr. George Lee. It was such a success that in 1807 what was probably the largest factory of its kind in the country installed Murdoch's gas-making apparatus.

That was the beginning; to-day, this great industry is of more importance and can contribute more to the common good than at any time in its long history, extending back over a century and a half.

North Thames Gas Board.

LAYING A MAIN

To supply gas to nearly twelve million consumers the gas industry uses 78,138 miles of mains, and new mains, as seen in this picture, are always being laid.

TESTING THE PRESSURE

The correct pressure of gas, steadily maintained at the same level, is highly important. Here we see a Gas Board official testing the pressure in a 24-inch main.

THE BUSINESS OF THE G.P.O.

BRINGING THE MORNING LETTERS

Every workaday morning, for every house in the land, a postman is available for the delivery of letters. The mail he carries may have come from any corner of the world and been carried by air, sea and land, yet it reaches its destination in the shortest possible time. In its inland business alone, our G.P.O. deals with twenty millions of letters and circulars every week-day.

LOOKING back through the centuries to the days of Imperial Rome we should find along the main roads that linked the capital with the provinces a series of posts, which might have been of wood, metal or stone.

At each of these stations there was always on duty a team of messengers, one of whom would run with a letter in either direction from his post to the next, when another courier took the missive and carried it on its way. If these men were called postmen, because during their hours of service they were to be found near a post, it would not be surprising, though there is no proof that such was the case.

Much nearer to the times in which we live and in our own country, before the coming of railways, swift dependable horses were kept at certain posts or places along a highway so that people could change steeds and thus travel without having to make a break in the journey whilst their hard-ridden animals were rested. Presently letters came to be dealt with at these posts and the name post office originated. If you journeyed from one point to another as fast as you possibly could you were said to be travelling post, or post haste. Riders entrusted with the mails invariably travelled post and so we have discovered two explanations of how the word post came to be used.

So far as the transport of letters is concerned, the work in remote times was in the hands of private messengers, and then there were people who for brief periods possessed the exclusive right of handling mails, a system that was soon found to be unsatisfactory. Thus it became necessary for the Government to have the sole authority to carry mails, to be granted the monopoly to the exclusion of individuals; and so, in 1657, the General Post Office came into being under the direction of a postmaster-general. At first, the Royal Mail was invariably carried by mounted post-boys and then arrived the four-horsed mail coaches, the first of them providing a service between Bristol and London, which began in 1784.

After the Mail Coach Days

This was the forerunner of a veritable network of mail coaches, sometimes driven at an average speed of ten miles an hour. Years later the steam locomotive began to run on the so-called iron roads and mail coaches had perforce to give pride of place to mail trains.

The first experimental dispatch of mails by trains was made in 1830 between Liverpool and Manchester. Railways still carry the bulk of our letters

G.P.O.

FIRST STAGE IN THE JOURNEY

Having written a letter, you drop it into the nearest pillar box and it starts its journey at the next clearance, as is depicted above.

and parcels but motor transport is also largely used and the air services for overseas mails have grown into a huge business. More recently, the helicopter air service has been used to carry mails between places awkwardly situated for rail or road transport.

Since the early days the Post Office has gradually extended its scope of services far beyond the carrying of mails. " Money letters " began in a small way as long ago as 1792 and eventually the Money Order department was established in 1838. It was not until 1881 that the highly popular Postal Order was introduced and rapidly became a big success. Telegrams were at first dealt with by private companies but about 1870 the Post Office took them over, just as eventually the telephone system was taken over, though it was not until 1912 that the Post Office became solely responsible.

So this huge business has steadily expanded through the years. Until 1840 the cost of sending a letter depended on the distance it had to travel. The charge for a letter from London to Edinburgh, for instance, was 1s. 3½d., and the amount was collected on delivery. Then, after a struggle, Sir Rowland Hill introduced his great scheme for penny postage throughout the kingdom, and soon afterwards the adhesive stamp as we know it to-day was introduced. Letter-writing increased enormously and in these days the Post Office sells 7,000,000,000 (seven thousand millions) of postage stamps in the course of twelve months and deals in its inland business with 20,000,000 letters and circulars and 650,000 parcels every working day, not counting the many other millions sent to places abroad.

How Your Letter is Handled

To turn from such breath-taking figures, let us imagine you have written a letter, placed it in its addressed envelope, affixed a stamp and dropped it into a convenient pillar box. If you

WHERE NIMBLE FINGERS SORT THE MAIL

The photograph above was taken in a Travelling Post Office van of one of the special trains from London. It shows the staff sorting letters and packages into their proper pigeon-holes. Bags of mail are taken aboard or dropped to the lineside by apparatus whilst the express travels at full speed.

Photos: G.P.O.

That letter you dropped into a pillar box has here reached the nearest sorting office. With other letters, it has been put up in a group, the addresses all facing the same way. The postage stamps have then been cancelled by a wonderful machine, and here we see deft workers sorting into frames each of which has 48 spaces.

have no stamp it is more than likely you can purchase one from an automatic machine attached to the familiar red box. You notice, as you leave, a printed time-table showing the daily clearances, whilst a little tablet in a slot informs you of the number or time of the next collection.

Presently, the postman who is responsible for the particular route comes along, possibly on foot, perhaps on a bicycle or maybe in a small motor van. With a special key he opens the box and sweeps your letter with all the others there may be into his bag, proceeding on his journey from box to box until eventually he reaches what is called a sorting office, usually in a busy centre and within easy reach of the railway station.

What happens to your letter now? First of all, the collecting bags as brought in by postmen are emptied in heaps on long tables so that they can be " faced," which means simply that

Post Office.
A POSTMAN OF THE FENS
Not all postmen can stick to the highway. The one seen above works in the Fenlands and has the help of a boat as well as a bicycle for his round of duty.

they are put up into neat, orderly groups with the addresses facing the same way.

This step is taken so that all the envelopes and cards of normal size can be passed through machines which cancel the stamps with indelible postmarks. Some of these machines are capable of dealing with 600 or more items a minute. Envelopes on which the stamps are placed too low down, too far to the left or on the back, cannot be dealt with by the machine and have to be set aside in order that their stamps may be cancelled by hand. So, if you do not take the trouble to put the stamp in its proper position you have only yourself to blame should your letter be delayed.

Once all the postage stamps have been cancelled the letters or packets must now be sorted according to their destinations. For this purpose, each of the sorters stationed at a long bench has in front of him a fitting which contains 48 pigeon-holes into which he sorts the correspondence. When a pigeon-hole has been filled he takes out the contents, ties them into a bundle and drops it into the appropriate bag. You will say, of course, that letters have to go to far more than 48 places and that is true enough, but what is called primary sorting divides correspondence into sections for large cities and towns, and counties or groups of counties, which have to be sorted again. Thus, you ought never to omit the county whenever you address an envelope, unless your letter is going to one of the largest cities. Further, London, Edinburgh, and most of our biggest places are now divided into numbered postal districts and such a number ought always to be given because it helps the sorting staff and prevents delay.

The Distributing Office

In due time, when the mail as collected has been transferred from the boxes in the sorting " fitting " to the

Post Office.

ALL PART OF HIS DAILY ROUND

In order to deliver letters to out-of-the-way places, the Post Office has various methods of transport, some of which are not lacking in novelty. In the above picture the postman is seen just after crossing the River Findhorn at Nairn in Scotland. The one-man power transporter bridge has just come to rest on its platform after the crossing.

appropriate bags, it is dispatched by road and rail, and then the bags find their way as quickly as possible to what is known as a distributing office, of which there is at least one in every large district. Here there is more detailed sorting, and bags are made up for all the places in the district, whether they are large towns, or small isolated villages.

Finally, there is the postman who delivers your letter in the area which he serves, the route most carefully arranged to save delay and known as the official's " walk." He takes his letters from the sorting boxes and arranges them according to the streets he has to traverse, tying them in convenient bundles for the purpose. Many postmen leave distributing offices by six in the morning and it is by no means uncommon for the first delivery of the day to be in full swing by seven o'clock.

When one considers that many of these letters were posted only the previous evening, perhaps hundreds of miles away, how is the miracle of such swift and efficient transport to be explained? It may well be, in the near future, that aeroplanes will shoulder some of the burden of the inland night mail, but at present most of the correspondence is carried by passenger train. In the case of at least forty-three railway expresses, special postal carriages are attached and the sorting of letters in these carriages goes on all through the journey. These postal carriages are called T.P.O.s (Travelling Post Offices).

What may be termed the main arteries of the night mail system are two trains which run between London and Aberdeen. These twin services are wonderfully organised entirely for postal purposes, except that passenger coaches are attached between Perth and Aberdeen in both directions.

Post Office.

THE LINE-SIDE APPARATUS

From special postal trains and from many expresses mails are dropped and picked up at great speed with the help of this ingenious apparatus at the side of the line.

The train long known as the Down Special T.P.O. leaves the L.M.S. London terminus of Euston every evening throughout the year, with the exception of Christmas Day and Boxing Day. It is always drawn by one of the heaviest and most powerful engines and consists of at least six postal coaches and as many again of ordinary brake vans—a dozen long vehicles in all. The guard is the only railway official who travels on the train, everyone else being a Post Office worker. Thus, the crew comprises a supervisor, who is in charge of the whole staff, and over forty sorters and two postmen to work the mail changing apparatus.

Actually, this apparatus is perhaps the most striking feature of the train. Outside the six letter vans, flat against the panelled sides, are two powerful electric binnacle lamps which serve to illuminate white boards set up as lineside markers. At speed and when

rounding a curve the lights give a snakelike appearance to the train. There are only a few stops on the long journey but at a number of points bags of mail are discharged from the train and others picked up.

If you can imagine the Down Special approaching one of these points, a postman will be standing at the open door of a coach with only an iron bar between him and the trackside, which is being left behind at the rate of a mile a minute or more. Like all the travelling staff, he knows every inch of the line whether the night be clear or foggy.

Presently, he detects a white board close beside the line and this serves as his signal. Immediately he fixes his pouches on to the dispatching arms of the apparatus; and, a moment later, pushes down a lever to open his receiving net. A bell then rings to warn the staff to keep clear of the door.

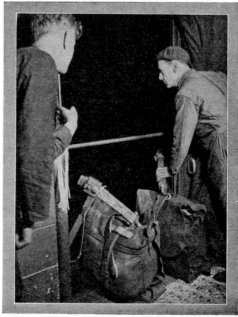

Fox Photos.

AWAITING THE MOMENT

Here we see the men standing by with the mail bags all ready to be ejected from the train and received by the net on the ground at the side of the railway.

SAFELY COLLECTED

The receiving net has caught the bag suspended from the rail-side apparatus and the photographer has snapped it at the moment when the mail-bag is falling safely inside.

Dispatching and Receiving Mails

It should now be explained that at the side of the railway is an apparatus corresponding with that on the train. Rising from the ground is a tall standard, with its top arched over like a gallows, from which a pouch containing bags of mail is suspended.

As the train sweeps by this pouch is caught in a capacious net so shaped that the load it catches is thrown through the open door of the passing coach, where it falls thuddingly upon an immensely thick mat. On the train is a dispatching arm much like the gallows; and, on the ground, a net is set to catch the pouch. In this way, by spacing out gallows and net at appropriate distances at the line-side, the exchange of pouches is made automatically, the dispatching arms swinging back into the resting position whilst the net is brought flat against the train merely by the movement of a lever. And, on the railways of this country, there are no fewer than 97 of these apparatus points.

In this magic handling of mails, there may be two, three, four or more of the familiar canvas bags. How many there are does not matter as long as the total weight does not exceed 60 lbs. for dispatches from T.P.O.s or 50 lbs. for dispatches to T.P.O.s. Each mail bag is secured with a leaden seal and the whole consignment then placed in a pouch of enormously thick hide, kept pliant and waterproof by frequent oiling. The pouch itself weighs 20 lbs. and one is not surprised at the reverberating thud with which it is thrown into a carriage on a train travelling perhaps at seventy miles an hour.

To begin with, the Down Special T.P.O. is well loaded with mails which reach it from most of the postal dispatching offices and railway termini in London. Loading begins an hour

GOOD-BYE TO THE T.P.O.

The Special T.P.O. has reached one of the big stations and the mail-bags, sorted and made up for different districts in this area, are being collected from the coaches.

before the train's departure, the bags to be sorted first being placed in the most convenient parts, with those for later sorting behind them. Bags of mail already sorted for particular destinations go mostly into the brake vans and there is on the train a posting box in which you can drop your own letter for a ½d. Late Fee.

Inside the long train as it thunders through the night the postmen are kept busy all the while, preparing for dispatch mail bags that are ready and taking to the sorters bags that have been picked up on the journey. As for the sorters, they are constantly at work, for some thousand bags must be handled between the Metropolis and the far north. There are no windows on this train except for those in the carriage doors, for the walls of the coaches on one side have sorting frames each made up of 54 pigeon-holes, the upper ones having glass bottoms so that no precious letter may be left behind because it has not been seen by the sorter.

There are no names of places on these pigeon-holes but merely numbers, and each sorter knows his own plan so thoroughly that the numbers are sufficient. On the other side of the carriage are many hooks from each of which is suspended a labelled bag. Thus, as bundles are sorted, they are dropped into their proper bags.

The Registered Mail

In one section of each coach, under a senior officer, the registered mail receives attention. In other sections, long large envelopes, packets, newspapers and anything unsuitable for the pigeon-holes are sorted from zinc-lined troughs not unlike kitchen sinks into special sorting frames with larger apertures than those provided for ordinary letters. There is no sorting of parcels on this train, but at least one of the brake vans is devoted to the needs of the Parcel Post. It is hard work sorting on a T.P.O., but

the staff responds loyally to whatever pressure is imposed upon it.

Crewe is the hub of our inland postal wheel. The Up and Down Specials between London and Scotland both stop there, though for only a few minutes. Between 11 p.m. and 2 a.m. no fewer than nine T.P.O.s attached to passenger expresses stop at this vast junction. Here mail services from Ireland, East Anglia, the west and north of England and of course Wales, dovetail into one another, together with postal traffic from London and the south. No wonder there is a depot at Crewe, where spare parts of every kind for the instant repair of mail-changing apparatus are kept to meet any emergency. Two other special P.O. trains are those which run nightly in each direction between Paddington and Penzance.

A P.O. Underground Railway

As far as London goes, the chief sorting office of the Inland Section is at Mount Pleasant, and some twenty millions of letters pass through this one centre every week. Here one finds mechanical conveyors of every kind to take correspondence from the stamp-cancelling machines to the various sorting and bagging positions, and it is interesting to know that the G.P.O. has in London its own underground railway, which naturally relieves the busy streets of still further congestion.

The line itself is upwards of six miles in length and connects Mount Pleasant and other sorting offices with several of the railway termini. Forty driverless electric trains run every hour in peak periods, some 80 feet beneath the capital's highways, and they normally carry 35,000 bags of mail a day. Further, the Post Office owns at least 21,500 motor vehicles, nearly 9,000 being used for the transport of mail alone, besides those hired from contractors and leaving out of account horse-drawn vehicles.

The efficient carrying of the Royal

A MAIL COACH OF 1832

Clarke and Hyde.

Couriers carried letters under an organised system even in the days of Ancient Rome; and in England there were posting houses in the reign of Edward I. We had our first regular inland post in 1635 and the G.P.O. was created in 1657. Yet, not much more than a hundred years ago, mails between London and Liverpool were carried by coaches, one of which is here depicted.

Post Office.

In this picture the sorters have paused for a moment to give the photographer an opportunity of recording the scene at London's chief Parcel Office at Mount Pleasant. It was taken at a time when the Christmas pressure had just begun and as soon as this collection had been cleared another would be ready for the sorting staff.

Post Office.

In this drawing the heights of some of the well-known high buildings and other erections in different parts of the world are compared with one of the Rugby Radio Masts. They are: 1, Empire State Building, New York, 1,248 feet. 2, Chrysler Building, New York, 1,100 feet. 3, Eiffel Tower, Paris, 985 feet. 4, Rugby Mast, 820 feet. 5, Woolworth Building, New York, 792 feet. 6, Cologne Cathedral, 515 feet. 7, Great Pyramid of Cheops, 450 feet. 8, St. Peter's, Rome, 448 feet. 9, Salisbury Cathedral, 404 feet. 10, St. Paul's Cathedral, 365 feet. 11, Forth Bridge, 361 feet.

LONDON'S SPECIAL POSTAL RAILWAY

In order to hasten its work the Post Office possesses its own tube railway far below the streets of London. The line runs between Whitechapel and Paddington, connects most of the important postal departments and deals with 35,000 bags of mail a day. The driverless trains are controlled by an official, as illustrated above, who operates a switchboard at Mount Pleasant.

Post Office.

Our picture affords you a glimpse of one of the underground stations on the P.O. railway and shows loading in progress. The trains run on narrow-gauge rails and attain a speed of 35 miles an hour. We should remember what a vast number of postal vans and lorries this tube railway keeps off the congested streets of Central London.

Mail is, as we know, but one part of the work of the G.P.O. Did you realise, for instance, that the British Post Office provides facilities for telephoning by submarine cable to most of the countries on the Continent of Europe and by radio-telephone to the United States of America, South Africa, Canada, Australia, India, and many other parts of the world, as well as to certain ships at sea?

The P.O. radio transmitting station at Rugby is one of the most powerful in the world, the station itself covering a site of 900 acres. The aerial is three-quarters of a mile in length, supported on four insulated steel masts each 820 feet in height. One must not forget, either, how the G.P.O. maintains a marvellous radio-telegraphic service, having no fewer than twelve wireless stations round our coasts. This service is of the utmost importance to ships at sea.

The G.P.O. is responsible also for well over three hundred submarine cables, over forty of them connecting Great Britain with the continent of Europe. Such cables connect Northern Ireland with Scotland and Scotland with many of its outlying islands; they also link up the Isle of Man, the Channel Islands and Eire with Great Britain.

Something like 345,000 men and women are employed by the G.P.O. and in this country there are about 25,000 Post Offices.

You go to a Post Office to buy a licence for your dog, gun, wireless or even for your car; to obtain a money or postal order; to transact business through your Savings Bank account or purchase National Savings stamps or certificates, to collect your pensions and allowances, or to buy Insurance stamps—and all this in addition to ordinary postal, telegraph and telephone business. Truly, the General Post Office is one of the most marvellous of all our public institutions.

Post Office.

AT RUGBY RADIO STATION

The Post Office radio transmitting station at Rugby is one of the most powerful in the world and provides radio communication with almost every part of the globe. The station itself occupies a site of 900 acres, and our photograph shows the main building with two of the four great steel masts, each of which is 820 feet in height.

HOW ELECTRICITY IS SUPPLIED

Fox Photos.

A MAZE OF CONDUCTORS

A view at one of the main power stations feeding the vast network of electric mains, called the "grid," which now covers a great part of the country. The steel lattice-work supports horizontal insulators, of great length, to which are anchored conductors designed to carry current at the enormous tension of 132,000 volts. The whole of the electricity supply industry in Great Britain is now controlled by the British Electricity Authority.

EARLIER in this volume we have read how long years ago scientists experimented with electricity and discovered the peculiar properties of the magnet. At that stage of course they had no practical value but when men such as Michael Faraday carried their experiments a few stages further it was realised that there were still great possibilities of a practical nature in these discoveries.

Two men, Joseph Wilson Swan in England and Thomas Alva Edison in America, share the credit for producing the first electric lamps suitable for use in homes and offices. There had been other lamps before this, however, and the Holmes arc lamp, driven by the Holmes machine, blazed out a beam with 1,000 candle-power from the South Foreland Lighthouse in 1858. It was not till 1878 and 1879 that Swan and Edison patented their new electric lamps.

There might have been trouble in the law courts between these two inventors but they settled their differences hap-pily and the Edison and Swan lamps, known later as Ediswan lamps, opened up a new era for indoor lighting. In other directions, too, progress was made in the use of electric power; machinery could be driven by electricity, and the steam engine and the gas engine had a serious rival. By the beginning of the present century the new source of power and illumination had begun to be fairly well used and it might be said that the Electric Age had dawned.

An Ever-Increasing Demand

Some idea of the growth of the public electricity supply in Great Britain can be gathered from the fact that in 1921 the total units supplied by public supply stations to consumers of electric current amounted to just over 3,000 million units. In 1950 nearly 45,000 million units were supplied; the demand for electric current had increased some fifteen times in the last thirty years. It is all within this period that wireless sets, vacuum cleaners, cookers, washing-machines, water-heaters and a host of other electric appliances had become articles of everyday use in thousands of British homes. Then, too, electric power was being used increasingly in steel-making and in many other industries.

It was all so easy; one just plugged in or touched the switch and the magic power did the rest. But this rapid development in the use of electric current created problems which the government had to tackle. In 1926 an Act of Parliament was passed to create a Central Electricity Board, and a National Grid system came into being around 1930. The object of this was to increase the amount of electric current available over the whole country and to enable it to be dis-tributed fairly and more economically.

Big new power stations were planned and schemes for the development of electric power from water were mapped out. How these hydro-electric schemes have come into operation is dealt with more fully in the section " Electric Power from Water " in Volume V.

Some sixty-five years after the supply of electricity to the public was first mentioned in an Act of Parliament, the Electricity Act of 1947 provided for full public ownership and operation of what had become a great and expanding industry. This Act came into force in 1948.

In a Power Station

The history of the current which

British Electricity Authority.

INSIDE THE TURBINE HOUSE AT BATTERSEA

The production of electricity on a large scale is based on a simple discovery made more than a century ago by Michael Faraday. This discovery led eventually to the building of our modern power stations in which turbines, driven by steam produced by coal-burning, drive large electric generators. In this photograph is seen the view inside the turbine house of " A " station at Battersea.

CONDENSING PLANT AT BATTERSEA

British Electricity Authority.

The pressure of the steam on the rotating blades of the turbines drives the wheels round at a high speed, usually either 1,500 or 3,000 revolutions per minute. By the time the steam has finished its task in the turbine its pressure and temperature have fallen and it is exhausted into the condenser, situated under the turbine, where it passes over numerous small tubes through which cold water is driven. The steam is thus condensed into water and pumped back into the boilers.

lights a lamp when you move a switch begins in a power station. In this country most electrical power is generated by steam obtained by burning coal in boiler furnaces. Water power is, however, being developed, especially in the North of Scotland, where water turbines drive electric generators and so enable more electric power to be fed into the Grid without using up more of our available coal.

A power station, as we know it here, is a great building, often found on the outskirts of a town, which gives out a loud humming noise, as of gigantic spinning-tops, from year's end to year's end. Close to it you may see great structures, somewhat like huge, squat chimneys.

These are cooling towers, used to chill water which has been heated by being circulated through condensers to change steam from the turbines back into water. If we could look inside a tower, we should see films of water trickling downwards over hundreds of thousands of wooden slats, and meeting a current of cold air rising through the tower. Many millions of gallons of water have to be used and cooled each day.

Some of these cooling towers are now fitted with eliminators which remove 95 per cent. of the vapour from the steam. In certain districts the clouds of steam from the cooling towers produced an artificial drizzle which could sometimes become a nuisance to people living in the near neighbourhood. The problem was studied by experts and new methods have been adopted which have already mitigated the trouble to a considerable extent.

The Boiler Room

Steam is raised by a battery of water-tube boilers. A boiler of this kind is made up largely of tubes, inside which is the water, and among which the furnace gases pass. In some stations one of these boilers may be as big as a

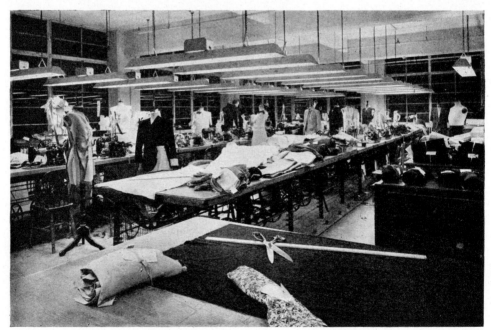

Morgan-Wells.

LIGHT AND POWER IN THE WORKROOM

When Thomas Hood wrote his *Song of the Shirt* he painted a grim picture of a garment-maker stitching with needle and thread by candlelight. In contrast to that non-electric age the photograph above shows a workroom where garments are made to-day with electrically-driven sewing machines and in the pleasant glare-free brightness of modern fluorescent lighting.

Metropolitan Vickers Electric Co., Ltd.

UNDERGOING A CHANGE

The high-tension alternating current generated in a power station must be changed into continuous current of much lower voltage to be suitable for use on our electric railways and tramways. This picture shows us three machines, called converters, used to bring about the change. They are, in effect, a combination of motor and generator. Alternating current makes them spin round, and their spinning produces continuous current.

good-sized house, and able to convert 200 or more tons of water into high-pressure steam every hour.

To give you some idea of what this means, let us explain that 200 tons of water would fill a trough a yard wide, a yard deep, and about 270 yards long. The coal for feeding the boilers is stored in great overhead bunkers, from which it passes down through chutes to mechanical stokers. These feed it into the furnaces at a steady rate. In some stations the coal is ground up into a very fine powder and blown into the furnaces in much the same way as oil fuel.

Among the Turbines

From the boiler-house we go into a huge chamber well lit through the roof. Ranged in orderly lines on its spacious floor are a number of steam turbines, each having its shaft connected to that of an electric generator. The turbines are entirely closed in, and the generator spins so fast that any visible moving parts are merely blurs.

There is very little to see here, as compared with the busy working of rods and cranks in the engine-room of a big steamer. But these quiet-looking and quiet-working turbines, on which one might stand a penny edgeways without it falling over, are doing great service. For every turbine-cum-generator unit may be converting anything up to 60,000 steam horse-power into electrical energy. One or more units may be standing idle, ready for starting up when the demand for current exceeds a certain limit, or to give one of the others a rest for overhaul or repairs.

Some distance from the turbine-room is the control-room, or switchboard room, containing panels which carry switch levers for controlling and directing the current, and instruments showing how much current is coming from each generator, what its pressure is, and so on. The switches themselves are, for safety's sake, housed in a separate building, and are operated from the panels by " distant control."

Through the Transformer

The current generated in the station is alternating; that is, it keeps changing its direction through the circuit many times a second.

Alternating current is used because, by means of a simple piece of apparatus, named a transformer, it can have its pressure increased and its volume lessened, or its pressure lowered while its volume is made greater. One may compare the process with changing copper coins into silver coins in the one case, and changing silver coins into copper coins in the other. The value remains unaltered in both instances.

As far as electrical power is concerned, it makes no difference whether one uses a lot of low-pressure current or a smaller amount of high-pressure current. But high-pressure current is transmitted with less loss than low-pressure current through long conductors, while low-pressure current is much safer to use. So the transformer plays a very important part in the distribution of electricity.

We will assume that current is generated at the power station at 6,000 volts, a volt being the unit of electrical pressure, corresponding to the pound per square inch of steam in a boiler.

Distributing Current

If we follow one of the conductors running from a power station it may lead us to a converting station in a " tube " or other electric railway. Here a motor and dynamo in one—a converter, it is called — changes the high-pressure alternating current into

Photopress.

MINIATURE LIGHTNING

This very interesting picture shows an electrical discharge taking place between an insulated ball and a plate on the ground. To cause the leap of only a few feet through the air an electrical tension of a million volts was needed. One of the difficulties associated with very high tension currents is that of preventing their escape from the conductors.

ELECTRICAL FIREWORKS

Fox Photos.

Another fine display of electrical energy breaking loose from its shackles. It is both streaming to earth in a cascade of fiery lines and leaping horizontally. You will note how closely some of the lines resemble lightning flashes, which are in fact the same phenomenon on a much larger scale, occurring between cloud and earth, or cloud and cloud.

METAL CHANNELS FOR ELECTRIC CURRENT

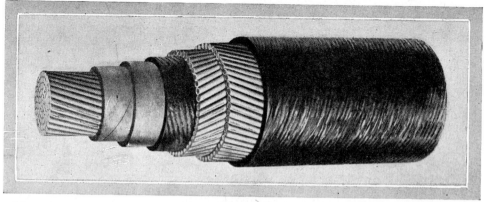

This is an end of an electric power cable, "stepped" to show construction. The central many-wire conductor is insulated by a wrapping of paper strip. Outside this is a sheath of lead to keep out damp: and then in succession come a layer of jute, two layers of armouring wire, and a wrapping of jute.

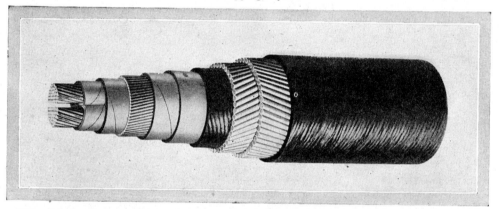

This cable has three conductors. Two, semicircular in section, are at the centre. Each has its own paper insulation, and the pair is further insulated by a wrapping enclosing both. Outside this wrapping are the wires of a third conductor, covered by paper, lead, jute, armouring, and more jute.

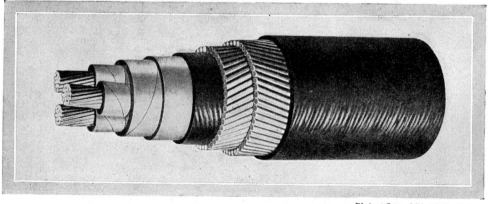

Photos: General Electric Co. Ltd.

In this three-conductor cable, designed to carry current at 11,000 volts tension, all the conductors are at the centre, insulated from each other and from the lead sheathing. The making of cables for the distribution of electrical power is now a very important industry.

HUGE ELECTRICAL SWITCHES

General Electric Co., Ltd.

These are three great steel tanks containing oil, in which are submerged switches for breaking circuits carrying current at 132,000 volts. The pressure and cooling effect of the oil prevent an electric arc forming between the parts of a switch as they are separated and destroying them. The gear for moving the switches is operated from the control board by means which prevent the high-tension current reaching the operator.

continuous current at, say, 600 volts pressure, for working trains or trams.

Some of the power station's output, again, may be wanted by a distant town. In this case the current goes from the generators to a transformer, and has its pressure increased to 11,000, 22,000, 33,000, 66,000, or even 132,000 volts before entering the conductors. On reaching the town it is "stepped down" say, to 3,000 volts at a transforming station, for distribution through the town.

The 3,000-volt high-pressure conductors or mains run from the transforming station about the town, and are connected here and there with transformers, housed in structures called kiosks, usually placed in open spaces at road junctions. A kiosk is 8 feet to 9 feet high, a yard or so in diameter, and entirely enclosed with iron plates. It is often used as a lamp-standard. In it the current is stepped down to, say, 415 volts, and passed on to low-pressure distributing mains running down neighbouring streets. In many places they pass through disconnecting boxes, which sometimes are contained in square iron casings, a yard or so high, standing on the pavement near the kerb. These disconnecting boxes make it easy to cut any part of the mains out of the circuit when work has to be done upon it.

The cables are lead-covered and armoured with steel tape, and are buried in the ground under the pavements. A cable contains three large conductors, with red, blue and white wrappings respectively, and a black-covered smaller conductor. There may be, and often is, a fifth conductor for special use as a switch wire for street lamps.

When a house is to be connected up with the electric supply system, the low-pressure cable closest to it is opened, and a small twin-conductor cable running to the house has one conductor joined to "black" in the main, and the other joined to "red" or "blue" or "white." This gives a pressure of, say, 240 volts. "Black's" partner is not chosen at random. A careful record is kept of all connections in a street, so that the total demand may be distributed as evenly as possible among the three "colours."

Somewhere in the street there may be a factory needing a large amount of power to

PUTTING AN ELECTRIC CABLE TO BED
Most power cables are simply buried in the earth, like water or gas mains. This picture shows us one being drawn by a large gang of workmen into a trench, the sides of which have been well shored with timber to prevent them falling in.

British Electricity Authority.

ONE OF LONDON'S ELECTRICITY SUPPLY STATIONS

Among the modern landmarks of London is the Battersea Power Station, with its fluted chimneys rising 300 feet above ground level. The building itself, 480 feet long, was designed by the distinguished architect, Sir Giles Gilbert Scott. Built in a populous area, it was important to avoid poisonous fumes, and the smoke passes through a filter plant which eliminates over 90 per cent. of the sulphur.

drive electric motors. In this case connection is made with " red " and " blue," " red " and " white," or " blue " and " white," " black " not being used. Between any of these two the pressure is 415 volts.

Electricity in the House

Now let us follow the branch cable to the house. After entering the house the conductors are joined to soft metal fuses which are designed to melt and break the circuit if the current should for any reason become dangerously great. Beyond these fuses—which the consumer cannot reach—is a meter for measuring the current; and beyond that a main switch which enables the supply to the house to be cut off.

Then comes a fuse or pair of fuses, which the householder can inspect and replace when necessary. Two wires connect these with what is called a distribution board, from which circuits branch out to various parts of the house. Each circuit is protected by its own fuse or pair of fuses, mounted on a board. From the two wires of a circuit two branch wires are thrown out to each lamp and its control switch.

We have now traced the distribution of electricity from the power station wherein current is generated to the points at which it is used.

Linking Up the Country

In the past the use of electrical power in Britain has been handicapped by the fact that power was supplied by a large number of quite independent companies, generating it at different pressures and at varying numbers of alternations per second. The result was that lamps, motors, and other electrical apparatus suitable for one district might be useless in another.

Imagine how difficult railway transport would be if each county had its

Central Press.

A THAMES-SIDE POWER STATION

One of the great new power stations which have been built in recent years is seen here. It is at Kingston-on-Thames, Surrey, and the first section was opened by King George VI in October, 1948. Its capacity is 123,000 kilowatts, and, despite its strictly utilitarian purposes, it has not been allowed to become a blot on the landscape.

own railway gauge, so that rolling stock in, say, Sussex, could not be used in Surrey or Essex, and it were impossible to move locomotives from one part of the country to another.

After the War of 1914–18 the question of bringing about a better state of things was taken in hand. Acts of Parliament were passed whereby all the 500 and more companies supplying power came under one great national scheme. A very large number of the old and less efficient stations were done away with, while some of the best were retained and their machinery was standardised to produce current at fifty cycles per second. Large new stations were built in various parts of the country and the supply of electric current steadily increased.

The demand increased also and after the Second World War of 1939–45 the supply was often inadequate for the huge amount of current required by industry and in the home. There were times, indeed, when the current in different areas had to be cut off altogether, but the building of new power stations is catching up with the demand, and power-cuts are much less frequent.

In order to carry the process of co-ordinating the supply of electricity to the whole country the Government decided to bring all the different undertakings under public ownership and from April 1st, 1948, the British Electricity Authority became responsible for the supply of electric current to the whole country. This national body, with its headquarters in London, is assisted by 14 Area Boards. There is a separate independent North of Scotland Board.

The big plans which were begun just before the World War had to be

AT CLIFF QUAY, IPSWICH

Another of our modern power stations in which the architect has nobly played his part is this station at Cliff Quay, Ipswich. Despite the great increase in the use of electricity the amount of coal used to produce the current is now only about one-quarter per unit compared with what it required 40 years ago, and further improvement in efficient production is being steadily achieved.

Photos: British Electricity Authority.

Here we are in the control room of the Power Station at Cliff Quay, Ipswich. It is in this room that action on load-shedding is taken when instructions are received from the Regional Grid Control Centre. The enormous increase in the use of electric current in recent years has imposed tremendous problems on those responsible for our supply of electricity.

MAN-HIGH INSULATORS

Fox Photos.

The huge insulators seen in this picture are needed to prevent the escape of high tension current to earth. Every such insulator has several " petticoat " storeys, each shaped to throw off water and keep dry on the under side. If the whole surface of an insulator were wetted, there would be serious leakage in rainy weather. The insulators are made of a special porcelain, glazed on the outside.

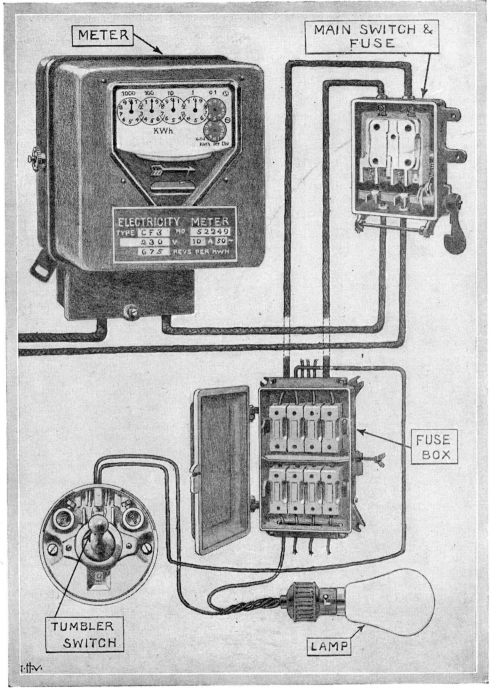

METER

MAIN SWITCH & FUSE

ELECTRICITY METER
TYPE CF3 Nº 52249
230 V 10 A 50~
675 REVS PER KWH

FUSE BOX

TUMBLER SWITCH

LAMP

Specially drawn for this work.

The current we use is first led through a meter which records, on dials, in " kilowatt-hours," the electricity consumed. Next comes a main switch (operated by the lever on the right) for breaking both sides of the circuit; and after this a pair of main fuses. At the fuse box the main circuit branches into as many sub-circuits, each guarded by its own pair of fuses, as may be needed. Every lamp on a sub-circuit is controlled by a tumbler switch.

suspended to some extent while hostilities were in progress, but work was resumed as soon as possible when peace came. The most interesting feature of this great scheme for linking up the power stations in one area with those in another is, from an engineering point of view, the main network of conductors named the " grid." This is made up of about 4,000 miles of " trunk " lines, corresponding with the arteries of the human body. A line has three conductors, each about ¾ inch thick, and made up of thirty bare aluminium wires twisted round a core of seven steel wires which give it the necessary strength. The conductors are carried on lattice steel towers, usually 70 feet

to 80 feet high, and set 900 feet apart, but larger ones are used also.

In some places, of course, the spans have to be much longer. At the crossing of the Forth, for example, a jump of over 3,000 feet is needed, and the conductors are supported by towers 358 feet high, to give plenty of room for ships to pass under them.

The electrical pressure in the grid is enormous—many hundreds of times greater than that used for ordinary electric lighting. So the conductors have to be kept well away from each other and from the steelwork of the towers. Between a conductor and the arm from which it hangs is a string of insulators, about 6 feet long, and the arms are so spaced that no conductor is within 12 feet of any other.

Some thirty-eight new power stations have been planned by the British Electricity Authority, and several are already in operation. In addition, a Supergrid employing an electrical pressure more than twice the original grid is now being constructed between Glasgow and London.

Besides the main grid there is a secondary network for distributing current, at half or a quarter of the pressure in the main grid, to centres where its pressure can be reduced.

Instead of having nearly 600 generating stations each supplying its immediate neighbourhood, we now have a comparatively small number of great power stations at work, each not only supplying its own neighbourhood, but able to contribute current to the grid arteries, to meet demands elsewhere.

British Electricity Authority.

" STEPPING-UP " THE VOLTAGE

By using high voltages on the national grid a great saving is effected. This photograph shows a transformer at a power station which raises the generator voltage from 11,000 to 132,000 volts to feed on to the transmission lines.

The World
and
Its Work

The Story
of Some
Great Industries

Shell.

AN OIL REFINING PLANT IN BRITAIN

Oil from Venezuela is brought to England in tankers, and in the photograph above is given a view of the Ester Salts Plant at Stanlow, in Cheshire. It stands on the Manchester Ship Canal. In the distance can be seen the Mexphalte Plant and the tanker discharge berths. The two Extraction Towers are on the left with the tank farm in the foreground.

THIS AGE OF OIL

PETROLEUM or rock oil has been known for thousands of years and the bitumen from it was used by the people of ancient Babylon to make mortar.

The Chinese knew something of the uses of oil more than 2,000 years ago and sank deep oil wells from which they obtained their supplies. But in the Western World the value of oil as a fuel was not generally recognised until about the middle of the 19th century.

To-day, oil is one of the most important of all our raw materials. Even in the most remote countries of the world the petrol-driven motor car has been seen and the jungles in tropical lands are being cleared by petrol-driven machines. The waters of the seas of the world are to-day being churned by the propellers of oil-driven ships while in the skies above, aeroplanes cover vast distances at amazing speeds owing to their petrol- or oil-driven engines.

Oil was discovered in boring for salt, and was considered a nuisance because it seeped into the salt wells and spoiled them. Then someone found that raw petroleum was a *lubricant;* that is, was good for oiling machinery. The result was that an oil-well was driven in the State of Pennsylvania, and oil was found at a depth of only 69 feet. This took place in 1859 and may be regarded as the first oil well to be sunk.

For Motor Car Engines

By degrees it was ascertained that

A STORE PARK AT A VENEZUELAN REFINERY

In comparatively recent years Venezuela has become one of the important oil-producing countries of the world and her oilfields are being rapidly developed. In this photograph is shown one of the store parks at a large Venezuelan refinery. Here are stored over £2,500,000 worth of different equipment and spare parts, most of which is bought in Britain by the company owning the concession.

the raw, sticky, ill-smelling stuff could be refined and used as lamp oil, and paraffin began to be burned in lamps. Its use increased until in 1905 the world was using some 215,000,000 barrels of oil yearly. Then the motor car boom set in. The "internal combusion" engine came into its own and the world went oil-mad.

The raw petroleum as it comes from the wells differs in quality according to the area in which it is found, just as coal differs in quality. Coal, we know, is the product of the forests of long cen-turies ago which have been buried be-neath the earth's surface until through long ages they have been turned into this particular and highly useful kind of rock we burn in our fires.

Just how oil came to be formed is not quite so clear. It is generally agreed, however, that it was formed during the course of millions of years from the large lakes which then existed. These lakes were gradually dried up as they be-came filled with decaying vegetation of all kinds. In some strange way all this dead material has been gradually changed during the long ages since it was buried beneath some great disturbance of the earth's surface, into a greenish-brown or rather darker liquid known as petroleum or rock oil.

As it is pumped from the earth this crude oil would be of no practical use in the high-powered engines of to-day. It has to be refined and treated by the chemist in various ways according to the kind of oil required, and, of course, according to the quality of the crude oil obtained in any particular area. " Refining " covers various kinds of treatment, but it is from the crude oil that the refiners obtain paraffin for lamps and stoves, petrol for the internal combustion engine, diesel oil for the big engines in ships as well as heavy lorries and 'buses, and lubricating oil for many purposes. Jet-propelled planes require their own special fuel, a heavier grade oil more like paraffin.

There is, too, the " high octane spirit " which is the outcome of the chemist's experiments to obtain a fuel most suitable for the wonderful engines designed for some of the high-speed aeroplanes. Without this high octane spirit the amazing speed attained by planes in recent years would be impossible.

In the early years of the oil age practically all the oil came from the United States or the shores of the Caspian, but then men began to bore for oil all over the world. Rumania, Trinidad, Persia, Venezuela, Canada and other countries were found to yield oil. Widespread districts were riddled with deep borings and gridironed with lines of steel pipes laid to carry the oil to the ports where it is pumped aboard " tankers." Great refining plants were built in which the crude oil is distilled. The petrol and benzine come away first;

Topical Press.

" ROUGHNECKS " WORKING AT THE DRILL

A great deal of hard and heavy work is necessary before the oil far below the earth's surface is reached. In this picture, taken during drilling operations in the Mene Grande, Venezuela, a team of heavy workers, known as " roughnecks," are seen in action. They are adding a new length of pipe as the drill penetrates to a greater depth.

OIL PIPES AT CURAÇAO

The largest island of the Dutch West Indies, Curaçao, lies forty miles north of the Venezuelan coast.
It has given its name to a well-known liqueur, but is known more to-day as a great oil distribution
centre. Here we see some of the loading-pipes which run from the tanks to the piers in the refinery
at Curaçao.

then, at a higher temperature, the
paraffin oil, followed by lubricating oils.

When a site is chosen for an oil-well a
tall derrick is erected and boring begins.
The boring tool is like a great chisel.
It is enormously heavy, as it is often
called upon to penetrate hard rock.
These bits vary greatly in size and shape
according to the type of sub-soil they
have to penetrate.

As the well is sunk metal casing is
driven down to keep the sides from
collapsing, and exclude water. This
casing is made up of sections which are

screwed on length after length. When
the friction becomes too great to allow
further driving, a smaller drill is used
to continue the hole, which is lined with
pipes fitting inside the first set.

Happily there are few dangers attached to drilling oil-wells nowadays.
Scientific aids of various kinds enable
drilling crews to be advised of any
trouble that may be expected, and,
when the conduct of affairs is in the
hands of an experienced oil company,
such events as a well getting out of
control and gushing forth a mighty jet

OIL FROM BELOW THE LAKE

Topical Press.

The South American republic of Venezuela has now become one of the greatest oil-producing countries of the world, second only to the U.S.A. Some of the richest strikes of oil have been made in the basin of Maracaibo, west of the Andes, and wells are being sunk below the waters of the lake. Our photograph shows a member of the Venezuelan National Guard gazing out across Lake Maracaibo towards the towering derricks.

Copyright.

A REFINERY FOR AERO-ENGINE OIL
The crude oil from the wells requires different treatment according to
its quality and the purpose for which it is to be used. Here we see a
refinery where the petrol used in high-speed aero-engines is prepared.
This particular plant produces what is known as 100-octane spirit.

of eight miles to leeward. The whole countryside was flooded with oil and people fled for their lives.

"Capping" a Well

An attempt was made to "cap" the well, but the thick steel lid which was drawn over the opening was soon bored through by the sand contained in the oil. A huge mast was then obtained, weighing no less than 70 tons, and was driven down the bore. This checked the terror, but only for a day or two; then the mast was blown out like a shot from an air gun and the oil rose into the air to a height of 300 feet. When at last this "gusher" was got under control, £1,000,000 worth of oil had been wasted.

The actual appearance of an oilfield is now greatly different from what it used to be. In former days, an oilfield was marked by a forest of huge, untidy derricks, with engines and gear on every side, and oil everywhere. To-day there is little to distinguish an oilfield from the rest of the surrounding country except for the presence here and there of a tall steel derrick, looking not unlike an ordinary electric pylon, but taller. Generally, no oil is visible anywhere; only a number of slowly oscillating pumps, looking rather like strange birds, which pump the oil from

of oil high into the air are very exceptional.

Some years ago a Tartar, named Tagiet, struck oil on the shores of the Caspian, and the oil spurted out of the bore-hole at the rate of 11,000 tons a day, a quantity which it was impossible to keep under proper control.

From the town of Baku, some miles away, the oil fountain looked like an immense pillar of smoke. Clouds of oil spray floated away before the wind and covered everything for a distance

BRITAIN'S GREATEST OIL REFINERY

At Fawley, near Southampton, a great oil refining plant was formally opened in 1951, and when finally completed will be easily the largest in Europe. Other refineries have been, or are being, built in this country, and Britain will soon be able to produce annually some 20 million tons of refined oil compared with 3½ million tons in 1948. At Fawley some 6½ million tons will be produced each year. In this photograph the fuel oil tanks and heaters are seen.

Photos : Topical Press.

This giant plant at Fawley has splendid berthing facilities in Southampton Water, and the crude oil can be brought right to the refinery while the refined product is sent in the same way to wherever it is required. At least one large ocean tanker discharges crude oil while others are constantly leaving with the finished products. Our picture shows an Esso tanker at No. 1 berth.

a depth of many thousand feet to pass through the gathering lines to the storage tanks.

Just as coal is found in every continent and almost every country, so is oil. While coal is known to be the fossilised remains of prehistoric forests, so oil is believed to have been formed from the decomposition of vast beds of seaweed or other marine growth. Oil is now being pumped from wells driven in the sea bottom off the Californian coast, and it is certain that there are huge supplies of this valuable fluid under the Gulf of Mexico.

Up to now, the country that has produced the largest quantities of oil is the U.S.A. For many years her output has amounted to more than 60 per cent. of the world total. But as her own consumption has increased, the amount of oil available for export has diminished. As a result, other countries have now to draw their supplies from elsewhere, chiefly Venezuela, Saudi Arabia, Kuwait, and the East Indies.

The situation to-day is that everybody is consuming more oil, especially in the U.S.A. As the output in the U.S.A. may be expected to decline

Topical Press.

AT ONE OF CURAÇAO'S REFINERIES

Concessions to work the oilfields of Venezuela have been granted to British and American Companies. A certain amount of the oil must be refined in Venezuela itself, while other refineries have been established on adjacent islands. Here we see the alkylation plant at a Curaçao refinery.

HOW THE GEOLOGISTS "SHOOT" FOR OIL

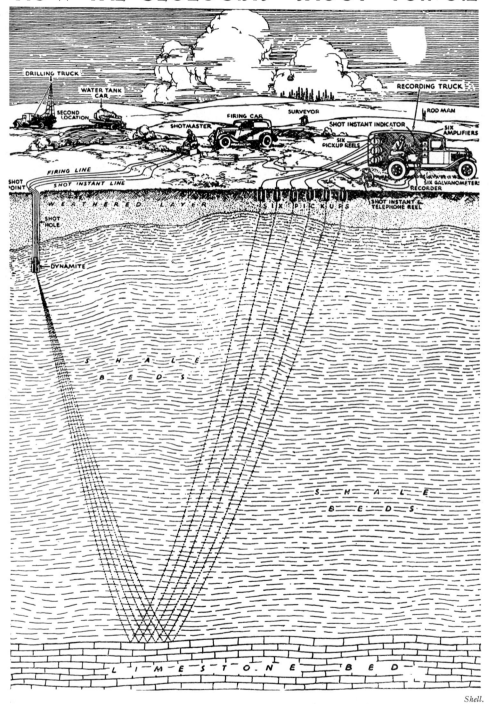

Shell.

A certain amount of intelligent guesswork has to be done by the geologists who assist the oil prospectors. Various tests are employed and the diagram above shows what is known as the seismic method. Into a bore-hole, not more than 100 feet deep, an explosive such as gelignite is placed and then fired. The result is a small earthquake, sound-waves from which are received in the recording van. The record tells the experts the exact nature of the ground far below, and whether oil is likely to be found.

Camera Press.

OIL IN THE DESERT LANDS OF KUWAIT

Under the sands of a desolate desert land where Bedouin tribes roamed, a rich treasure-chest has
been discovered. To-day, Kuwait, a small sheikhdom on the Persian Gulf, is being rapidly transformed.
A joint British-American corporation is working the great Burgan oilfield, and the Sheikh enjoys a
fabulous income which is being spent on his people. Above are seen the pipelines leading from the
Kuwait refinery to the storage tanks.

gradually, she may have to look elsewhere for part of her supplies. This is
the reason why so much attention is
being paid to-day to the Middle East
as a source of supply. It contains the
largest reserves in the world as far as is
known at present.

Prophecies regarding oil supplies must
always be taken with caution. The
United States authorities, while looking
elsewhere for oil supplies in case their
own wells run out, have not relaxed
efforts in their own country. In March,
1948, for instance, it was officially
announced that an oil shale deposit in
Colorado was being developed and that
this new source was believed to have a
potential output of about ten times the
volume of all oil so far drilled in the
U.S.A.

It is possible, so the experts believe,

that this may become the largest
mining operation in the world. The
method employed in the case of this
deposit is to mine the shale rock and
transform the nearly solid petroleum
contents into crude oil. Such a source
of supply, when fully developed, might
solve all the American problems of an
adequate oil supply for many years to
come.

In Canada, too, the production of oil
is increasing. Alberta's oilfields are
being steadily developed, and the
Athabaska tar sands are believed to
contain one of the largest known supplies of oil in the world. The development of these deposits holds tremendous
possibilities. Large reserves are known
to exist in South America also and
intensive exploration and development
work is being carried out there.

THE DRILLING CREW AT WORK

Shell.

Oil is not found in pools or lakes below ground, but is always absorbed in sand or sandstone, which holds the oil as a sponge holds water. This sand or rock may be anything from 60 to 70 feet to nearly three miles below ground. To reach it a hole has to be drilled, and here we see a drilling crew at work, fixing the tackle which will drive the hole, no more than 8 or 10 inches across, right down to the oil-soaked sand or rock from which it will later be pumped.

CONSTRUCTING A PIPELINE

Shell.

In various countries huge pipelines have been constructed to bring the oil from the place where it is found to some port where it can be conveniently taken aboard a tanker for transport to wherever it may be required. In this picture we see part of one of these long pipelines during construction. The curious-looking engine is a pipe-cleaning machine in action.

Shell.

Here we have another view of a big oil-refining plant. This photograph shows the Dominguez Refinery of the Shell Company in California, U.S.A., where Iso-octane is manufactured to form the basis of 100-octane aviation spirit.

Shell.

A TANKER WITH OIL FROM VENEZUELA

The big oil companies have their own fleets of specially-constructed vessels to bring the oil from overseas to the countries where it is needed. Our photograph shows one of the Shell Company's fleet of tankers. It is carrying a cargo of oil from Venezuela to a British port.

One of the most important oil strikes of recent times occurred in the Exmouth Gulf area of Western Australia. This was the first successful large strike to be made in the island continent, and it was the work of a joint Australian and American company. It took place in November 1953, but remained a carefully guarded secret while samples of the oil were sent to America and tested. Not until December 4th, about three weeks after the strike, was the world told that Australia now had a large-scale field of high-grade oil.

Australia's Search for " Black Gold "

It had been known for many years that this part of Australia might contain " black gold," as oil is sometimes called. During the early years of the present century a State Government geologist named Gibb Maitland made many survey trips by camel and showed that sedimentary rocks, necessary for any oil deposits, were present in the Exmouth Gulf area. Sedimentary rocks occur in layers (" strata "), and for this reason are also called stratified rocks. They are made from materials from other rocks which have been deposited, in both prehistoric and modern times, on sea or lake or river-beds. Some sedimentary rocks may be the sand of prehistoric deserts which has been hardened into sandstone by the pressure of later deposits.

Other Australian geologists developed the study of the area. Among them was Dr. H. G. Raggatt, the present secretary of the Department of National Development, who worked in the Exmouth Gulf area during the mid-1930s. He was so impressed with the possibilities that he devoted much of his time to urging the setting up of test drills.

By 1948 an Australian company had obtained oil rights over a large stretch of Western Australia. This area extended from Joseph Bonaparte Gulf, in the north, to Cape Leeuwin, in the south, and reached inland for about 500 miles. The total area was about 325,000 square miles. A base camp was established at Learmonth, where the oil company took over the buildings and airfield of an old Royal Australian Air Force Station.

By 1951 the Americans had joined forces with the Australians in their search for oil around the Exmouth Gulf. By 1953 everything was ready for the first drill. Equipment had been brought by sea from California and hauled across rough roads to the site near Learmonth, where it was assembled into one of the largest and most modern oil drills in the world. The completed rig was 142 feet high. When drilling started on September 5th, the oil men were prepared to go down to a depth of 12,000 feet, but their first strike was actually made at a depth of 3,605 feet, in a layer of oil-bearing sands. The production of the strike was tested for

a period of twenty-four hours, and during that time oil was coming out at the very high rate of twenty barrels an hour. By this time more than £A.1,500,000 had been spent on survey work and drilling in the Exmouth Gulf area.

The Search goes on

The success of the Learmonth drilling spurred the efforts of oil prospectors in many parts of Australia and her overseas territories. Many years before the Exmouth Gulf strike, oil had been produced from time to time at the Roma field, in southern Queensland, and at Lakes Entrance, in Victoria, but the quantities were so small that the fields could not be worked profitably. Interest in these fields has now been revived. In December, 1953, it was said that a Melbourne company intended to prospect for oil in the Port Keats, Daly River and Fitzmaurice River districts of the Northern Territory. In New Guinea, at Omati, near the head of the

Planet News.

THE SCENE OF AUSTRALIA'S FIRST LARGE OIL STRIKE

This picture shows us the drilling site in the Exmouth Gulf area, where an important oil strike was made in November, 1953. The drilling rig, which reaches a height of 142 feet, is one of the largest and most modern in the world. The black mass to the right of the derrick is shale from the outlet pipe.

Planet News.

HIGH-GRADE AUSTRALIAN OIL

Drilling at Exmouth Gulf is the work of a joint Australian and American company. In this picture we see an American drilling superintendent showing a visiting air pilot a specimen of the crude oil from the large new field. Oil samples were sent to America for classification before the strike was made public.

Gulf of Papua, work has been resumed on the test well. Drilled to a depth of two and a half miles, the well is the deepest test drilling in the Southern Hemisphere.

Prospecting also continues in Western Australia, where the Rough Range area and Fitzroy Basin are being investigated. Drilling of the sea bed off the West Australian coast may take place also, for oil-bearing rock formations sometimes reach out under the sea. A similar search for underwater oil was being conducted during 1953 off the coast of Qatar, in the Persian Gulf, and still continues.

New Refineries

Australia may soon be almost independent of overseas refineries. A large new refinery, capable of handling 1¾ million tons of crude oil every year, was opened on March 18th, 1954, at Geelong, Victoria, to process supplies from British Borneo and the Middle East. At this time, other new refineries were being built at Altona in Melbourne, Sydney and Brisbane, and at Kwinana, near Fremantle, in Western Australia.

Home-produced Oil

Great Britain normally needs some 3,000 million gallons of oil every year and could no doubt use very much more if supplies were unlimited. Practically all this quantity has to be brought to our shores in the specially-built oil-carrying ships known as tankers. Everywhere the demand for oil is increasing.

Oil has been discovered in Britain but the prospect of obtaining sufficient supplies for our needs at home is highly remote. In 1911 an experimental boring was made in Nottinghamshire and in 1918 the first real oil-well was drilled in Derbyshire. The experts continued their search and by 1945 there were some 240 wells in this country, mainly in Nottinghamshire and Lancashire. Over 25 million gallons

UNLOADING OIL AT A BRITISH PORT

In modern times great pipelines have been laid from the oilfields to the ports where the tankers take the oil aboard through flexible pipes, wire-covered to guard them against injury. After its journey in the tanker across the seas, the oil is unloaded, and in this photograph is seen a tanker at a British port. The oil pipeline from the shore is being lowered by a crane in readiness for the task of taking the cargo of oil ashore.

of petrol were produced in a year, but this is not a hundredth part of the total amount we require.

A certain amount of petrol is being made from coal in England, but the supply is limited. In Scotland a particular substance known as oil-shale was dug from the ground years ago and a certain amount of oil extracted from it. When large quantities of petrol were easily imported from America no one troubled very much about shale-oil. To-day with new methods of extraction

the shale-oil industry is being developed. The shale is dug from comparatively shallow mines in much the same way that coal is mined; later the shale is treated in retorts and various products are extracted during the process of distilling, condensing and refining.

We speak of petroleum as a " mineral oil," and not only does it give us petrol, paraffin and fuel oil for steamers, locomotives and different kinds of heavy engines, but it also affords paraffin wax, from which candles are made.

Specially painted for this work.

COTTON GATHERING IN EGYPT

Cotton grown in Egypt ranks among the best in the world because the climate and soil admirably suit the needs of this invaluable plant. We see above the gathering-in of the harvest by girls and boys. Most of the work such as seed-sowing, thinning-out seedlings and hoeing is still carried out by hand. Channels are cut to bring water from the Nile to thirsty roots, and it should be noted that gatherers wear special aprons in which to collect the seed-heads. Camels convey the crop to warehouses where the cotton is baled ready for shipment.

Specially painted for this work.

TAPPING A TREE FOR RUBBER IN MALAYA

South America was the original home of the trees from which raw rubber is obtained. There are several trees and plants which yield the "latex" or milky sap, but the *Hevea brasiliensis* is the one chiefly grown. In this picture a worker on a large Malayan rubber plantation is seen tapping a tree in a district where they are tapped on half circumference on alternate days. As will be seen, the bark is pared away to expose the tubes in which milky latex collects, and this drains into the cup attached to the tree.

THE EVER-USEFUL RUBBER

Rubber Growers' Association.

MAKING A RUBBER PLANTATION

A short time ago this land was covered with jungle. It has now been cleared, and coolies are planting it with rows of evenly-spaced young rubber trees from the estate nurseries. These plants have been reduced to stumps, but they will send out shoots and grow into sturdy trees.

ABOUT the year 1500 the Spanish adventurers who were conquering Mexico brought home to Spain some small, hard, black balls which *bounced* in a way which was new to all beholders. They were made, so the travellers said, from the black resin of a tree, called by the natives "Ulaquahuil."

This was the first rubber seen in Europe. It was looked upon merely as a curiosity, and it was a great many years before it was thought of as anything else. Priestley, the great English chemist, found that it was good for rubbing out pencil marks, and that is how it got its name "india-rubber," "Indias" being the old Spanish name for South America. That was about the year 1770, but another seventy years had to pass before it was discovered how to *vulcanise* india-rubber.

Rubber is a peculiar commodity. It will not dissolve, like so many vegetable saps, in water or alcohol. It was discovered, however, that by heating it with sulphur, it could be handled quite easily. It became more elastic, was not hardened by cold or softened by ordinary heat, and it could be made into thin sheets which, when applied to cloth, made the cloth waterproof.

It could also be made into "vulcanite," the hard form of rubber which is good for making combs, penholders, buttons, paper-knives, etc. Vulcanite can be moulded or carved into a hundred forms, and one of its advantages is that it is a *non-conductor* of electricity.

From the Amazon Valley

So began the use of india-rubber. For the first time in history men had overcoats through which no rain could penetrate; goloshes, shoes which were impervious to wet; garden-hose which could be coiled up and made of any length desired; belting for machinery better than any yet made; and, as time went on and motor cars came in, air-filled tyres on which these vehicles could travel at considerable speed.

Several different trees supply the "latex," or sap, from which india-rubber is made, but the most important is the *Hevea brasiliensis*, which is a native of the Amazon valley. For many years Brazil was the sole source

MILKING A RUBBER TREE

Topical Press.

This method of " tapping " a rubber tree is called the herring-bone system. Sloping grooves are cut in the bark of the tree on both sides of a central vertical channel, which leads the exuding latex or milky juice down into a collecting cup at the bottom. The coolie in charge of a section makes his rounds periodically and empties the latex from the collecting cups into his pail.

A RUBBER PLANTATION IN MALAY

Here we see the seedling rubber trees growing in the nursery beds of a plantation near Kuala Lumpur, Malay. The weeds are kept down by Indian coolies.

Another method of tapping the rubber trees is by removing a small section of the bark in a full spiral. The latex appears at once and drips into a small cup hanging on the wire below.

Photos : Topical Press.

In this picture the tappers are returning with their pails of latex after the morning's work on the plantations.

Inside the plantation factory, the latex is mixed with formic acid, then passed through rolling mills to make into sheets.

ROLLING AND DRYING

The blocks of coagulated rubber are here being rolled out like pastry and then passed through rollers, while being washed, to flatten them further into thin sheets of " crepe " rubber. Various methods of rolling are used, to produce different kinds of crepe and sheet, in which forms raw rubber is sold to manufacturers of rubber articles.

Photos : Rubber Growers' Association.

Crepe rubber hung up on racks in a drying house. What is called " pale crepe " is dried by a natural draught of air circulating among the sheets, while " smoked " sheet is exposed to the smoke from wood fires burning on the ground below. The smoking gives the rubber a dark reddish-brown colour.

BRINGING RUBBER TO MARKET

The sheets of cured rubber are carefully sorted, weighed, folded, and packed into strong ply-wood cases, each containing from 1½ to 2 hundredweights of rubber. In this picture coolies are seen carrying cases from a native craft called a wallam into a storehouse, where they will remain until required for shipment.

Photos : Rubber Growers' Association.

The scene is now shifted from the East to a warehouse in London. The raw rubber is here being unpacked, weighed, sampled and got ready for inspection by buyers. London is one of the greatest rubber markets of the world. Well over 150,000 tons of rubber enter London docks in a year.

of the world's rubber, and great fortunes were gained by tapping the wild trees.

Terrible work it was, and is, in those steaming tropical forests which reek of fever and pestilence. For hours daily the rubber gatherers work in swamps where they sink over their ankles, amid rivers swarming with alligators, surrounded by poisonous snakes and clouds of stinging insects, threatened by all kinds of disease, especially that terrible one called "espundia." For the wild rubber tree attains greatest perfection in conditions that are most terrible for human beings.

The Smuggling of the Seeds

This sort of thing could not go on, and in 1876 it was decided to endeavour to transplant the rubber tree to India. The authorities at Kew entrusted Mr. Henry Wickham with the task of collecting rubber seeds from Brazil. Now, the Brazilian Government, well aware

Dunlop Rubber Co., Ltd.
RUBBER FOR CAR TYRES
A wide band of unvulcanised rubber being passed between huge rollers and slit down the middle into two parts, each of which will be cut up into lengths for covering tyre walls and treads.

of the value of rubber, had made laws against allowing any of the seed to leave the country, and Mr. Wickham did not know how to get past the Customs' examiners.

Chance came to his help. While far up the Amazon he was surprised by the arrival of a large steamship, the S.S. *Amazonas*, which had been sent from England to trade up the Amazon. She could find no cargo, however, and was on the point of being abandoned when Wickham chartered her on behalf of the Government of India. With great secrecy he got a quantity of rubber seeds aboard and hid them. Then he sailed for home. Somehow he managed to evade the officials at the river mouth, though this was not easy, because the only *navigable* mouth of the Amazon is very narrow—the big mouth you see on the map is shallow and full of sand banks. Eventually he delivered his seeds at Kew, where they were germinated in hot-houses. For this great service Mr. Wickham was afterwards knighted.

Sent to India

The young plants were, in due time, sent to India in "Wardian" cases, like small portable greenhouses, and set out in botanical gardens in Ceylon, Singapore and elsewhere. Here, it is now difficult to believe, no one would bother to grow them. Planters were all too busy with tea and coffee. Then came the coffee-leaf disease, which destroyed all the trees in Ceylon and forced growers to look for some other crop. They started rubber, and to-day most of the world's rubber comes from countries of the East. The Malaya plantations produce over 600,000 tons a year, about one-third the total natural production of rubber in the world.

A rubber tree is first tapped when five or six years old. The bark is pared away, a bit at a time, to expose the tubes in which the milky, rubber-yielding latex collects. The "milk" drops into a cup, and in due course

TWO STAGES IN TYRE MANUFACTURE

In this picture we see the raw rubber as it is received in this country, being " masticated " at the works. It is passed between heated steel rollers to make it fit for the next stage.

Dunlop Rubber Co., Ltd.

This shows a later stage in the manufacture of a heavy truck tyre. A newly-built tyre is being lowered into the mould ready for vulcanisation.

Dunlop Rubber Co., Ltd.

Here we see another of the various stages in making a motor car tyre.   The tread rubber and the sidewalls are being laid on a flat collapsible " Forma " on to which the rubber-impregnated cotton casing has previously been laid.

TAKING OUT A VULCANISED TYRE

Dunlop Rubber Co., Ltd.

On a previous page we saw the tyre being lowered into the mould for vulcanisation. In this picture the great press is seen more fully as the freshly vulcanised tyre is removed from the mould. In the vulcanisation process sulphur is added to the rubber.

these cups are emptied into pails, which, in turn, are emptied into tanks. The fluid is later coagulated (made firm) by adding a little formic acid, and is then washed and rolled into sheets, which take on a pale yellow colour. Sometimes the sheets are smoked and are then known as " smoked sheet."

The sheets are shipped to Europe or America for making up into various objects, from elastic bands to great motor tyres. Vulcanising, which used to be a slow process, is much hastened nowadays by mixing with the rubber certain chemicals called " accelerators."

The Value of Rubber

The cycle and the motor car could not exist without rubber tyres, while football, tennis and golf would be equally impossible without rubber to make balls used in these and other similar games. Electrical engineering depends largely on rubber, and so does the medical profession. Rubber gloves,

rubber sheeting, rubber tubing for administering anæsthetics, rubber castors for operating tables, rubber mattresses —these are only a few of the many uses of rubber in modern medicine.

For Paving Roads

In the home we have rubber hot-water bottles, rubber sponge bags, rubber bath mats, and many other rubber-made articles. Rubber soles our shoes, often replacing leather for that purpose. In the office you find rubber erasers, rubber stamps, rubber bands and often rubber flooring. Nearly all fountain pens are made of vulcanite. When rubber was plentiful we began to pave our roads with it. Rubber is in truth one of the most useful substances known to man.

One may start a rubber plantation from seeds, but a quicker method is to plant trees. These are cut down and trimmed to mere stumps but develop quickly and grow into strong trees.

Dunlop Rubber Co., Ltd.

A BATTERY OF TYRE-BUILDING MACHINES

Many thousands of tyres are required each year for motor vehicles of all types, as well as bicycles and motor cycles. This picture shows the scene in a factory at Fort Dunlop where a battery of tyre-building machines is in operation.

From about 1873 onwards, wood pulp has been used more and more for the making of paper. In this picture are seen the great stacks of baled wood pulp as it looks when brought to the papermakers from abroad. In the countries where the cone-bearing trees flourish, the wood is chopped up then made into pulp by chemicals. This pulp is dried and shipped to the papermakers overseas.

PAPER is one of the world's oldest inventions. The Chinese, who usually claim most of the big inventions, certainly made paper hundreds of years before the time of Christ, but it is doubtful if they were ahead of the ancient Egyptians, who manufactured papyrus paper out of reeds fully 4,000 years ago. They cut the pith out of the reed called papyrus, laid the thin slices side by side, moistened them with water, rolled them flat and polished them with an elephant's tusk.

The Chinese formed their first paper out of mulberry trees and sprouts of bamboo, and later discovered a way of pulping silk waste and turning it into paper. Tsai Lun, a Chinese inventor, who lived about 100 years after Christ, found out how to make paper of bark, hemp, rags, and even from worn-out fishing-nets. Chinese artisans crossed Asia and took the invention to Samarkand, where paper-mills were erected more than 1,000 years ago.

The Arabs made paper of rags, and the Moors brought the invention to Spain. At last, in or about the year 1460, the first paper-mill was established in England, and in 1590 the mills at Dartford were started. Since then Britain has become one of the greatest paper-makers and users in the world, and in 1889 an English maker showed in Paris paper made from sixty different materials.

Pulp for Paper

Almost any vegetable growth has a fibrous structure or framework which can be converted into paper. To be of any use to paper manufacturers, however, it must be cheap and in plentiful supply. For centuries nearly all our paper was made from cotton and linen rags, but as the demand for paper increased the supply of rags became totally inadequate. About the year 1839 experiments were made in producing paper from Esparto grass, a very long, thin, wiry grass that grows in the swampy areas of North Africa.

Esparto grass proved highly suitable as it contained a very good proportion of fibre, and about the year 1890 we were importing approximately 220,000 tons yearly. To-day it is largely used in the manufacture of good quality paper for books and other better-class publications.

In 1873 wood pulp was first introduced for paper-making, and by degrees was found to be by far the cheapest and most satisfactory material for that purpose, so that nowadays nearly all paper, except the best note, is made from wood. But all woods will not do for paper-making. Oak, ash and beech are practically useless for the purpose. The fibre is not long enough. Only the wood of certain cone-bearing trees is suitable, and, in point of fact, most of the world's paper-making material comes from Scandinavia, Newfoundland and Canada.

Wood to be used for paper-making is first chopped up and sliced by machinery, then pulped with chemicals, such as caustic soda or bisulphate of lime, in vats heated to a high temperature. To save cost of carriage, this is usually done at works close to, or connected with, the saw-mill, and the pulp only is brought across the sea.

Making the Paper

The pulp has to be carefully bleached before it can be used. It is then mixed with water to about the consistency of cream, and this pulp is run out on to a table made of wire cloth. On this wire cloth the pulp is carried along and strained and dried as it goes. It passes between rollers, which squeeze out the remaining water, and after this it looks like very thick, rough blotting-paper. It is then called "half-stuff."

Copyright.

THE FIRST PROCESS AT THE MILL

Wood pulp in its natural state is a greyish, dirty hue, and altogether too lumpy. The first task at the mill is to break up this raw material by a process of beating in great tanks, as seen above. In these tanks certain chemicals have been mixed with the water and these chemicals are absorbed by the pulp and act as a bleaching agent to give the necessary whiteness.

MAKING PAPER BY THE MILE

In the two pictures on this page the machine which really makes the paper is shown. The material starts at the " wet end " as a creamy liquid stream. It is carried forward on an endless wire cloth through which the water drains, assisted by suction boxes. The fibrous film then travels round steam-heated cylinders and rollers that drive off the rest of the water and make the sheet firm.

Photos : Copyright.

Eventually the material which began as the creamy pulp arrives at the other end of its long journey through the machine, which, as can be seen above, is of truly tremendous length. This photograph shows the " dry end," and the paper comes steadily forth to be wound on the great reel.

We are all familiar with the process of ironing starched material such as collars and cuffs so that a perfectly smooth, shiny surface is produced. The big rolls of paper seen in the picture above are going through a very similar process. The heated rollers press the paper and dry it, giving to the paper what is known as a " calendered " surface, smooth and shiny.

This is broken up again with a quantity of pure water, dried and rolled out afresh.

It is during this second process that any necessary colouring matter is added as well as the " filling " or " loading." China clay or calcium sulphate is used for filling, and makes the paper more solid. " Size " is added also. The last process is to run the sheets between smoothing rolls and polished rollers of chilled iron, which give it a smooth surface.

The pulp made in this way is known as chemical wood; it is of good quality and will retain its colour for a long time.

Pulp for Newspapers

In the case of newspapers it is not so important to use a paper of good quality, as the daily papers are usually bought, read, and then thrown away. For newsprint an even cheaper and quicker process is employed, producing what is known as mechanical wood pulp because it is made by the mechanical process of grinding logs of wood on revolving wet grindstones. Many millions of tons are made in this way every year.

Pulp made in this way is practically a fine sawdust, with torn fibres that are too short to use entirely alone. This pulp is therefore mixed with chemical wood pulp; approximately one part of chemical pulp is mixed with four parts of mechanical, and the longer chemical fibres give the necessary strength to make the finished sheet hold together. Paper made from this mixture is known as " newsprint," and the machines making newsprint have gradually become larger and increased the speed at which they run. One machine in Britain makes a sheet 300 inches wide at the rate of 1,250 feet per minute.

This is only a very brief description. A glance at our pictures of paper-making machinery will give a better idea of the many processes through which the pulp passes before it comes out, ready to be cut into sheets for printing newspapers or books.

Made from Rags

The best sorts of notepaper, and paper for special illustrated books, is made of linen and cotton rags, which are first freed from dust, then carefully sorted and cut up by a machine. They are next boiled in caustic soda, and a solution of bleaching powder (chloride of lime) is added, in which they soak for some time.

The " half-stuff " now is fed into beating engines, then strained and run out upon the paper-making machine. All these best qualities of paper are " tub-sized "; that is, put through a bath of gelatine size and afterwards dried. The sheets are placed between zinc plates and rolled or glazed between heavy rollers before being sent to the finishing department, where they are sorted and counted into reams. Notepaper is usually packed in quires of 24 sheets. In every ream there are 20 quires.

The amount of paper used in the world is enormous. As an example, one mill in Britain, and that not the largest, produces about 3,000 tons a week, and to make this it uses 4,000 tons of coal and uses 200 million gallons of water.

Thousands of Miles of Paper

We think of paper for printing and writing purposes, for making bags for the tradesmen, and brown paper for household use. If you were asked to make a note of other uses, you might

Copyright.

CUTTING UP A REEL OF PAPER

For newspapers the paper required is usually made in great reels measuring a particular width. Other paper-users require different sizes, and in the picture above we see the first huge reel as it came from the paper-makers' machines, being fed through another machine, fitted with knives adjusted to the particular widths required.

perhaps put down wall-paper, paper for wrapping cigarettes and blotting-paper.

But these are only a few of the vast varieties of paper. There is paper for currency and Bank Notes, very specially made for the Bank of England, and every inch has to be measured up and accounted for. There are drawing papers, carpet felt, cartridge paper, butter paper, tracing paper, chart paper. Nor must we forget millboard, paste-board and cardboard, in all kinds of thicknesses and varieties.

For cardboard, brown paper, wrappings, and to fortify pulp for newsprint, the waste paper collected from homes and offices has become highly important in recent years. Over 15,000 tons of waste paper can be dealt with weekly by British mills.

During war-time strong sandbags were made of paper, as well as twines, cords, ropes, and petrol jettison tanks for aeroplanes. Paper is now fashioned into stair carpets, trunks and bags, milk bottles, towels, handkerchiefs, and even wearing apparel.

By Smokeless Engine

In a paper-works fire would be a particularly terrible happening, and the air has to be kept as free from smoke, soot and sparks as possible. In one large paper mill the bales of wood-pulp are hauled on narrow-gauge rails from the ocean-going ship to the stackyard, and from this yard to the " beater " or mixing-room by a small though immensely powerful locomotive that has neither fire nor smoke and yet is a steam engine.

Instead of having a furnace the engine is taken every four hours to a boiler-house to be charged with super-heated steam.

Messrs. Stonhill and Gillis Ltd. and Messrs. R. T. Tanner & Co. Ltd.

ESPARTO GRASS FOR HIGH QUALITY PAPER

For centuries nearly all our paper was made from cotton and linen rags, but in 1839 experiments were made with Esparto grass which grows in the swampy areas of North Africa. Esparto is still used in large quantities for the manufacture of good quality paper. In this picture a cargo of Esparto grass, brought from Sfax in North Africa, is being unloaded into barges in Britain.

By courtesy of British Railways.

A PAPER-MAKING MACHINE IN A MODERN MILL

The history of paper goes back almost as far as civilisation itself, though the earliest kinds of material on which writing was inscribed differed consider-ably from the paper used to-day. Papyrus, from which the name "paper" is derived, was made by the ancient Egyptians from reeds. Parchment, used in Europe much later, was made from the skins of animals, but the Chinese method of making paper from a fibrous vegetable pulp eventually spread to Europe. To-day wood pulp is largely used, but Esparto grass as well as cotton and linen rags are the raw material for better quality papers. Our picture shows a paper-making machine from the wet end, with the pulp flowing on the endless wire belt to the drying cylinders in the distance.

N.P.K. VI, p. 352.

SHEEP-SHEARING IN AUSTRALIA

Wool is a valuable commodity because it enables us to endure the cold of our northern winters. Though we still produce much wool at home, the immense flocks of sheep in Australia and New Zealand now yield about one-fourth of the world's supply, much of which finds its way to the mills of Yorkshire. Our picture shows mechanical shearing on an Australian sheep station.

COTTON GROWING AND SPINNING

H. J. Shepstone.

COTTON-PICKING IN CALIFORNIA

The cotton harvest in full swing at Fresno, in the San Joaquin Valley. The pickers are pulling off fully ripened bolls, seeds and all. Harvesting cotton is not a matter of a day or two, as with grain crops, for the bolls ripen at different times, and the first may be picked months before the last.

THERE is nothing particularly noticeable about an ordinary cotton bed sheet, considered merely as a sheet. It is just two sets of threads, crossing one another at right angles. If you look at any one thread closely, you will see that it passes alternately over and under the threads in its path.

But, like many other common things, it becomes quite interesting when its story is explored. Who first discovered how to twist the fibres gathered from the ripened bolls of the cotton-flower into a thread of cotton no one knows. It happened long centuries ago and most probably in India. Long before anyone in England knew what "cotton-wool" was like or how to spin it into cotton and weave it into cloth, the making of garments from cotton material had become quite an industry in India and other parts of the East.

Calico and Muslin

Cotton cloth was being made at Calicut on the West coast of India when Europeans landed there at the end of the fifteenth century. It was from this town that the name "calico" came, just as another kind of cotton material, muslin, first took its name from Mosul in that country not very far from India known to-day as Iraq.

Since those days the cotton industry has become a great and important industry in many countries and nowhere more so than in Britain. Lancashire is said to owe much of its success as the great centre of the cotton-spinning industry to its humid atmosphere, which prevents the fine threads in the early stages from breaking too easily. In drier climates where cotton-spinning was at first a failure this humidity has to be produced in the factories by artificial means. The cotton plant itself grows best in sub-tropical climates.

Look at a piece of cotton cloth—a sheet or a handkerchief. If a single thread be pulled out and untwisted, it is found to be composed of a number of very fine fibres. Under a microscope each fibre resembles a tiny flattened tube with a corkscrew-like twist in it. This twist is found only in cotton fibres and is a great help in spinning, as it makes them interlock and cling to one another.

The cotton used for our sheet came most probably from the southern part of the United States, which produces about half the world's supply of raw cotton. The cotton-growing district there covers about 500,000 square miles, or, say, ten times the area of England. In one year it may yield as many as 16,000,000 bales, each weighing 500 pounds; that is, over 3,500,000 tons of the material.

In case you should wonder where the rest of the world's cotton is grown, we will add that India comes next to America as regards quantity produced, while Egypt supplies cotton of the highest quality. To make the list of cotton-growing countries fairly complete, we must include in it the West Indies, Mexico, Brazil, Peru, Nigeria, British East Africa, Russia, Persia, the East Indies, Asia Minor, China and Japan. Australia also has become a cotton-growing country, and in Queensland, which has long been well-known for its wool-producing sheep, the farmers are now cultivating the cotton-plant as well. Nearly all the cotton that Australia needs is produced on her own land.

How the Cotton Grew

Last April, on a certain cotton estate, machines were busy drilling seeds in rows about 4 feet apart. From these seeds sprang little plants, which were thinned out with hoes till only one remained every foot or so. Now and then the farmer cleaned the ground between the rows with a machine called a cultivator, to keep down the weeds which grow so quickly in these parts.

Two months after sowing, the plants were bushes 18 inches high, with leaves rather like those of ivy. On them flowers presently began to open— creamy-coloured, suggesting hollyhock blooms, but with longer bells. The shrubs went on growing till they were 3 feet to 4 feet high, and the earliest flowers dropped their petals. At the centre of each flower was a seed capsule or fruit, called a boll. By August many of the bolls had split open, and out of them burst masses of white down, clinging to a large number of black seeds. The down was raw cotton.

Coloured people — negro men, women and children— then began to pick the cotton, and the picking lasted till well on into the autumn. As fast as the cotton was gathered it was passed through a machine named a gin, which separated all the seeds from the fibres. The seeds weigh a good deal more than the lint, that is, the cotton itself.

Will. F. Taylor.

THE MOST USEFUL OF FLOWERS

A " close-up " of cotton flowers just come into bloom. Seen from this point of view they resemble poppies, but actually they are more like hollyhock blossoms.

At one time they proved themselves a great nuisance to farmers, who were at their wits' end to know how to get rid of the huge piles of seed that collected round the ginning-mills. But to-day the seed is a valuable part of the crop. Oil squeezed from it is used for cooking, soap-making, and many other purposes; the spent pulp makes a splendid cattle food ; and even the husks have a use as fertiliser.

Enemies of Cotton

The ginned cotton is put into bales, which are squeezed in a powerful press to reduce their size, and sewn up in

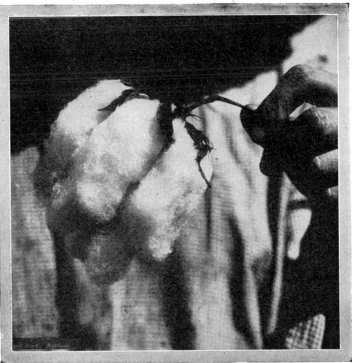

Commonwealth of Australia.

WHAT COMES FROM THE FLOWER

The ripened seed-capsule or boll of the flower has here opened, and masses of the white down which we call cotton have burst out of it. This particular boll was grown in Queensland, Australia.

sacking. It is then ready for sending out into the cotton markets of the world.

The cotton-farmer, like other farmers, is more or less at the mercy of the weather, which may be too dry or too wet, and may favour the spread of the pests that attack the cotton plant.

Some of these pests are kinds of fungus, others are insects or their caterpillars. The worst plagues of all are the cotton-worm, which gnaws away the leaves; the boll-worm, which devours the buds and young bolls; and the boll-weevil, which feeds on the lint, and is the greatest enemy of American cotton-growers. It invaded Texas in 1892, and since then has spread so much as to wipe out altogether the finest variety, Sea Island cotton, which fetched the best prices because its fibres were exceptionally long.

Some planters now use aeroplanes to scatter poisonous powder over their fields and destroy some, at least, of their tiny foes.

Cleaning the Cotton

Imagine now the bales of cotton to have travelled some thousands of miles by land and sea and to have reached one of the many spinning-mills in Lancashire, which for the last 150 years has been the greatest cotton-spinning and weaving centre.

The cotton in the bales contains a good deal of dust and dirt, fragments of seed, shells and leaves. The fibres run in all directions, and many of them are knotted together. Before the cotton can be spun, it must be both cleaned and " straightened out."

So it is flung into a bale-breaker, which mixes different grades of cotton together, and tears any lumps apart. Then it undergoes a good beating in another machine, and has most of the dirt and rubbish knocked out of it. A third machine finishes the beating and converts it into a thick and delightfully soft sheet of " cotton-wool," such as one buys for packing purposes. If you examined a piece of cotton-wool under a microscope, you would see that the fibres still lie " anyhow," in a regular jumble.

Straightening the Fibres

So the sheet of cotton-wool is fed into a carding machine, between a great revolving cylinder and an endless belt travelling close to the top of the cylinder, and in the same direction, but at a different speed. Both of these parts bristle with millions of short wires. The difference of speed makes the wires act like combs and drag on the fibres, pulling them so that they all tend to lie in the direction in which they are moving. The cotton leaves the machine in the form of a web or veil about as thick as stout paper. This web is drawn through a funnel, which compresses it into a " sliver," as the workpeople call it, 1 inch wide and $\frac{1}{2}$ inch thick.

But the straightening is still far from complete. In another section of the mill you will see the slivers being " drawn." If a person holding one end of a piece of elastic walks faster than a second person holding the other end, the elastic will be extended and become thinner. The same principle is used in drawing cotton slivers.

Six slivers are passed together through three parallel sets of rollers, placed one behind the other and turning at different speeds, the front set six times as fast as the back set. The single sliver into which they are mingled is of the same size as each of the original slivers, and this means that every one of the partners has been lengthened six times. The process is repeated twice more and the drawing-out does not cease till a sliver is a mixture of 216 original slivers. All this dragging at the fibres has straightened them out wonderfully.

Spinning Cotton into Threads

Before the cotton can be spun, the slivers have to pass through four other machines, which convert them into coarse, loose threads, slightly twisted, called " rovings."

The drawing out of the rovings, and the twisting of them into threads fit for weaving, are done by either a ring frame or a mule, both of them very ingenious devices.

Let us glance at the first of these: on it are hundreds of upright steel spindles, each carrying a bobbin and revolving thousands of times a minute inside a hole in a horizontal rail which moves slowly up and down. Encircling each spindle, and fixed to the rail, is a steel ring, with a grooved lip. A small curved piece of wire, known as a " traveller," is clipped loosely over the lip and is able to slide freely along it. The roving being spun passes through the " traveller " to the bobbin.

As the bobbin revolves it pulls on the roving, and the roving makes the traveller fly round and round the edge of the ring. If the traveller could keep up with the bobbin, the roving would merely be twisted, but there is friction between traveller and ring, and the ring is therefore always losing ground. The result of this is that the thread, besides being twisted, is wound steadily on to the bobbin. The up-and-down movements of the ring ensure that the winding is done evenly from one end of the bobbin to the other.

Now a few words about the other kind of spinning machine, the self-acting " mule." It is a very large apparatus, being about 200 feet long and 12 feet wide and consists of a fixed frame on which are up to 1,200 bobbins of rovings and a moving carriage with as many spindles on it. The carriage keeps travelling a few feet away from the frame and then back again on wheels

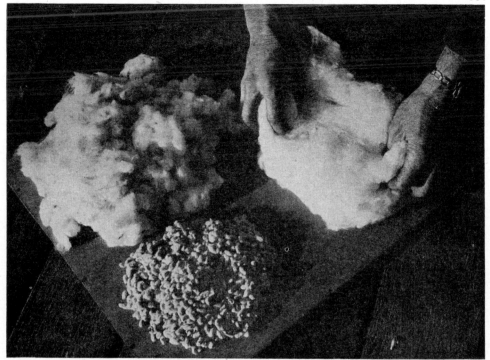

Australian News and Information Bureau.

COTTON GINNING—SEPARATING THE SEED FROM THE FIBRE

In this photograph we have on the left the seed cotton as it comes from the flower. After being dealt with at the ginneries, the seed, seen in the centre, is extracted and the raw cotton lint or fibre, on the right, is ready for the next stage in the various processes of cotton manufacture. This sample was grown in Queensland, Australia.

running on rails. During an outward journey the spindles draw out and spin the rovings, and during an inward journey they wind the spun threads on to the bobbins. A single mule spins and collects several miles of yarn every minute.

Weaving the Yarns

A woven fabric is made up, as we have noticed already, of two sets of threads, the *warp* threads and the *weft* threads. The warp threads run from end to end of a piece, and the weft threads cross and are interlaced with them.

The threads intended for the warp of a length of cotton cloth are wound side by side on to a weavers' beam, which is placed at, say, the south end of a machine called a loom. If we take any thread and follow it northwards through the loom, we see that it passes first between two horizontal rods (lease bars) then through an eye at the centre of a vertical wire (a heald), next between two of many upright wires in a swinging frame, named a reed, and on to a winding-on roller at the north end of the loom.

For weaving a simple fabric, such as a sheet, all the " odd " healds are attached to the same rods top and bottom and move together, and all the " even " healds to another pair of rods.

The bottom bar of the reed, named the sley, is wide enough on the north side to form a ledge, on which a shuttle slides to and fro from a shuttle-box at one end of it to a shuttle-box at the other. The shuttle is pointed at both ends and contains a " cop " or reel of weft thread.

Now let us watch the operations

of actual weaving: first the mechanism of the loom "opens the shed" by pulling the "odd" heals up and drawing the "even" heals down. The warp threads, seen sideways, now enclose a lozenge-shaped space, and the even threads are all pressing against the sley. An arm, called a pickling-stick, gives the shuttle a jerk. It flies over the "even" threads, paying out thread behind it.

Immediately afterwards, the reed moves northwards, its wires pressing the weft thread just laid by the shuttle into the north angle of the lozenge. While the reed is swinging back the "odd" heals are lowered and the "even" heals raised, and the two sets of threads cross round the last weft thread, holding it firmly in place. Everything is then ready for the next throw of the shuttle.

This series of operations is repeated as long as the weaving continues.

In a Weaving Shed

The weaving shed of a mill is a very noisy place. It may contain as many as 2,000 looms, all going clickety-click, as their shuttles fly backwards and forwards 200 times a minute—too fast for the eye to watch them.

The looms are probably of several different sizes, the largest of them able to weave cloth up to 12 feet wide. Some of them have very wonderful mechanisms. Here is one which automatically supplies the shuttle with a fresh cop of weft yarn when required, and stops instantaneously should a warp thread break. Over there is a loom using weft threads of several different colours, and changing the shuttles automatically whenever a change of colour is needed.

Will. F. Taylor.

IN THE DRAWING SHED

The machines in this picture are each taking in six slivers, or ribbons, of cotton wool and combining them into a single sliver, which is the same size as an original sliver, and therefore six times as long. The pulling-out action straightens the fibres.

Topical Press.

MODERN MACHINERY IN LANCASHIRE'S MILLS

The manufacture of cotton goods began in Lancashire soon after 1700. Since then the industry has undergone many changes: machinery first came into use about 1780, with the inventions of Hargreaves, Arkwright and Crompton. The improvement of cotton spinning machinery is still going on, and this photograph shows a new model Nasmith comber in operation in a big Lancashire mill.

By it stands a loom fitted with the wonderful Jacquard apparatus, which enables the most elaborate patterns, and even pictures or facsimiles of writing, to be woven in one colour or different colours. It is controlled by a series of cards, with holes punched in them, which cause certain warp threads to be raised before each trip of the shuttle.

Like a Piano Player

One may well compare it with a piano " played " by a punched roll of paper, the difference being that in the loom a hole relates to one or more warp threads, whereas in the other case the holes control notes in the piano.

To return to our sheet, or, rather, to the cotton cloth out of which it will be made : After leaving the loom it has the rough nap burned off it by gas burners. It then goes to the bleaching works, where it is washed, treated with chemicals, bleached, starched, dried, damped again, beaten, folded and pressed. It is then ready for the market, and for making into sheets.

King Cotton

The cotton-spinning and cotton-weaving industries are of enormous importance to Great Britain. There are in the world about 165,000,000 spindles for spinning cotton, and about 3,000,000 power looms for weaving cotton fabrics. Great Britain contains nearly 60,000,000 of the first and 800,000 of the second, and so is by far the greatest cotton-manufacturing country.

The products of her spindles and looms easily take first place, as regards value, in the list of her exports. In post-war years it has become even more important to keep up our exports of cotton goods to those countries, such as America, from which we obtain large quantities of the food we cannot grow ourselves as well as the raw materials on which our industries depend.

Lancashire was for long years the greatest cotton-spinning area in the world. It may be that her claim will be challenged sooner or later by other countries where the manufacture of cotton goods has made rapid strides in recent years. Even to-day, however, it is safe to say that from China to Peru the people in many lands are wearing cotton garments made from raw material which was spun and woven in Lancashire.

Nor is Lancashire relying upon her reputation of the past to maintain her position against increasing world competition. New machinery has been devised and many mills have been thoroughly modernised. A Cotton Manufacturing Commission, set up by the Government, has studied every aspect of the organisation of the industry.

Experimental trials were made of new systems and the Cotton Spinners' and Manufacturers' Association has

Topical Press.

WARP DRAWING IN A COTTON MILL

From the raw cotton the mills produce sheets, shirtings, towels, pillow-cases and the cloth for many articles of wear as well as for industrial purposes. Women, with their deft fingers, have always played a great part in the Lancashire cotton industry, and in this photograph is shown the process of warp-drawing: the reacher is selecting a thread for her fellow-worker, the drawer, to draw through the eye of the heald.

prepared instruction manuals in the new methods. At a stage in Britain's history when the standard of living for the whole nation depends upon exports to other countries, the great textile industry, which has contributed so much in the past to Britain's prosperity, is determined to maintain its lead.

Some idea of the quantities of cotton piece goods which Lancashire mills produce can be judged from the fact that in one month alone in 1949, just on 90 million square yards of these goods were exported. In comparatively recent times other countries have developed the manufacture of cotton goods, but those made in Lancashire still hold first place as far as quality is concerned, and it is to maintain this supremacy that the leaders of the industry are striving to-day.

Topical Press.

WINDING FROM RING TUBE TO BOBBIN

The cotton yarn from approximately eight spinning tubes is joined together and run on to a flanged bobbin in one continuous length as part of the process of preparing the warp—the threads that run lengthwise in the cloth. A girl worker is seen using an automatic hand-knotter to tie the yarn from a ring tube to the bobbin.

Apart from the manufacture of cotton goods there are a number of by-products which come from the wonderful cotton flowers. We have seen how the seeds, which were once a nuisance, are now taken out in the first process of "ginning" and become the raw material for manufacturers of cattle cake, cooking oils and other purposes. Cotton which has not been spun into thread or yarn is specially dealt with to rid it of greasy substances and make it absorbent. This is the cotton-wool which is used in hospitals and in the home. This same harmless cotton-wool when treated with certain acids becomes gun-cotton, a dangerous and powerful explosive.

The clean clippings from factories where cotton garments are manufactured are not by any means wasted. High-grade papers are made from this "waste," and our banknotes are printed on this type of paper, which differs considerably in quality from the wood-pulp paper used for newspapers and most of our books.

In this age when the scientist is discovering new methods of manufacture and new uses for old materials, a great deal of research work is being carried on in the cotton industry. The story of the fluffy cotton-boll with seeds clinging to its twisted fibres has not yet come to its end. Other chapters will one day be written about the new discoveries and developments in the uses to which the flower of the wonderful cotton plant can be put.

Imperial Chemical Industries Ltd.

FINISHING TOUCHES

After being woven, cotton cloth has to undergo about twenty processes—which include singeing, washing, boiling, bleaching, pounding and rolling—before it is ready for market: that is, unless it is sold in the unbleached condition. This picture was taken in the finishing department of a mill, and shows cloth passing through rollers under heavy pressure.

FROM SILK TO RAYON AND NYLON

ALL MADE FROM NYLON

Nylon is one of the most recent and one of the most amazing discoveries to be made in the textile world. Its fine strong thread is used not only for garments and stockings, but, as this picture of various kinds of brushes shows, it can be used in many other ways. The full list of the articles which can be manufactured from Nylon fibres is almost endless.

AN old legend of the China of four thousand five hundred years ago tells how the wife of the Yellow Emperor Huang-ti, the lovely lady of Si-ling, began the Chinese silk industry. The empress is said to have encouraged her people to grow mulberry trees to provide food for the worms which spun the wonderful silken thread. The legend says that she herself reared silkworms and even invented a loom for weaving the thread into fabric. After her death, the empress was revered as Yuen-fi, the goddess of silk, and was worshipped down the centuries by the Imperial Court in the Forbidden City of Peking.

Whatever the origin of the silk industry—and none can say who it was that first discovered the real value of the grubs of the mulberry-feeding moth—we know to-day that the rearing of silkworms, sericulture as it is called, and the developments to which it has led, have given us clothes and fabrics of unsurpassed quality. Now, thanks to miracle discoveries by scientists and chemists, beautiful textiles are no longer luxuries which only the rich can afford, but are within reach of everyone. To-day nearly every one of us has something in his or her wardrobe or house which is the equal of such silk as was once an expensive commodity available only to the privileged few.

How the Silkworm Lives

In its naturally produced state, silk comes from the silkworms hatched from the eggs of the mulberry-feeding moth, the *Bombyx mori* as scientists properly call it. This moth, white in colour and with brown-striped wings, lays from between four and seven hundred eggs each so small and so light that nearly half a million would be needed to make a pound in weight. When the silkworm is hatched, it begins eating almost at once and continues eating for about eight or ten days. Then it sleeps for two days, wakes up, and—starts eating again. After thirty-two days of this life, the worm has developed from a tiny hairlike thing

into a large amber-coloured caterpillar. It now coils itself up, horseshoe fashion, and begins to spin its cocoon, sending the silk from two openings above its mouth and joining the two threads together and spinning them about itself. One caterpillar spins nearly two miles of silk, but much of this cannot be recovered. The silk thread is so fine that as many as 1,100 cocoons may be needed to make a pound of raw silk.

If the industry depended upon the silkworm, delicate and lustrous silk fabrics would probably still be beyond the pockets of most of us. But to-day, in *Rayon*, we have a man-made textile fibre that has all the shimmering richness of silk produced by the *Bombyx mori* caterpillar and which constitutes a world-wide industry employing hundreds of thousands of workers.

Even as long ago as the seventeenth century an English scientist, Dr. Robert Hooke, was wondering whether there might not be some other way of manufacturing silk, whether it might not be possible " to make an artificial glutinous composition, much resembling, if not fully as good, nay better than . . . whatever substance it may be out of which the Silk-worm wire-draws his clew "; but it was not until 1855 that the first artificial process was patented by a Swiss named Audemars, and not

Courtaulds Ltd.

WHERE RAYON BEGINS

The story of Rayon, the fine man-made textile that has all the richness of natural silk, begins in the spruce forests of Canada and Scandinavia. This picture shows typical Northern Canadian spruce ready for felling. At the pulp mills, cellulose will be produced by the many processes to which the logs are submitted. The large cellulose sheets will then be baled up and sent to the rayon factory.

until the early eighties of the last century that the hopes of Dr. Hooke were to be realised. Sir Joseph Swan, a famous English chemist and electrician, produced a silken thread in the course of his experiments in 1884 with materials for making electric-light filaments: a remarkable achievement which, however, he did not attempt to use commercially.

First Artificial Silk

In the following year, Count Hilaire de Chardonnet produced artificial silk yarns and later had them woven into finished garments which he exhibited in Paris. At first, he copied the silk-worm, using mulberry leaves as his raw material, but later he found other substances which could be obtained more easily and cheaply. Count Chardonnet was the first to exploit artificial silk commercially, and his factories rose in France, Belgium, Switzerland, and our own country.

Meanwhile, another process was discovered and put to use in Germany, and in 1892 three British chemists, Cross, Bevan and Beadle, found a way of obtaining a smooth thread from a cellulose solution which they called *viscose*. Literally, cellulose means *containing cells*, and it is the name given to the carbohydrate main element of the cell membrane of plants and wood.

Cross and Bevan now sought the help of one of Sir Joseph Swan's former

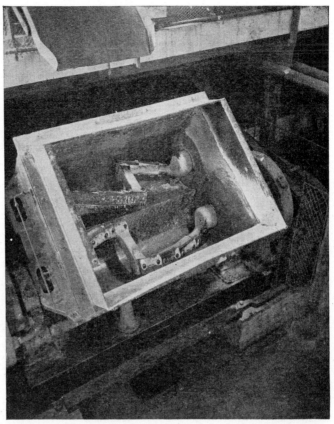

Courtaulds Ltd.

THE BLADES OF A PULVERISING MACHINE

Alkali Cellulose is in sheet form. After it has been squeezed in hydraulic presses, it is torn and ground by the blades of a pulverising machine called a Pfleiderer. These reduce the Alkali Cellulose sheets into creamy-white alkali cellulose " crumbs " which are then stored in large bins for a time to allow the caustic soda to complete its work.

colleagues, C. H. Stearn, whose associate, C. F. Topham, devised the method of rayon spinning that is most widely used to-day. This viscose process yielded its first yarn in 1898, and at the beginning of the present century, British rights over this process were bought by the old-established and famous firm of Courtaulds, which to-day is known the world over for the quality, variety, and richness of the rayon which it produces.

How Rayon is Made

There are various processes for making rayon: the *Cellulose-Acetate Process,*

RAYON IN THE MAKING

When the cellulose reaches the rayon factory it is inspected and carefully stored until it is needed. Then it is batched and weighed, and steeped in a bath of caustic soda. This picture shows the sheets of cellulose being put into the bath before the liquid caustic soda is run in. The caustic soda removes impurities and combines with the cellulose to form Alkali Cellulose.

Photos: Courtaulds Ltd.

In these churns, carbon bisulphide converts the alkali cellulose crumbs into an orange-red mass called Cellulose Xanthate. Cellulose Xanthate will dissolve in water to produce a honey-like substance called Viscose which gives its name to the Viscose process of manufacturing rayon illustrated in these pictures.

in which the cellulose from cotton linters or spruce wood is used with acetic acid and acetic anhydride to produce a thick liquid which yields cellulose-acetate flake which, dissolved in acetone, forms the spinning " dope " from which the rayon filaments come; the *Cuprammonium Process*, in which pure cellulose is mixed in a solution of copper sulphate and ammonia to produce a sticky viscose solution for spinning into rayon filaments; and the *Viscose Process* invented by Cross, Bevan and Beadle.

The story of Viscose Rayon begins in the spruce forests of Canada and Scandinavia where large pulp mills process the felled trees, stripping them, cutting them, crushing, cleansing, washing, scouring, and bleaching them; drying the product over cylinders heated by steam, and baling up the resulting cellulose —which looks very like large sheets of thick blotting-paper at this stage—for its journey to the rayon factory.

The cellulose requires careful handling; its weight and temperature are checked when it reaches the factory, and until it is required it is kept in a specially controlled atmosphere and submitted to frequent tests and checks. When manufacture begins, the cellulose is batched and weighed: then steeped in a bath of caustic soda. Caustic soda is used in vast quantities by the rayon industry and the part it plays in the manufacturing process is a highly important one. Not only does it remove any impurities —elements which are not required in the process: it combines with what is left to form Alkali Cellulose. This comes from the " bath " (which is really a long deep metal trough) in sheet form. Hydraulic presses squeeze part of the soda from the pulp sheets which are then torn and ground by the spiral blades and tooth-edged bars of pulverising machines. At this stage, temperature is still very important and is carefully controlled. The caustic soda has still not completed its work and the creamy-white alkali cellulose " crumbs " which come from the pulverising machines

Courtaulds Ltd.

VISCOSE

The honey-like substance flowing from the glass palette is Viscose. Two British chemists, Cross and Bevan, discovered that Cellulose Xanthate, when dissolved in water, would produce viscose, and it is on this fact that nearly ninety per cent. of world rayon production depends.

RAYON SPINNING

Forced through the holes of a spinneret, the viscose emerges as Viscose Continuous Filament Rayon Yarn. The number of filaments in the yarn is determined by the number of minute holes in the spinneret. Spinnerets are usually made from platinum-gold alloy. The actual size of a spinneret is about a third larger than that of the one shown on the right of the picture.

Photos: Courtaulds Ltd.

C. F. Topham invented the method of rayon spinning that is most commonly used to-day. As the viscose is forced through the spinneret, it is drawn into a spinning box which twists and winds the yarn into " cakes " ready for " doffing " (removing from the spinning boxes). The picture shows a spinning machine which has just been " doffed."

are therefore stored in large bins for a time.

When the " crumbs " are ready, they are put into six-sided churns where carbon bisulphide converts their creamy-whiteness into an orange-red mass called Cellulose Xanthate. It was Cross and Bevan who discovered that this Cellulose Xanthate would dissolve in water, and it is on this fact that nearly ninety per cent. of world rayon production depends. For when the Cellulose Xanthate has been dissolved in water in large mixers, the honey-like substance that is the result is the Viscose which gives its name to this particular process.

But the viscose is not yet in its purest form. Air or gas may have crept in, and there may be particles of undissolved matter and other impurities. The viscose is therefore

DOFFING *Courtaulds Ltd.*

This picture shows a " Doffer " removing a " cake " of rayon yarn from a Topham Spinning Box. Notice the covering lid and ring of the box, that he is holding in his right hand. After it has been " doffed," the yarn undergoes further cleansing processes on which depend its natural whiteness and thus the success of any dyeing processes to which it may be submitted.

stored for several days in " caves "— special cellars whose atmospheric conditions are carefully regulated. In the caves, the viscose passes through perforated layers of cloth between which are thick sheets of wadding. This is done several times, and simultaneously vacuum pipes draw off any gas or air.

This done, the viscose is forced through a spinneret. Spinnerets, made usually from platinum-gold alloy, are about the size of a thimble and are shaped like top-hats. Each spinneret may have up to 500 holes in its head, and it is from these that the thread emerges as Viscose Continuous Filament Rayon Yarn. The number of filaments in the yarn is fixed by the number of minute holes in the head of the spinneret; the yarn is called " continuous filament " because it is manufactured in a continuous thread. Metering pumps force the viscose through the spinneret, which is in an acid bath. As the threads emerge, they are drawn together and led out of the bath to pass round two wheels called *godets*. The surface speed of these godets also plays a part in determining the size of the yarn, which is measured, in the industry, in *denier* (the weight of 9,000 metres of yarns in grammes). From the godets, the threads drop down a glass funnel, the lower end of which dips into a circular metal cup with straight sides. This cup revolves several thousand times a minute, and the funnel is kept moving up and down by a lever.

This cup is more properly called a spinning box and is the invention of Topham. What happens is this: the thread already in the spinning box is pressed hard against the inside by centrifugal force and pulls on the thread coming down through the funnel. The thread is thus drawn into the cup as fast as it is formed, and, at the same time, given a twist. The up-and-down movements of the funnel cause layers of thread to be laid evenly one on top of the other, each layer a little nearer the centre of the box than the previous one. In this way, the spinning box twists and winds the yarn into " cakes " which are " doffed " (removed) from the boxes, wrapped, washed, bleached, dried and inspected before being packed ready for processing, dyeing, or dispatch to the spinning or weaving mills.

These final stages of washing, purifying and bleaching are most important, for on them depends the natural whiteness of the rayon and so the success of subsequent dyeing processes which provide rayon in such a wide range of lovely tints and shades.

Spun Rayon

Not all rayon is required in continuous filament form. For making fabrics similar in texture to cotton, linen, and woollen cloths, for working in with cotton, linen, and wool, and for making new crease-resisting fabrics, *Spun Rayon* has been found to have many advantages.

Spun rayon yarns are made from viscose rayon staple. That is to say, from equal lengths or staples of cut rayon filament. Spun rayon is made in the same way as continuous filament rayon up to the spinneret stage. But as the thread emerges from the spinneret, it is gathered into an untwisted rope, about the thickness of one's thumb,

VISCOSE RAYON STAPLE   *Courtaulds Ltd.*

Not all rayon is required in continuous filament form. For certain things Spun Rayon, made from Viscose Rayon Staple, is better. Viscose Rayon Staple is made up of rayon filament cut into equal lengths or staples. This picture shows a bale against which has been placed a card showing the size of the yarn and its quality.

and is then cut into staples whose length is determined by the kind of textile spinning system subsequently to be used. Spun rayon, so important for its adaptability, is yet another of the developments which we owe to the firm of Courtaulds which has built the rayon industry in our own and other countries.

The Rayon Industry

In 1947, the world production of rayon filament and rayon staple amounted to 1,990,710 thousands of lbs. The largest producer was the United States of America, with Great Britain second. But it was from Britain that America derived her rayon industry. The American Viscose Corporation was an offshoot of the British firm of Courtaulds and passed into other hands only as a result of the second world war, when British assets abroad had to be sold to provide food and munitions.

Rayon in Britain is inseparable from the name Courtaulds. This famous firm was founded at Bocking, Essex, by the descendant of a refugee Huguenot family. To-day, the organisation is the largest of its kind in the British Commonwealth, with more than 20 factories and 25,000 employees in the British Isles alone. Coventry was the site of their first rayon factory and is still one of the chief Courtauld centres; a second great centre is Flintshire, North

I.C.I.

NYLON MONOFILS

Nylon fibres can be made in various sizes, ranging from gossamer, which is about four-thousandths of an inch, to extra stout, which is one-fiftieth of an inch in diameter. This photograph shows the single filament known as " Monofil," but for textile purposes multi-filament is used, a number of filaments being twisted together.

Wales. Overseas the firm has factories in Canada and in France. One of the most recent developments in which the firm has taken a major part is the establishment of British Nylon Spinners —a new organisation which has its headquarters at Pontypool, Monmouthshire.

Nylon, the New Textile

Nylon is the wonder fibre that made parachutes and glider cables during the war. We think of it first as a yarn for making the sheerest stockings, but it actually has more than a hundred other uses—not only for dress fabrics, underwear, and umbrellas, but for tarpaulins, whaling ropes, canvases and in industry generally.

What exactly is nylon? Nylon is different from all other textile fibres. It is something quite new, made from the product of coal, air, and water. In Britain, for instance, the basic raw material in the manufacture of nylon yarn is benzene. We might be tempted to think that nylon is just another man-made copy of some natural fibre, that it is no more than just another "artificial silk." But nylon is neither of these; it is an entirely new textile fibre of surprising lightness, strength and beauty, which we owe to the research work of a number of American chemists.

In 1928, these chemists, under the leadership of Dr. Carothers, were working in their laboratories at Wilmington, Delaware, on the structure of certain natural materials. They were studying the process called *polymerization*—that is to say, the way in which chemical changes can unite a mass, whether large or small, into a substance that is permanently set. They began by studying *polyesters*—that is to say, the products of condensation from the reaction between dibasic acids and glycols—and they discovered that they could spin fibres from the polyesters: and that when these fibres had cooled, they could be stretched to several times their original length and, while remaining very strong, had become lustrous and transparent. A new textile fibre had never been the main purpose of their research, but this was what Dr. Carothers and his associates had discovered.

This was only the beginning. They wanted a stronger fibre and one with more elasticity, and they therefore sought to produce a *super-polymer* which would yield the desired fibre. (A *polymer* is one of a series of substances which are alike in composition, but which differ in molecular weight. A *super-polymer* is one which has a greater molecular weight than 5,000.) At last

MAKING THE NYLON HANKS   *I.C.I.*

When the nylon filaments or monofils have been produced, they are cut into lengths and arranged in hanks ready for sending to the manufacturers. This picture shows a hank of Nylon monofil fibres, suitable for toothbrushes, etc., being tied before dispatch.

Fox Photos.

GUMMING NYLON HOSIERY YARN

The headquarters of the British nylon industry is at Pontypool, Monmouthshire, and in this picture we see some of the machinery used in preparing nylon yarn for stockings.

telligibly, we can generalise by saying that nylon is a complex structure of carbon, nitrogen, oxygen and hydrogen which is built up into nylon polymer chips. Save that they are hard and not soft, these chips resemble soapflakes. They are melted, and the molten polymer is pumped through a spinneret. As the streams of liquid come from the tiny holes of the spinneret, they are cooled by air currents so that they form continuous filaments. These filaments are then processed to produce nylon yarn.

When production of nylon began in Britain, they lighted on polymer "66," from which they produced nylon in their laboratories in 1935. Commercial production of the fibre and of garments made from the fibre did not begin until 1939, and we all remember the wonder and delight with which the ladies greeted the nylon stocking.

Chemists would tell us that polymer "66" is "obtained by heating the reaction product of adipic acid and hexamethylenediamin," that "each molecule of these reagents contains six carbon atoms." But speaking less scientifically and—for those of us who are not chemists, at any rate—more in-

Fox Photos.

THE LAST STAGE IN NYLON SPINNING

In this picture we see nylon yarn being wound on to spinning cylinders, which is the last stage in the spinning process. Nylon is used to-day for more than a hundred different products.

Fox Photos.

TESTING NYLON

Like rayon, the size of nylon yarn is measured in the industry in *denier* (the weight of 9,000 metres of yarn in grammes). This picture shows us a worker in a British nylon factory testing yarn for denier. It seems incredible that so light and fine a yarn should have so many uses and such powers of resistance to wear and strain.

rayon and nylon is becoming an important industry in countries of the British Commonwealth.

Since nylon is a new fibre, with new qualities, many questions have been asked as to how things made from nylon should be treated and how they will wear. We know that nylon is strong, that it is very fine, and that it is extremely light (an American firm has recently marketed a nylon nightdress weighing as little as five-sixteenths of an ounce). But it is also tough and resists rubbing. It is so smooth that when it is washed the surface dirt comes away very easily. It also dries very quickly after washing and, what is more, dries crisply and smoothly so that

every bobbin of yarn made was urgently needed for war purposes. But to-day, this yarn that is finer than silk is being used for dress materials, curtains and coverings, brushes, underwear, ties and eiderdowns, as well as for tents, hammocks, blood filters, raincoats, and many industrial purposes. Moreover, nylon can be combined with wool, silk, or rayon to make special high-quality fabrics.

Imperial Chemical Industries Ltd. and Courtaulds have together founded the firm of British Nylon Spinners Ltd. Through the world-wide connections of these companies the manufacture of

it does not have to be ironed. The housewife who washes her stockings, for example, will find that they dry in an hour or two—if they are made of nylon; and she will know that since they are made of nylon, she must never attempt to iron them.

Nylon fabrics can be ironed, however, and they have the advantage that they will not attract moths or other fabric-destroying insects. Nylon, too, is damp-resisting, and many yachts now have their sails made from the wonder fibre. It has indeed so many advantages that the uses of this amazing textile discovery are continually increasing.

THE ROMANCE OF WOOL

PROVIDERS OF WARMTH AND WEALTH

For long centuries the making of wool into cloth has employed thousands of men and women—and all the wool has been provided by sheep. Britain's early prosperity was due to her wool trade; Australia's amazing growth during the last century and a half is based on the wool from her sheep. Our photograph shows two prize Australian Merino rams—and the Merino reigns supreme in the main sheep-raising areas of Australia.

OF all the animals in this world the sheep is one of the least respected. " Silly as a sheep " is as common an expression as is " Brave as a lion." Yet the lion is of little use in the world while the sheep is one of the most valuable. There is nothing in the history of the British Commonwealth of Nations which records the important part played by lions, but sheep figure prominently in the development of the prosperity of the British race in various parts of the world.

It is to the sheep and their coats of fine wool that one of the most important textile industries in the world owes its existence. Here we are not concerned with the sheep's value as food, which is important, but with the part it has played in clothing the human race.

The industry of wool-making has been associated with the British Isles for many centuries. There are references to it in the writings of Pliny, the Roman historian. Wool was used by the ancient Britons before the Romans came, but it was they who probably introduced new methods. Winchester became a centre for the manufacture of woollen clothing for the Roman armies and Britain became known for the wool it supplied.

In the time of Edward the Confessor definite regulations were laid down for the conduct of the wool trade, and from the twelfth to the fifteenth century England's main commercial undertaking was the export of raw wool. In the fourteenth and fifteenth centuries an ever-increasing proportion of the wool clip was retained for the manufacture of cloth and felt, and later the export of raw wool was restricted and even prohibited. British cloth was becoming famous and, as the trade in raw wool declined, the trade in cloth increased and London became one of the chief trading centres in Europe. Britain was becoming an industrial and commercial nation.

Different types of woollen goods were made in different districts. The West of England, Wales, Scotland, and Ulster in Northern Ireland all have to-day their distinctive types of woollen manufactures, but for more than a century the West Riding of Yorkshire, with adjacent parts of Lancashire, has been the main centre of Britain's wool industry.

Australia Comes In

Before the end of the eighteenth century Britain needed not only all the wool produced in the country but was willing to buy from other countries. The romance of wool at this stage switches to the little-known and undeveloped land of Australia. An English officer,

John Macarthur, who held the post of Commandant at Parramatta, was granted two small blocks of land, one of which, " Elizabeth Farm," became important in Australian history as the birthplace of the great sheep and wool industry of Australia.

When Macarthur visited England in 1803 the woollen manufacturers of Yorkshire were keenly interested in the prospect he put before them of New South Wales becoming an important source of supply. That was the beginning of the Australian wool industry. Less than fifty years later Australia was the world's chief exporter of wool, and to-day the sheep of the Commonwealth produce one-quarter of the total wool supply of the world.

The production of wool is now Australia's greatest industry and her sheep population of over 100 millions is more than double that of the next two most important wool-producing

Australian National Publicity Association.
PRODUCERS OF THE WORLD'S BEST WOOL
One-quarter of the world's wool is produced in Australia where on the sunny plains covered with sweet herbage record wool clips are obtained. A century and a half ago the average fleece weighed only 3 lb.; to-day Australian merinos yield over 9 lb. of the finest wool. In this picture sheep are being yarded for shearing at Koroit in Victoria, Australia.

SHEEP=SHEARING IN QUIET PASTURES

Central Press.

As far back as the Norman Conquest wool-growing was a main source of wealth in England and our earliest prosperity as a trading nation was due to our wool and cloth exports. In the picture above is seen the first stage in the great woollen industry when the fleece is taken from the sheep with the aid of a clipping machine which has now displaced the old-time shears.

International Wool Secretariat.

SORTING THE WOOL

The wool from Australia, New Zealand, and even from Britain itself has arrived at the mill. The first to deal with it are the sorters who work by a north light as their judgment of the different grades is based on what they see. The wool in each fleece is sorted into different qualities and then passed on to be scoured and cleaned until it is ready to be made into yarn.

countries—the United States of America and Argentina, which have about 50 million sheep each.

Australia herself uses for home manufacture about 12 per cent. of the wool she produces, and the remainder is exported. This single commodity, Wool, represents nearly 40 per cent. of the total Commonwealth exports of merchandise and is the basis of Australia's prosperity and her international solvency. Her biggest customer is Britain, and, with the producers of New Zealand and South Africa, Australia helps to finance technical research in Britain into the problems and improvements in the manufacture of woollen goods.

In New Zealand a missionary, Samuel Marsden, tried to establish a small flock of sheep in 1814, but it was not very successful. It was not until 1834, six years before New Zealand came officially under the British flag, that John Bell Wright permanently established a sheep flock. To-day there are more than 32 million sheep in New Zealand and sheep-farming is the Dominion's principal industry, while Britain is, and always has been, her best customer.

The manufacture of woollen goods is still one of Britain's great industries and British breeds of sheep are the foundation stock of sheep-breeding in all parts of the world. The Merino type of sheep, which is not a British breed, is also prominent and has been used to improve the wool in many British breeds. Merinos have been largely used in Australia, while New Zealand's own special breed, the Corriedale, which gives both excellent meat and wool, comes from the crossing of Merinos with English Lincolns and Leicesters.

To come back to wool, which is the fleece or coat of the sheep, the first task is the removal of this from the living animal. Some preparation is necessary before this is done. The sheep are brought in from pasture and herded together in an immense pen (or railed-in enclosure), next to which is a long, narrow tank of water. Then, one at a time, they are driven along an enclosed passage which leads from the pen to the tank, and as they pass along a strong spray of hot or warm water is shot over them. The purpose of this is to loosen the dirt in their thick and curly coats.

Next, still in single file, they pass into the tank of water and swim towards its distant end. The friction thus set up causes the loosened dirt to fall from their coats; finally, as each sheep scrambles from the tank, a strong douche of pure water thoroughly rinses it.

After washing, the sheep are put to pasture on land entirely free from straw and gritty matter, so that the wool remains clean while it dries in readiness for shearing.

Until a few years ago sheep-shearing was a long, slow task, each animal having to be clipped by hand. To-day hand-shearing is still practised, but the shears are driven by electricity, allowing each man to shear anything up to two hundred sheep every day. The record of 456 sheep in nine hours was made in New Zealand in 1953.

Farewell to Winter's Coat

To watch a skilled sheap-shearer at work is a really fascinating experience. Holding his shears lightly in one hand, he stoops over the animal, slips the shears into its coat—and the thick and heavy fleece immediately begins to peel off, just like the skin of an orange. Since the highest prices are paid for fleeces in one piece, an important part of his job is to see that he does not break the long and even process.

As far as the living sheep is concerned

International Wool Secretariat.

MULE SPINNING

After the wool has been thoroughly scoured and cleaned it may be dyed, or it may be left until it has become cloth before being dyed. In any case it must go through certain processes which make it into a rope-like " roving " of soft wool, almost too soft to handle. It must be transformed into a thread or yarn by the spinning mule. The bobbins of roving are fitted to the standing part of the machine, and each roving is drawn out, twisted and wound on to the bobbins as yarn.

there is, of course, not the slightest pain or discomfort. In fact, since shearing is done only in the warm weather, the sheep is no doubt only too pleased to be rid of its heavy winter coat!

Now, one of the most dread diseases known to mankind lives in wool; some wools, indeed, are so prone to carry the germ that the British Government enforces their disinfection before they are passed into factories for the manufacturing processes which follow. Persian lamb is one of these wools; the germ it carries is known as *anthrax*, and was, until a few years ago, a terrible enemy of the wool merchant.

Cleanliness, therefore, is the first consideration of the experts who sort the wools into different grades; indeed, cleanliness in its highest possible form is maintained throughout.

When the manufacturer receives the wool his first task is to clean or *scour* it; for despite the washing it received when on the back of the sheep, and the careful pasturing which followed, it has naturally picked up all sorts of stray foreign matter.

Scouring calls for great care; bad treatment can injure the texture of the wool, and also, unless the cleansing is both thorough and gentle, the various dyes to which it will possibly be subjected will not take properly.

A scouring machine is a tank about 60 feet in length, its interior fitted with a series of rollers and nozzles. The end into which the wool is fed contains very hot water, which, like the hot spray originally given to the sheep, loosens the dirt. The wool is steeped in this water, after which the rollers move and carry it forward into warm water, then on into water slightly colder, and so forth, again and again, through waters whose temperatures gradually decrease, until, at the far end of the tank, it meets with pure rinsing water. All this

International Wool Secretariat.

HOW WEFT YARN INTERLACES WITH THE WARP

The " weft " yarn is wound on bobbins which fit in the weaver's shuttle and take the weft yarn backwards and forwards across the loom to interlace with the warp threads. Here we see the weft thread and shuttle passing through the " shed " created by the raising and lowering of the warp threads, leaving the weft yarn behind.

IN AUSTRALIA'S WOOLLEN MILLS

Carding is one of the most important processes in the preparation of the raw wool for making into garments. The wool is teased out and any burrs or seeds still adhering to the material are removed. Here the carding machinery in an Australian mill is seen in operation.

Australian News & Information Bureau.

The manufacture of woollen goods made its first modest beginning in Australia nearly 150 years ago and has steadily progressed until to-day it represents one of the Commonwealth's leading industries. In this photograph is seen one of the circular combing machines at work in an Australian mill.

International Wool Secretariat.

PREPARATIONS FOR WEAVING THE CLOTH

Before cloth can be woven the warp must be built by arranging the yarns parallel and equidistant, and running them on to the warp mill at an even tension. The " warp " is the collection of threads which run lengthwise in a piece of cloth, and here we see the warp threads being placed on to the " balloon " before weaving begins.

time the nozzles have been ejecting water on to the wool, maintaining the correct temperatures and forcing the dirt from it in preparation for its next process.

The grease in wool has a good commercial value and the water in which the wool is washed is afterwards treated with acid to separate the fats. Crude brown wool grease is useful as a lubricant, but when refined the substance is known as lanolin which is more readily absorbed than most other fats when rubbed into the skin. It is also antiseptic to some extent. For these two important reasons it is largely used as a basis for face creams and ointments.

After washing comes the drying process—and although drying would seem to be a simple matter, in this case it is governed by a strict, stern rule: namely, that gentle and even drying *must* be enforced; for wool carelessly dried, either too much or too quickly, is considerably lessened in value.

There are many types of machine in use, but one of the most popular in this country is known as the *Jumbo*. It is a massive, churn-like construction into which the wool is emptied following its passage through the washing apparatus. Once it has received its precious cargo, the machine is set in motion; it rolls and rolls, the great masses of wool slide through it, and warm air, ejected into the Jumbo, gently but firmly rids the wool of its moisture. When it is finally withdrawn, the wool is soft, clean, and correctly dried.

From this stage onwards the various processes through which the wool passes depend upon the ultimate uses to which it will be put; knitting wools, for instance, receive vastly different treatments from wools destined for carpet manufacture.

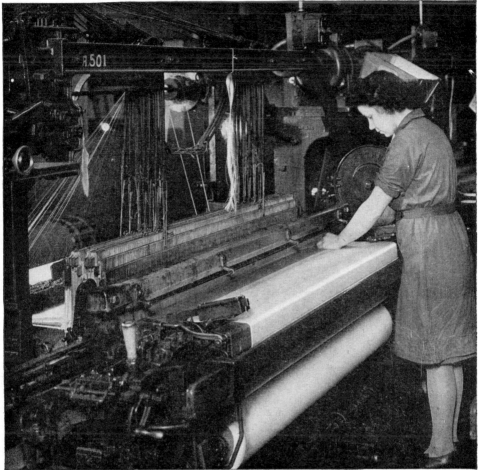

International Wool Secretariat.

WHEN THE CLOTH IS WOVEN

Here we have the final outcome of the interlacing of warp and weft during the weaving process, and it is this interlacing which constructs the cloth. There is still much to be done after the cloth leaves the loom. The dyer and the finisher play their part and then the cloth is inspected for faults before going to the burler and mender who make the cloth as perfect as possible.

It should be mentioned here, however, that woven wool cloth may be either woollen or worsted. Woollen cloth is made from yarns in which the fibres lie in all directions, thus producing a relatively rough surface. Worsted cloth is made from yarns in which the fibres lie more or less parallel, thus producing a comparatively smooth surface. The shorter-fibred wools are generally used for the woollen cloth industry. For worsted cloth the longer-fibred wool is preferably used.

Having sorted the raw wools into their respective grades, the worsted manufacturer subjects them to a process of combing, known as *carding*. This is to open out the mass of fibres and eventually produce a uniform sliver or ribbon of wool, and to remove any vegetable matter which may be adhering to the material.

This carding is probably the most important process in the preparation of wool for the manufacture of cloth. The wool is teased out and shredded as it passes through the steel claws of a machine which eventually reduces the wool to a fine web of fibres, free from lumps. This comes from the machine as a thin veil 5 feet wide, and is then split into narrow strips about half-an-inch wide; the same mechanism then proceeds to rub these strips into thin, soft ropes, called rovings, which are then wound on to large bobbins.

To make a thread or yarn from a roving it has to be made strong, and to give it strength it must be twisted. This is done on a spinning mule (a machine developed from the Hargreaves Spinning Jenny). Revolving spindles spin, that is, twist the yarn, thus binding the fibres tightly together and making the thread strong.

From these single threads many kinds of yarns are made. Some of the yarn must be dealt with to make the " warp " —the threads which run lengthwise in a piece of cloth. Some must be wound on bobbins (called pirns) which fit in the weaver's shuttle to take this " weft " yarn backwards and forwards across the loom to interlace with the warp threads.

When eventually the cloth comes from the loom it is harsh and thready to the touch and has to be " finished," another fairly complicated series of processes which produce the finished effect desired. All cloths also undergo " cropping " in which high-speed knives, operating rather like a lawn-mower, go over the cloth and crop the surface hairs to a uniform level.

Everything possible is done during the manufacture of woollen cloth to preserve the character of the yarns and to display the structure of the weave. The talent of the designer has full play, and each step in the complicated processes adds its part to the beauty and value of the finished cloth, ready for the tailor to manufacture into suits to clothe mankind.

Yorkshire Evening Post.

IN THE CHIEF CENTRE OF BRITAIN'S WOOL INDUSTRY

For more than a century the West Riding of Yorkshire has been the chief centre of the British wool industry and nine-tenths of the worsted and two-thirds of the woollen goods produced in Britain are manufactured in this area. The photograph above shows a typical night scene of the factories in the Colne Valley, looking towards Milnsbridge in the West Riding of Yorkshire.

PLASTICS—A MODERN INDUSTRY

Chad Valley Co., Ltd.

MOULDED IN PLASTIC MATERIAL

Plastics are not by any means a new discovery, but within the past ten years a great many new plastics have been evolved. Certain kinds are particularly suitable for children's playthings and the toy train and motor lorry, seen in the picture above, are typical examples of the use of plastics in this field.

SOMETIMES, in the progress of world affairs, man seems to demand something more than nature can provide from her rich stock of timber, minerals and other raw materials. In such a case science often rises to the occasion, finding in its harvest of knowledge garnered through patient research a fruitful means of fulfilling man's requirements and giving to nature just a small measure of respite.

What we to-day call plastics for the want of a better word is an excellent example of such a happening, and there is every indication that in the future we are likely to depend more and more upon plastic products. At the same time, let us understand that we are not about to explore in this chapter an undeveloped field. For many years now we have had things made from plastics, and you have only to think of the flexible material with which photographic films are backed; of table-tennis balls, gramophone records and the fountain-pen barrel to recall some very important uses for various substances that fall within this group. Sealing wax is, by the way, a natural plastic product and there are seals in

perfect condition now that were impressed upon documents long centuries ago.

You will first of all wish to know what plastics are. They may perhaps best be described as a range of materials that in the course of manufacture can be rendered plastic or soft with heat and then moulded to the required shape under great pressure.

Strangely enough, modern plastics first came into being because there was a world shortage of ivory and the price of this natural commodity became too high for the commercial needs of the time. A scientist thereupon produced what we call celluloid by treating cotton cellulose (taken from the cells of cotton down) with an acid. You will know how valuable celluloid is. It is used for billiard balls, piano keys, handles of knives, combs and other articles, and was invented in 1868.

Discovered by Accident

More than twenty years later another scientist discovered a second plastic called casein. It is said that he found out his valuable secret through mingling by accident in his laboratory some sour

A NEW GARAGE IS OPEN

E.V.B. Plastics Ltd.

For the modern boy interested in motor-cars and everything connected with them the toy-makers have produced the roadside garage seen in the photograph above, complete with petrol pumps. The cars and motor lorries are in various colours. For these the plastic material used is cellulose acetate.

Punfield & Barstow (Mouldings) Ltd.

Here we have another example of the use of plastics in the manufacture of toys for children. The table and four chairs seen above are light, practically unbreakable, and are made in a variety of different colours.

milk and a substance known as formalin, and here was an artificial product to take the place of horn and possibly even of tortoiseshell, for both of which we had previously looked to nature. Later, camphor was used in connection with cellulose and so there arose xylonite, a plastic everyone will know.

We must go to America to follow up the next vital stage of development. Here, in 1909, Dr. Leo Hendrik Baekeland was busily conducting experiments in an effort to discover an artificial substance that would materially advance the science of plastics. He too used formalin or formaldehyde (largely produced from coal) in close combination with phenol (a product of coal tar) which he blended together in certain proportions under heat.

It was in this manner that there came into being one of the principal plastic materials, a man-made resin or resinoid which is known by the trade name Bakelite, a name that is now a household word in the realms of plastics all the world over.

You will all know natural resin, which is a kind of gum that comes from trees and plants. You may often have seen the stuff oozing from a plum or cherry tree in the garden and have

noticed some of it in the house when prepared for commerce for floor-polishing and other domestic purposes. If you play the violin, you may have rubbed the hairs of your bow with a piece of refined resin, and the synthetic product can be seen in lumps of a dark amber hue, almost transparent, and both hard and brittle.

Good Dr. Baekeland, after whom Bakelite is called, at first mixed his precious resinoid in small test tubes in his laboratory. It is now produced

Hydraulic Press Mnfg. Co.

A HOT PLATE PRESS FOR PLASTICS

In this picture we see one of the big presses used by the Plastic manufacturer. It is equipped with eleven steam plates, each measuring 44 inches by 40 inches by 2 inches, and is capable of squeezing the moulding material at a pressure of many tons.

to understand that in the industry we are exploring together there are thermo-plastic and thermo-setting materials. The term thermo need not bother us at all, for it means merely something that has to do with heat. Thus, the former substances, of which celluloid is one example, can be softened by heat and hardened by cooling again and again, and lose little or nothing in the process.

In the second group, however, the materials are moulded under heat and pressure and this brings about polymerisation. This is a long and perhaps puzzling word, but it means simply that chemical changes take place and the entire mass, however large or small it may be, becomes one substance that has set permanently.

United Ebonite & Lorival Ltd.

PREPARED FOR A RAINY DAY

The use of plastics has been extended to many articles of wear and in this picture are seen examples of their use in the manufacture of waterproof coats. These are very light to wear or carry yet proof against showers or heavy rainstorms. The material in this case is P.V.C., which is a convenient abbreviation of the chemical name Polyvinyl Chloride.

Wood Flour for Filling

Having got thus far, it will be clear to you that the foundation of thermo-setting plastics is artificial resin, but this is not all by any means, for the resin itself would be much too brittle if used alone, and none of the desired effect could be obtained. This resinoid requires what is called a filler and so there are mixed with it certain other commodities in powder form according to the purpose the finished article will be called upon to fulfil.

Wood flour is such a filler, and the name explains itself. Mica (a glass-like mineral) and the fibres of cellulose (obtained from plants) are other fillers,

in whole batteries of large stills, and the chemicals which feed them are stored in monstrous containers, each having a capacity of some thousands of gallons. The resinoid comes from the stills in a sluggish, treacle-like substance which hardens as it cools in giant trays. When cold it is in appearance not unlike barley sugar. Next, for the making of plastics, the resin has to be passed through a powerful crushing machine until it is converted into a powder as fine as flour.

At this stage, it will be well for us

and when asbestos is used we obtain a plastic that will resist a great deal of heat. As for the cellulose fibres, they serve almost to reinforce or strengthen, as do steel rods in concrete.

To go on to the next stage, the resinoid, when it has been reduced to a fine powder, has the filler and such colouring matter as is required mixed with it and the mixture is fed in a continuous stream on to the heated rollers of a special appliance. The heat renders the whole mass plastic, causing the resin to impregnate the filler, and it leaves the rollers very much in the same form as would a sheet of crude rubber. It has then to pass, by means of a conveyor belt, to another crushing machine and thence through a sieve after which it is ready for the final process.

If you had the privilege of watching the making of moulded plastics you would stand in a room at a factory near an hydraulic press capable of exerting a squeeze of some 70 tons, though there are presses in use for exceptional purposes that can squeeze at 1,500 tons, and even more, whilst moulding pressure may be anything from 1,000 pounds to 4,500 pounds to the square inch of the material. On the base plate of this press you would see moulds of heavy steel, with the counterparts in the upper jaw, and you could detect for yourself if the

press were heated by steam, gas or electricity.

The advance of plastics as a commodity of everyday use has brought into being a new and highly-skilled operative known as a moulder, and you will be able presently to watch him as he places in the bottom part of every mould a carefully measured quantity of the materials required.

The moulds themselves are hot before the powder goes into them and the press is brought down and left for a period that may be as much as fifteen minutes or less than one minute, according to the nature of the articles being made. Then, as the upper part of the press is raised, the completed items, whilst still hot, are ejected mechanically from the moulds.

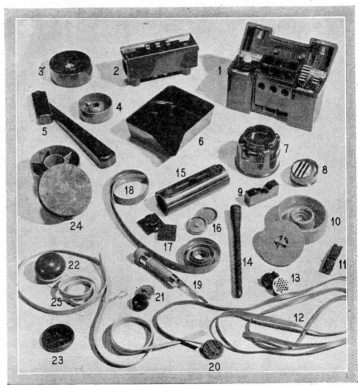

United Ebonite & Lorival Ltd.

IN WIDE VARIETY

It would be impossible to list all the articles in everyday use which are to-day made in plastics. Our photograph shows an interesting range of mouldings for various uses, most of which will be easily identified. Among them are: (1) Water-testing box assembly; (8) Telephone mouthpiece; (18) Belting; and (24) Cigarette box and cover.

AEROPLANES, SHIPS AND CARS

This is a small selection from a wide range of children's toys. All are made in plastic material with " Celastoid " Injection Moulding Powder. What colour is required is incorporated during the course of manufacture and is therefore permanent. The toys shown above were made by Cascelloid Ltd., Fraser and Glass Ltd., and Fairylite Ltd.

On the other hand, if you had been a fascinated spectator of the thermo-plastic process, the material would have been put into cold moulds and left in them after the processing until they had given up all their heat. The highly-polished appearance in both classes of article is due entirely to the fact that the surface of the steel mould is perfectly burnished.

By Mass Production

What sort of articles are moulded in this way by the thermo-setting method ? We can think at once of the stan-dardised telephone instruments, the outside cases and inner component parts for radio sets, caps for bottles, camera cases, electric bell boxes, automatic lighters, trinket receptacles and so on. All such useful items are made on mass production lines in their hundreds or thousands and the high cost of steel moulds is amply justified.

It would not, however, be profitable to make such moulds for the casting of only a very small number of articles and we must never run away with the idea that plastics are necessarily cheap; actually, in many instances, they are produced only at very considerable expense.

There are plastics now to represent china, porcelain and even glass, most of the articles being produced by moulding, but other and equally valu-able types reach the market without moulding at all. Thus, in the case of some sheets formed by the thermo-plastic process, the material can after-wards be softened by heating and then finished in steel moulds or wooden formers to make glass-like enclosures for aircraft, children's dolls, babies' rattles and so forth. Where a hollow article is being made it is moulded in two halves, steam being admitted to force the halves into the moulds, the edges needing merely to be welded. As a matter of fact, welding is a simple process with such plastics for whilst the edges are soft through heat they join readily together.

Yet another most useful form of plastic material is that known as laminated plastics. In this instance sheets of paper or of fabric are saturated with the artificial resin and allowed to dry. They are then assembled and arranged in a pack one sheet above another until there are sufficient to form a board of the required thickness. The laminated or built-up packs are next placed between burnished steel plates and subjected to heat and pressure, the result being a panel much stronger than one produced by moulding.

Such boards, up to 8 feet by 4 feet in area, are most effective when used for surfacing walls, forming table tops, counter tops, doors and even ceilings. They can be seen in the saloons and corridors of some of our crack railway trains and in the lounges on ocean liners, whilst as decorations to bathrooms they are ideal because no steam can affect them and a mere wiping down is sufficient to keep them clean. These laminated boards vary in thickness from that of a postcard to about 6 inches.

Moulding by Injection

Another process of great interest is

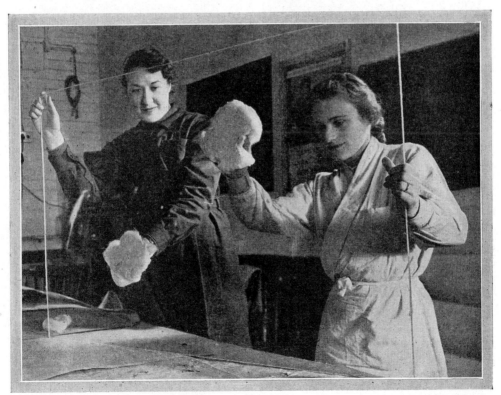

I.C.I. Ltd. (Plastics Division).

AS CLEAR AS GLASS BUT STRONGER

Among the more recently discovered of the many plastic materials now in use, Perspex has become most widely known owing to its use in aircraft. It is much lighter than glass, can be produced in sheets of various thickness and moulded into any desired shape under gentle heat.

I.C.I. Ltd.

CORRUGATED PERSPEX

Here we see a sheet of corrugated "Perspex" (methyl methacrylate) mainly used for factory top lights set in corrugated iron roofing. It has also been used successfully for partitions and screens in restaurants.

that known as injection moulding. Here the cold moulding powder in its appropriate mixture is fed into a hopper from which it passes to a heated cylinder where it quickly becomes fluid. It is then, by means of a piston, forced through a nozzle into a mould at a lower temperature so that the plastic hardens at once. Combs, frames for spectacles, ashtrays and even thimbles are made in this way and at a speed that seems almost impossible, the machinery employed being in the main automatic. Incidentally, in a thermo-setting ashtray, a lighted cigarette may be allowed to burn itself out and not leave the slightest mark.

There are several other processes in our new world of plastics, but sufficient has been written to give some idea of the vast field opened up by this artificial material, and we must all realise that in the future it is going to be still more important. We may even be approaching an age of plastics, for chemists are constantly finding new combinations of materials.

In Pastel Shades

Let us remember that almost any colour, including the pastel shades, may be incorporated into plastics in the course of manufacture so that no subsequent painting is required. If desired, as in the case of table tops and wall panels, an artist's design can be included as the moulding is fashioned and the resulting picture permanently protected by a film of resin. In our homes we may have plastic skirting boards and decorative wall tiles, whilst pipes and cisterns for the domestic water supply can be made of the same substance.

Varnishes, lacquers and cements are made from the resinoid and are available for innumerable uses, being applied by spraying, brushing or dipping. The varnish is excellent for insulating electrical fitments, whilst the cement is employed for fitting the bulbs of electric lamps into their sockets and many similar purposes.

The use of plastics for gear-wheels in machinery has recently come very much to the fore, largely because of the silence of such gears when in operation. Small gears can be moulded and it should be remembered that when a suitable base mixture is utilised plastic material can be drilled, turned on a lathe, planed, cut with a saw and shaped with a chisel, rasp or file as might be the case with ordinary wood. Moreover, a plastic substance can be faced with metal when such a step is necessary. Even the bearings of certain classes of machinery can be formed of plastics and bearings of laminated plastics are said to wear as well as those of bronze, water being frequently used as a lubricant. Further, the electro plating or spraying of bearings with metal is well within the range of the industry.

There does not appear to be any limit to the uses of plastic materials. We already use plastic window frames, dashboards and instrument fascias in our cars and plastic coachwork will probably be a feature of many cars in due course. As far as aeroplanes go, this type of material is extensively employed and reinforced panels for the fuselage have proved their worth, whilst plywood panels interleaved with resinoid instead of glue are noted for their strength and durability.

During the past ten years a great many new plastics have been discovered. Three of the most widely known of these are Perspex, P.V.C. and Nylon.

Perspex, the Glass-like Plastic

Perspex became most widely known owing to its use in aircraft. It is a substance which resembles glass in appearance, but it is very much lighter. Its chemical name is methyl methacrylate. It can be produced in sheets of various thicknesses and it has the interesting property that when sheets of Perspex are slightly warmed they become pliable, so that they can be moulded into any desired shape.

One of the most interesting applications of this material to peacetime uses is illustrated in the pictures shown in these pages. Here we see a section of corrugated Perspex suitable for use in the roof covering of a factory. This forms a skylight which is practically unbreakable.

P.V.C. in War and Peace

Here is an interesting story about

I.C.I. Ltd.

UNBREAKABLE TOP LIGHTS

In this photograph we see the " Perspex " sheets shown in the previous picture in actual use on the corrugated iron roof of a locomotive shed at a London station. As it is practically unbreakable and easily fixed its advantages are obvious.

DASH PANEL   INSTRUMENT   CONTROL   WINDSCREEN   WINDOW
                PANEL   BUTTONS   FINISH   STRIP   FINISHER

ASH TRAYS

PACKAGE TR
FINISH STRIP

HAND BRAKE
LEVER HANDLE   GEAR CHANGE
                                     LEVER KNOB

HORN BUTTON
SURROUND

Ford Motor Co., Ltd.

FITTINGS FOR MOTOR-CARS

The motor-car manufacturers use a considerable number of fitments made in various kinds of plastic material. In the photograph above some of these fittings are seen from the viewpoint of the driving-seat and their purpose is indicated. The use of plastics in aeroplanes and cars is steadily expanding and the all-plastic car is a possibility of the future.

P.V.C. These initials are an abbreviation of the chemical name of Polyvinyl Chloride, a plastic made from hydrochloric acid and acetylene. This substance has properties very similar to those of India rubber. During the war, when our rubber supplies were cut off, manufacturers of electric cables and also rubber tyre manufacturers were faced with the problem of finding a substitute for the rubber which up to then had been considered indispensable for their products. P.V.C. proved to be the plastic which most nearly fulfilled their requirements. Many thousands of tons of P.V.C. were used by cable makers during the period of rubber scarcity.

The peace-time uses of P.V.C. are very varied. In addition to its use in the electrical industry it is used for chemical piping, and for lining tanks to protect them from corrosion. It has been made up into useful articles, such as tobacco pouches, braces, belts, wrist watch straps, and garters.

By passing the material through hot rollers it can be spread out into sheets and many beautiful colourings can be given to the material which can then be used for manufacturing waterproof garments, curtaining materials and so on.

Not the Cheapest, but the Best

Many people have the impression that plastics provide a cheap substitute for other materials. This may have been true in the very early days of plastics when, for instance, white celluloid was often used as a substitute for ivory.

It is not true to-day. The materials which are now being produced by plastics manufacturers are new materials which have properties not possessed by any materials used before. For instance, laminated plastics are being very largely used for the panelling of rooms in public buildings and in luxury liners, such as the *Queen Elizabeth* and the *Queen Mary*. These plastic materials were selected by the designers not because they were cheaper than other available materials, but because they were the very best materials available for the particular purpose in view.

To take another example, Perspex was used during the war for pilots' windscreens, gun turrets and bomb-aiming windows not because it was the cheapest material available—glass is much cheaper—but because it had properties not possessed by any other material known to science.

Nylon, the Wonderful Fibre

Nylon is another of the new plastics which has become very widely known. Nylon stockings are highly valued not because nylon is cheaper than silk or rayon (artificial silk), to which it provides an alternative, but because the nylon fibres have qualities which are not found in real silk or rayon. These qualities provided the reason for the extensive use of nylon during the war. Parachutes, parachute cords and ropes for towing gliders were made of nylon fibres because these fibres possessed the requisite strength and resilience which were necessary for these particular applications. The question of cost was a secondary consideration. Weight for weight, nylon is stronger than steel.

Since the war, nylon fibres have been applied to many other purposes. For instance, tooth-brush bristles, hair-brush bristles and surgical sutures, *i.e.*, for sewing up wounds, instead of the silk or cat-gut fibres which were previously used.

One of the most important things about nylon, like many other plastics, is that the raw materials from which it is made are very plentiful. In order to make nylon, the plastics chemist takes salt, coal, water and air and by a complicated series of reactions he causes these substances to split up and to form new combinations resulting finally in this wonderful modern substance.

P. B. Cow & Co. Ltd.

GUARDING THE FORT

Toy soldiers have always been popular but the days when they were made of lead and tin are fading and plastics are being largely used nowadays. The soldiers seen above are in khaki and were moulded in Polythene, one of the new plastics.

Plastics for Water-softening

One of the most surprising applications of plastics is in connection with water-softening. Certain plastics when suitably treated can be used in a water-softening plant, so that water passed through the water-softening equipment becomes for all practical purposes as good as distilled water, *i.e.*, free from any trace of "hardness." One type of this apparatus has a battery of water-softening tanks which use synthetic resins or plastics as a water-softening medium. An especially interesting feature of this method of water-softening is that the plastic reagent can be regenerated, that is, made as good as new, at intervals by treatment with a suitable acid.

British Industrial Plastics Ltd.

A TOY HOUSE BUILT IN SECTIONS

A doll's house has been a popular gift for children for many generations, and here we have one made of plastic material in sections so that the child can become a builder when fitting the different parts together.

Plastics from Sand

The very latest developments in this field are silicone plastics. The basis of this new series of plastics is silica or sand. When sand is heated with coke in the presence of chlorine gas, a substance called silicon tetrachloride is formed. When this chemical is treated with a magnesium compound a new substance called chlorosilane is produced. From this a number of plastic materials can be produced by suitable chemical reactions.

Some of these plastic substances are liquid and can be used in place of insulating oil in electrical apparatus, whilst others are solid and have properties which render them of particular interest to electrical manufacturers who wish to obtain materials with good insulating properties. Such materials can be used by the electrical manufacturer to prevent the electric current from leaking away from the wires and other conductors which he uses on his electrical machines.

It is not possible yet to make plastics which are as strong as steel or which can be beaten into different shapes as copper can. But many qualities, such as resistance to moisture, transparency, lightness, colour, high electrical resistance, ability to withstand heat, can all be obtained by selecting the correct plastic and combining it with certain other substances known as fillers. For many purposes plastics are taking the place of metals and wood, and it is not an exaggeration to say that, in view of the developments taking place, we are at the beginning of a new era, the Plastics Age.

MACHINES FOR THE FARMER

By courtesy of the David Brown Corporation (Sales) Ltd.

PULLING A TRAILER AND GREEN-CROP LOADER

Britain has an important agricultural engineering industry which makes tractors and tools not only for her farmers, but for those of many other countries. The picture shows a British tractor pulling a trailer and green-crop loader. The spring tines of the loader revolve just clear of the ground, picking up the crop, which is delivered into the trailer.

OUR visit to the farms of Britain showed us that farmers now do more and more of their work with machinery. We saw, too, that Britain's farmers are generally much better equipped than those of other countries. To-day, practically every major farming operation can be done either entirely by machine or with machinery doing most of the work.

So it is not surprising that making of tractors and other farm equipment is an important British industry employing thousands of workpeople and using many large factories. The number of tractors and agricultural implements made in Britain is so great, and their design so good, that we send large quantities abroad every year. Farm machinery made in Britain can be seen at work everywhere. Only the United States does more than Britain to equip the world's farmers.

Man was not naturally a farmer. He was a hunter. But as his numbers grew, the wild life that was his food became less plentiful or retreated farther into the deep forests where it was no longer the target of his primitive hunting weapons. It was then that Man began cultivating the land, not as farmers cultivate it to-day but scratching the surface with a pointed stick to prepare the soil for his seeds.

The First Plough

Presently he found that he wanted to turn the soil to a greater depth than his pointed stick would permit. The shoulder-blade of a deer was of suitable shape and strength for this work, and it thus became his first shovel. Later, he made furrows for his seeds by pushing a tree branch through the soil, and because pushing was hard work, he tried pulling. His tree branch had become a plough.

An implement which is said to be almost as old as the plough is the harrow, and like the plough it began with a tree branch—or rather, several branches. These were laced in a wooden frame and drawn across the ground to level the ridges left by the plough and make the surface soil into a finer seed bed. In time, iron pegs, or tines, took the place of the branches. Another implement which has come down to us from the earliest times and is still widely used in many different forms is the hoe. It had its origin in the pointed stick that was Man's first cultivating implement.

Power for the Plough

If you watch a modern plough at work, you will notice that it not only cuts the furrow but inverts, that is, turns over, the slice that has been cut and exposes a new surface to the beneficial action of air, rain and frost. The crude, wooden ploughs of early times did nothing more than cut a shallow furrow, throwing up one or two inches of soil in ridges on either side of a sliding block. Ploughs of this kind are still used in the less advanced parts of the world, especially in the Middle East and Far East. Not until the eighteenth century did a plough which inverted the soil become popular in England. It came to us from the Netherlands and because it was improved at Rotherham, in Yorkshire, it was known as the Rotherham plough.

It was made almost entirely of wood, but the share was faced with iron and plates of the same metal encased the mouldboard. (The share is the part of the plough which cuts the underneath of the furrow slice; the mouldboard, the part which turns the slice over). By 1803, when Robert Ransome patented his self-sharpening ploughshare, the way was open for experiments with many kinds of plough bodies and fittings.

Although the plough, as the farmer's chief cultivating implement, must claim most of our attention, we must not forget the many other improvements in English farming during the eighteenth century. Among the notable figures who strove to improve farming practice was Jethro Tull, a Berkshire farmer, writer and

By courtesy of Ransomes, Sims & Jefferies Ltd.

PLOUGHS IN THE MAKING

These works at Ipswich, Suffolk, are world-famous for their ploughs and other farm machines. They were founded in 1789 by Robert Ransome, the inventor of the self-sharpening ploughshare, and are one of the oldest farm engineering enterprises in the country. This picture shows us the plough assembly line.

A LARGE TRACTOR FACTORY

This aerial view shows us one of the large factories where tractors are made. The plant is at Dagenham, on the banks of the river Thames, and produces cars as well as tractors. Note that the factory has its own loading jetties.

Photos by courtesy of the Ford Motor Co.

Here we see a finished tractor coming off the assembly line. It comprises more than 2,400 component parts made to an accuracy of a thousandth of an inch. At every stage in its manufacture, from basic raw materials to the completed tractor, it has been subject to rigid check and inspection.

inventor. At the very beginning of the century, he devised a machine that would sow seed in drills, or rows, sufficiently wide apart to allow hoeing and ploughing while the crop was growing and, in fact, almost until it matured. He published an account of his experiments in 1731 under the title, *Horse-hoeing Husbandry*, a work which did much to advance farming theory and method.

But let us return to the plough. Once invented, the plough had to be pulled, and Man naturally sought the easiest possible way. At first he had no farm animals, so the task fell to his wife, who dragged the plough through the soil much as she still does in some parts of the Continent and North Africa. Then donkeys, oxen and other animals took her place, as many as eight oxen being required for the heavy ploughs mentioned in Domesday Book. Mechanical power was not applied to farming until about the middle of the last century, when engineers began to design steam traction machines for such work as ploughing. In Britain steam traction engines were first used with ploughs about 1865, and then only on very large acreages. By modern standards, the method was cumbersome and expensive. Steam ploughing demanded two engines, one stationed opposite the other, and between them, the full width of the field. From a winding drum on each engine, a cable ran to the plough, and by working the drums the plough could be pulled from one side of the field to the other.

The Modern Tractor Appears

Britain really felt the need for farm tractors during the First World War, when she was experiencing the most serious food shortages she had ever known. By 1916, German U-boats had become so active that something had to be done to increase the quantity of home-grown food. So the pace of tractor design and construction quickened, for mechanising the farms was now of

By courtesy of the Ford Motor Co

A TRACTOR ON TEST

This unusual " caravan " plays an important part in testing a tractor. It is a dynamometer car and it is coupled to the tractor to test its pulling ability. During the test, the amount of fuel used by the tractor will be recorded also. Before a new tractor is put into production, a few prototype tractors will be made and tested on work under actual farm conditions.

ANIMALS THAT GIVE US WOOL AND HAIR

The fine Merino Sheep (top, left) comes from Australia. It is really a Spanish Sheep, introduced into Australia from South Africa in 1797. On the right is an English Southdown Sheep. The Shepherd lives on the steppes or grasslands of central Asia, and below him are the dark Alpaca and white Llama of Peru. The silky hair of the Angora Goat from Asia Minor (bottom, left) gives us mohair, from which articles ranging from bootlaces to velvet are made, while to the right is the long-bearded Barbary Sheep of the semi-desert tracts of North Africa.

N.P.K. VI, p. 400.

WEAVING FIGURED FABRIC ON A JACQUARD LOOM

Furnishing brocades and other fabrics in which the design is woven in during manufacture are made on Jacquard looms. This type of loom was invented by Joseph Marie Jacquard in 1804. The design is worked by the introduction of various coloured yarns, the arrangement of yarns differing in either quality or thickness, and variation in the interlacing of the warp and weft yarns. Any design is translated on to cards which cause some warp yarns to be lifted and others depressed, thus forming a passage through which the weft yarn can pass (by means of a shuttle) and make the interlacings which result in the figured design as seen in this picture.

By courtesy of the David Brown Corporation (Sales) Ltd.

HOW POTATOES ARE LIFTED

This implement is a potato spinner. Because it is fitted to the tractor linkage it can be quickly transported from field to field. As the tractor moves along, the spinner, which is driven from the tractor power take-off, brings up the potatoes. The main tines of the spinner are rubber-covered to prevent damage to the crop.

national importance. An all-purpose tractor, called the " M.O.M." because it was sponsored by the Ministry of Munitions, was built in large numbers and sent out to speed the ploughs of Britain. And in 1917, the first Ford tractors to be used in this country joined in the fight to defeat the U-boat blockade.

Henry Ford was undoubtedly one of the greatest American inventors and manufacturers, and you will probably at once think of him in connection with cars. Although his fame and fortune came from such inventions as the Model T, or " Ford car " and its successors, he experimented with tractor design before he drew up the plans of his first passenger car. The companies which bear his name to-day, not only in America, but in Britain and many other countries, play a very important part in providing tractors and other machinery for the farmer.

After the first World War, the cause of mechanised farming was taken up by

British motor-car manufacturers, who, in October, 1919, organised trials for farm tractors and " self-contained motor ploughs " at South Carlton, near Lincoln. It makes us smile now to see pictures of the pioneer machines which were entered for these tests, for most of them bear little resemblance to the compact, stream-lined tractors to be seen on our farms to-day. But the popularity of the trials showed that engineers in many parts of the country were striving to help the farmers, who for their part were equally interested in mechanisation and its future.

Among the men who helped to make that future was a farmer, engineer and inventor named Harry Ferguson, who had seen the out-of-date methods used by farmers in Ireland, where he had been making a farming survey for the Irish Department of Agriculture, and was convinced that the answer to their problems lay in machinery of revolu-tionary design. By 1920, he had designed a linkage that enabled a farmer to mount a plough on his tractor quite easily, and after many years of experiment Ferguson produced a light tractor which has become the basis of a whole system of farming, popular in many parts of the world.

His greatest achievement has been the invention of what agricultural engineers call the " hydraulic 3-point linkage," and this was naturally the great feature of his tractor. This remarkable invention, which has been described by a United Nations Economic Commission as " one of the most significant contributions to the mechanisation of agriculture," was quickly taken up in principle by other British engineers. It is one of the reasons why British wheeled tractors are so popular throughout the world.

Tractor and Implement

Now let us see exactly what the phrase " hydraulic 3-point linkage " means; understanding it is certainly much easier than you might at first think.

Have you ever pushed a stick into the ground and then tried to pull the stick along ? If you have, you will know that the soil resists the stick and makes pulling very difficult. The same thing happens when a farm implement is just towed (trailed is the word that farmers use) behind a tractor. The soil opposes the passage of the implement, sometimes so severely that the front of the tractor is lifted off the ground.

One answer to this problem, of course, is to build heavy weights on to the front of the tractor, but this is not a very good answer. Extra weight on the tractor means that more power is taken from the engine for moving the tractor, leaving less power for pulling the implement. Again, a weighted tractor sits more heavily on the soil, pressing it down hard; crops will not grow well in soil that has been packed in this way. This was the problem that Harry Ferguson solved with his hydraulic 3-point linkage.

The first point about this linkage is that the implement—a plough, for example—is actually linked, or attached

By courtesy of the David Brown Corporation (Sales) Ltd.

PLOUGHING ON A STEEP SLOPE IN NEW ZEALAND

British tractors and farm implements are exported to all parts of the free world. Here a crawler tractor and double furrow, semi-swamp plough are reclaiming steeply sloping land in New Zealand. After the swamp plough had broken the rough surface, a disc plough was used.

DRYING GRAIN

This experimental " platform " dryer handles grain threshed by combine harvesters. Sacks of grain are laid over openings in a large air chamber into which hot air is blown by a fan. The air passes through the grain, drying it in three to six hours.

Photos by courtesy of the National Institute of Agricultural Engineering.

This is a hay and straw pick-up baler. It is driven from the power take-off shaft of the tractor and is here seen picking up straw from a windrow left by a combine harvester. The bales of straw are being automatically tied with twine and then ejected from the baler.

to the tractor at three points. It is not permanently attached, of course; the linkage is quite simple and can be connected or disconnected in a few minutes so that the farmer can change from one implement to another without wasting time. The tractor is thus a mobile power unit which can be fitted quite quickly with whatever implement the farmer needs. Many British tractor manufacturers make or recommend a full range of implements for work with their tractors: a range which covers practically every farming operation.

An implement mounted on the tractor in the way described can be raised or lowered by the hydraulic lift, which is operated by a simple control lever. The combined effect of the linkage and the hydraulic lift is to transform pressure of soil against the implement into a downward pressure on the tractor wheels. The front of the tractor does not therefore want to rise, and the depth at which the implement works is constant—unless the driver raises the implement or puts it in deeper by using his hydraulic lift.

Not all tractors are wheeled; many tractors have caterpillar tracks, very much like those you see on tanks, and these are known as crawler tractors. Caterpillar tracks spread the weight of the tractor over a much larger area of ground, and pressure at any one point is therefore less than it would be with a wheeled tractor. The advantage of the crawler tractor is thus that it may be able to work on very soft or marshy ground, where a wheeled tractor might quickly become bogged down. Generally speaking, though, crawler tractors are more expensive to operate and maintain.

How a Tractor is Made

There are, however, thousands more wheeled tractors at work on British farms than there are crawlers. So let us go now to a big factory in the Midlands to see how wheeled tractors are made.

What a huge place the factory is!

By courtesy of Massey-Harris-Ferguson (Sales) Ltd.

A FARM TRACTOR IN THE MAKING

Another important tractor factory is at Coventry. In the two large machine shops of this factory parts are made ready for assembly into tractors. The shop seen in this picture is concerned with the heavier components.

By courtesy of Massey-Harris-Ferguson (Sales) Ltd.

THE ELECTRONIC BRAIN OF A MODERN TRACTOR FACTORY

From this central control room, the delivery of parts from the large component store to the assembly line is controlled. Delivery by the wonderful Monorail system can be slowed down or speeded up so that the work of putting the new tractors together can proceed smoothly at all times.

Thousands of people work here, and the machinery they use and the buildings they work in are together worth literally millions of pounds. The factory is capable of making nearly 320 tractors a day; every two and a quarter minutes, a finished tractor comes off the assembly line and is at once ready to start work on the farm. But tractors—and most farm machinery, for that matter—do not normally go direct from the factory to the farm. The factory usually supplies dealers and distributors at home and abroad, and they in turn supply the farmers and help them to keep their tractors in good order.

The factory covers ninety acres and its buildings are amongst the finest in the country. In fact, from the road, the front of the factory looks more like an imposing government building than a place where farm tractors are made. We shall find as we go round with our guide, who meets us in a beautifully panelled entrance hall, that everything possible

has been done to make for the comfort, welfare and efficiency of the workpeople. The huge hall which we see on our way to the factory proper is their fine dining and recreation room, where the catering is so well organised that it takes only about eight minutes to serve a three-course meal to 2,000 people and where dances, plays and parties take place in the evenings. The interior of the factory buildings and the machines themselves are painted in colours that are restful to the eyes. There are special bus services to take the people to and from their work. There are welfare and social schemes.

The Machine Shops

The story of the tractor begins in No. 1 Machine Shop, where castings and forgings made in foundries outside the main factory are tempered, machined and cut into components for the tractor transmission and gearbox. A great many fully automatic and self-feeding machines

TRACTORS TAKE SHAPE

These men are preparing the gears and central transmission, which are the first tractor components to be put on the main tractor assembly conveyor. Above them runs part of the Monorail system, which conveys on its hooks the various parts needed on the assembly line.

Photos by courtesy of Massey-Harris-Ferguson (Sales) Ltd.

Now the tractors are really taking shape, for they have reached the final stages of assembly. When complete, each tractor will undergo thorough tests and inspection before it is passed as being ready for the farmer. Some will be used on farms at home, others in distant lands.

A FARM MACHINERY SCHOOL

Not far from the great works at Coventry, the tractor-manufacturing company maintains a school where its own workpeople and those of its dealers and distributors can learn about handling and maintaining the tractors. As the picture shows, there is plenty of practical out-of-doors work.

Photos by courtesy of Massey-Harris-Ferguson (Sales) Ltd.

Provided that you have an instructor, one of the best ways of learning how a thing works is to take it to pieces and then fit it together again. That is why this stripped-down tractor proves of such interest to these students at the school.

are used in this shop, and some of the automatic gear-cutting machines may be worth nearly £20,000 each. Precision is essential in making the components of the tractor, and one part of the shop is concerned with checking and regrinding the cutting tools so that they work always to a fine degree of accuracy. It is important, too, that the components are strong enough and hard enough to stand up to the stresses and strains of farm work. So after tempering, machining and cutting, the parts undergo heat-treatment and are case-hardened.

In the No. 2 Machine Shop we can see the heavier parts of the tractor taking shape. Some of the machines used do a number of operations at once, others can operate in four directions simultaneously.

The Assembly Shop

From the machine shops, the finished parts go to a large components store where they are kept until required on the assembly line. This brings to our notice one of the most amazing features of the factory—the Monorail conveyor system. Its tracks—eleven miles of them!—run overhead and carry, suspended on moving hooks, the various parts that are needed on the assembly line, delivering them there at the very moment at which they are required. The conveyor system is regulated electronically from a central control room, the delivery of parts to the assembly line being speeded up or slowed down so that the work of assembly proceeds smoothly at all times. The progress of each stage is recorded in the control room so that there is no danger of the assembly line being held up through lack of certain parts or sub-assemblies. If this happened, the whole line might be held up and both time and money be lost.

The main assembly line is fed from a number of sub-assembly lines where individual units of the tractor, such as the gearbox, have been put together. The gears and transmission are the first components to go on the main line, and from then on, the tractor gradually takes

shape until the first stage of assembly is complete. The conveyor system then takes the partly-finished tractor through the paint-spraying booths and drying-ovens, after which the final stages of assembly begin.

Complete engines, made at another factory not far away and already tested, are fitted to the tractors on the assembly line and while this is being done, the rear axle assemblies are also fitted. Each tractor then passes off the line and on to a hydraulic platform where the large rear wheels are fitted. Then, under its own power, it is driven off for test and inspection. This final stage is most important, for every tractor that leaves the factory must be mechanically perfect. Thorough testing and inspection ensure that the farmer receives a tractor on which he can rely.

More than thirty different implements, ranging from a two-furrow plough, cultivator and harrow to a hammer mill, earth scoop and post-hole digger, are available for use with the tractors that we have just seen in the making. These implements are not made at the tractor factory or, indeed, by the tractor company. They are made by other agricultural engineering firms which co-operate with, and build to designs approved by, the tractor company. The latter does much more than the mere making and selling of tractors and approved implements. Not far from the factory it maintains a school where its dealers and their staffs can be trained in working and looking after the tractor and its implements. The school has lecture rooms, stores, a cinema, a fully-equipped workshop, living accommodation for the students and, of course, plenty of land where practical work can be done with the tractor and its equipment.

Better Farm Machinery

The firms who make machines for the farmers are naturally always striving to produce more efficient tractors and implements, but there are also independent research organisations which test

HARVESTER AND HEDGER

This is a self-propelled combined harvester and thresher working on a crop of barley. The machine cuts the crop with its 8-foot long cutter-bar, then threshes it and delivers the grain into bags.

Photos by courtesy of the National Institute of Agricultural Engineering.

This machine cuts hedges vertically, horizontally, or at an angle. The cutter-bar, which is guided by an operator, is mounted on a boom carried on the front of the tractor and is driven and counter-balanced by a small engine.

new machines, carry on design and development work of their own, and collect and publish reports of experiments and improvements. The main centre of this kind is the National Institute of Agricultural Engineering, which has its headquarters at Wrest Park, Silsoe, Bedfordshire. Another centre, the Scottish Machinery Station, at Howden, Mid Calder, Midlothian, is particularly concerned with hill farming in this part of Great Britain.

The testing of new machines at these centres is obviously a great help to the manufacturer and is often done at his request. The centres have special equipment which makes possible a detailed and scientifically accurate report on every aspect of a new machine and its performance under varying working conditions. They may discover that one or two minor changes will greatly increase the efficiency of the machine; knowing this, the manufacturer can make these changes before he puts the machine into general production and offers it for sale. Quite often the test reports are published and become a valuable guide to any farmer or dealer thinking of buying the machine in question; by reading the report, he knows at once what sort of work the machine can do and how well that work is done.

In Other Countries

The soils and climate of Britain are very different from those, for example, of India, and the problems facing farmers there are equally different from those which our home farmers have to solve. Why, then, is Britain able to make farm machinery that is suitable for these distant and different parts?

One reason is that her agricultural engineers themselves study conditions abroad and are often able to adapt or design machines to meet the requirements of farmers in other lands.

By courtesy of Massey-Harris-Ferguson (Sales) Ltd.

FOR SOWING THE SEED

This seed drill can sow most kinds of seed from grasses to root crops. It can sow up to thirteen rows at a time. The seed is carried in the long box on top of the drill, and is fed accurately into the earth scuffled by the coulters. If he wished to put fertiliser on the land at the same time, this farmer could fit a special attachment which would make a single operation of fertilising and sowing.

The World
and
Its Work

Agriculture—
Producing Food
from the Land

By courtesy of David Brown Tractors Ltd.

HARVESTING IN THE MODERN WAY

" The old order changeth, yielding place to new," is as true of farming as of any other British industry.
Britain's agriculture is the most highly mechanised in the world. This picture shows us a combine
harvester at work. It reaps, threshes, pours the corn into the truck travelling alongisde, and bales
the straw.

THE FARMER'S BUSY YEAR

THOSE of us who live in towns
and cities often like to visit the
country for a rest or a holiday.
The leafy lanes, broad fields and old
villages are so peaceful after the noise
and bustle of the crowded streets and
there are many interesting animals and
activities to be seen.

But we should not be deceived by
the quiet and gentleness we meet there.
Our green and pleasant countryside is
much more than a playground for
tired town-dwellers. It is the busy
workshop of a most important British
industry. For most of our countryside
is farmland, where nearly a million
workers and a vast amount of machinery
are employed in producing food.
Although we still have to import considerable quantities of food from overseas, more and more of our needs—
in milk and dairy produce: in meat,
poultry and eggs: in corn, fruit and
many other crops—comes from our
own farms. To-day the cash value of
the products of Britain's farms is greater
than that of the farms of Australia.
Remembering what a great food producer
the Commonwealth of Australia is, you
will at once realise the size and importance of our own farming industry.

Some British farms are small, others
large ; sometimes several farms are
banded together and worked as a single

farm of perhaps as much as 10,000 acres. The *type* of farming varies according to the locality, its soil and its climate, and the markets available for the products of the farm. The west of Britain, for example, contains rich plains and lowlands and has a kinder and moister climate that favours good crops of grass and roots. Here dairy-farming and stockbreeding are most common. But in eastern England, where the climate is much drier, arable farms predominate, that is, farms where most of the land is ploughed. From the farms of eastern England comes much of our home-grown wheat, barley and oats; here, too, sugar-beet is grown.

Sheep flourish on the short grass of Britain's limestone hills and chalk Downlands. Sheep, also, and hardy breeds of cattle will be found on the mountain pastures. Fruits are grown in Kent, the famous "Garden of England," and in our rich and sheltered valley lands. Market garden farming is found near the cities and large towns, which are a ready market for vegetables,

flowers and the like, and where the buyers are easily reached by modern transport.

Remember, however, that these are only general examples. Dairy farming goes on in some parts of eastern England, and land in some parts of the west is put under the plough. The fact is that by far the greater number of British farms are *mixed* farms. They do not rely on one or two crops; they produce various grain and root crops, grow fruit and fodder crops, rear stock, and keep sheep and poultry.

The Dairy Farmer

Milk is produced in all parts of Britain, so let us look first at the dairy farmer. His herd may well be of the Shorthorn type, for this breed is the most numerous, producing males that make first-rate beef and females that are good milking cows. Pure-bred dairy Shorthorns, red or brownish-red in colour, are seen at their best in districts where they have long been bred; for example, the hilly parts of Westmorland and Cumberland.

Another popular breed is the British

C. Hosegood.

A FINE HERD OF JERSEY COWS

Like the Guernsey, the Jersey cow originated in the Channel Islands and is noted for its rich milk. Although Britain has about twenty distinct breeds of cattle, her dairy herds can generally be divided into two types: those producing both milk and beef, and those more suited to milk production alone.

Harold Burdekin.

A SHEEP AND TWO LAMBS

The townsman may think that all sheep look alike, but there are at least a dozen distinct breeds in Britain. Those with long wool and heavier fleeces, like the ewe and lambs in this picture, were originally developed by Robert Bakewell (1725–1795). Their most common representative to-day is the Border Leicester.

Friesian, black and white in colour and larger than the Shorthorn. As its name suggests, this breed had its origin in Holland. Guernsey and Jersey cattle, fawn coloured but with darker patches, are found mostly in the south and west. They came first from the Channel Islands and are noted for giving good yields of rich milk. The Red Poll, a hornless breed that is raised for both beef and milk, is found mostly in eastern England. A famous hardy breed is the Ayrshire, found especially in south-west Scotland. Ayrshires are usually brown and white in colour and are generally considered to be second only to the Friesians as milking cows.

When a dairy cow is in milk she needs food that is rich in protein. Before the Second World War much

food of this kind came from abroad in concentrated form, e.g. cake or meal. But war cut off these supplies and although " concentrates " are again coming from overseas, the British farmer himself is growing more food for his herds and, more important still, is doing all he can to improve his grassland. For properly-managed grass can give more protein than any other crop.

How does he preserve his grass crop for use in the winter? Haymaking is no real answer, for this robs the crop of much of its goodness. On large dairy farms you may therefore see special kilns for drying the grass crop as soon as it has been cut. Grass so dried has a high protein content and is a valuable feeding stuff.

But most dairy farmers cannot afford

to instal expensive plant for grass drying. Instead they use a system called ensilage that has come to us from abroad. This method involves keeping the grass in shallow pits, under a covering of earth—a cheap way of safeguarding the food value of the crop.

Housing the Herd

Except in the south, the dairy farmer has to keep his cattle indoors for half the year, in clean, well-lit and airy cowsheds. Some farms in the south, where it is warmer, use the open-air bail system invented by that famous farmer, A. J. Hosier. Instead of driving the cows in twice a day for milking, a portable milking shed complete with fence, milking machinery and power, is taken to the cows in the fields. This saves much time and labour, and means that the herd lives out in the open all the year round.

Milking is done mostly by machinery. Well-padded cups are attached to the cow. Suction obtained by power through vacuum pipes causes the milk to flow from the patient animal through spotlessly clean tubes to the cooler in the dairy. Everything possible is done to make sure that the milk is pure and clean. The cowsheds will be washed down frequently, and the cows themselves washed before milking. The milking machines and all utensils will be cleaned and sterilised regularly. The milk is usually collected from the farm by lorry and taken to town where it is pasteurised and bottled ready for delivery to the customers the day after it has been taken from the cows.

As long as the bin in front of her contains some tasty snack, a cow does not object to the milking machine. Each individual cow is known to the farmer and his dairymen by name. Each receives an amount of concentrated food that is calculated in relation to the milk yield. Careful records are kept of the milk yields of every cow.

Beef Cattle

What about our meat supplies? About half the beef produced in Britain comes from cattle which are no longer required in the dairy herds, and the

John Topham.

A PORTABLE GRASS-DRYING MACHINE

One of the problems which always faces the British farmer is how to overcome the vagaries of our climate. Sunny days are needed at haymaking time. A spell of wet weather may ruin or endanger the crop. Here is a drying and baling plant which tours the farms and deals quickly and efficiently with the mown grass on which the sun has failed to shine. Three weeks' work can be done in three days.

GOING TO MARKET

This young calf will travel to market in a trailer behind the farmer's car, but help is needed to get him on to the comfortable straw bed prepared for him.

Market day brings farmers, dealers and merchants to the country towns. The picture shows a typical scene at Chelmsford, Essex, during a sale of beef cattle. The auctioneer stands on a platform from where he can see every bidder.

best comes from breeds that have been specially developed for the purpose. Among these are the famous Aberdeen-Angus cattle, black from head to tail and without horns, which are found in north-eastern Scotland. Farther south, in the border country and Northumberland, they are often found cross-bred with Shorthorns. Another famous breed is the Hereford, whose name tells us what part of the country they come from. Their faces and underparts are white, the rest of their coats usually being a reddish colour. Then there is the hardy Galloway ; and in Scotland's Highlands and western isles, the shaggy, long-horned Highland breed. Devon has its small, reddish North Devon. The Welsh Black is the breed of the Welsh hills.

Sheep and Pigs

Sheep have always played an important part in British farming. In 1951, the United Kingdom had nearly 20 million sheep, of many different breeds, helping to provide us with wool and mutton. Sheep can be raised in many places quite unsuitable for other stock. With their small mouths they can graze off the short grasses of the Downs and hill country that cannot provide a good feed for cattle.

Sheep can be found in most parts of Britain, even in London itself, where they are sometimes put to graze in Hyde Park. But to see them in really large numbers you must go to the hilly and mountainous parts of the country.

The many breeds include the hardy Blackface sheep of the Scottish Highlands, producers of fine quality mutton ; the Cheviot breed, which takes its name from the range of hills along the border between Scotland and England ; Cotswold, Leicester and Wensleydale sheep, all bearers of long wool : and the downland sheep—Southdowns, Suffolk and Dorset Horns.

One of the most fascinating sights on a sheep farm is to see the shepherd at work with his dog. How well the two understand each other ! The dog responds at once to the signs and whistles of his master, rounding up the stragglers and bringing the flock to just where the shepherd wants it. Every

Harold Burdekin.

FEEDING TIME WITH THE PIGS

We have ten or a dozen separate breeds of pigs, some varieties associated with particular parts of the country. The young pigs seen above have not long left their mother.

By courtesy of Massey-Harris-Ferguson Ltd.

HARVESTING IN THE MODERN MANNER

This harvest scene is typical of the larger British farms, where it is profitable to use the most up-to-date combine harvesters. Two of these wonderful machines are seen at work in this picture, cutting and threshing the corn, putting the grain into sacks, and laying the straw aside in neat windrows. The combines in this picture are self-propelled ; they move along under their own power and do not need tractors to draw them, like some other types. They are being followed up (right) by a tractor-drawn baler, which is gathering up the straw, compressing it and baling it for stock.

Reece Winstone.

RICK-BUILDING ON A KENTISH FARM

The corn has been harvested and stood in stook to dry. The golden sheaves have been loaded on wagons and trailers and brought to the stackyard where rick-building is well under way. Indeed, one of the ricks (left) has been completed and thatched already. The man standing on the load of sheaves finds it easy to toss them on to the elevator, whose moving spikes carry them to the rick-makers. In the background are the oast houses, typical of Kent where hops are an important crop. This photograph was taken in August; but farther north, harvesting and rick-building may not take place until September.

year sheepdog trials are held in many parts of the country, including London, and it is truly wonderful to see these wise and well-trained animals work perfectly with their masters in the most difficult tests.

Pigs, like poultry, do not require much land. They are bred mainly to provide us with pork and bacon, pork coming from such breeds as the Middle White and Berkshire, and bacon from the Large White, Essex and Wessex breeds. Other noted breeds associated with particular districts are the Tamworth, the Gloucester Old Spot, and the Lincolnshire Curly Coat.

The male pig is called a boar ; the female, a sow. Instead of saying that a sow gives birth to a litter of young, we say that she is farrowing. All round the sty is a low farrowing rail beneath which the little ones can take shelter so that their mother does not crush them when she lies down.

Harold Burdekin.

TWO PROFITABLE NANNY GOATS

Male and female goats are known respectively as billies and nannies and form profitable livestock on some farms. Goats' milk is very rich and especially good for infants and invalids.

Other Animals on the Farm

You can probably think of many other animals you will meet on the farm —goats and rabbits, perhaps: cats, for keeping down the vermin. There may also be chickens, ducks, geese and turkeys, and perhaps guinea fowl and bantams.

What about horses ? Sturdy breeds like the Suffolk Punch can still be found on many farms, ready to take their share of the work. But the number of working horses on our farms is now small compared with what it was before the coming of machinery. Ploughing and cultivating and many other jobs that were once work for the horse are now work for the tractor.

The tractor is the key to all farm machinery. It can do all sorts of jobs and can take practically every kind of implement the farmer will want to use. Britain has played a leading part in developing the modern farm tractor. In its most popular form, it has what is known as a " hydraulic 3-point linkage "; that is to say, implements can be mounted—one at a time—on the tractor, which will lift them by its hydraulic mechanism, carry them to work, power them for the job to be done and then bring them back when the job is finished. Changing over from one implement to another is usually a very simple matter of withdrawing three pins and bolts, dropping the implement off and hitching up the next implement that is required.

Most tractors are simple to handle and are built to stand up to hard conditions—for there is often tough work to be done on the farm. Many tractor manufacturers make whole ranges of farming implements to go with their tractors so that the farmer can do practically all his work by machine. Thanks to these manufacturers, Britain now has the most highly-mechanised agriculture in the world and, in addition, sends all kinds of tractors and farming implements to farmers all over the world. In the amount of farm machinery that she exports, Britain is second only to the United States.

Most farmers have little time to be idle. There is work to be done seven days a week and fifty-two weeks a year. Livestock must be tended regularly, land must be cultivated and crops sown, tended and harvested. At no time is farm work really finished.

Life on the Farm

The modern farmer has to be a very knowledgeable man. He must know the land he farms, how he can get the best results from his particular type of soil and climate; he must know his stock, how they should be fed and cared for ; and he must know his machinery, how his tractors and implements should be maintained and what should be done when there is a breakdown. He must also be a business man, who can work his farm so that it will give him a good living ; and he must always be looking ahead and planning carefully for the future.

Let us see how the year might run on

Topical Press.

A HORSE PLOUGHING MATCH

Whether horse or tractor is used, ploughing is skilled work. In many parts of the country, ploughing matches are held every year and prizes awarded to the champion ploughmen. Nowadays there are not so many horse-team entries because most of the ploughing is done by tractor.

By courtesy of Harry Ferguson Ltd.

THE FARMER AND HIS TRACTOR

It might almost be said that the farmer's best friend is his tractor. The tractor can pull his plough and other implements, tow trailers of the kind seen in this picture, and do no end of useful work about the farm. Britain has played a leading part in modern tractor development.

a typical mixed farm. The actual times at which the various jobs are done will vary, of course, according to where the farm is situated, because of the differences in climate in our country. For example, fields in the north might still be snow-covered when those in the south were being sown to barley; and cows in the Midlands and the north might still be in farm buildings when herds in the south were in the meadows. The weather decides what farm work can be done at any particular time of the year.

For most of us the new year begins on January 1st, but for farmers it usually begins in October. Farm rents are payable from this time of Michaelmas onwards, so this is the time when the farmer can make a change and rent a new farm if he wants to.

October is the time when the farmer is gathering in the last of his harvest. Turnips and the large yellow mangolds are pulled and stored away as feed for the cows when there is no longer good grass. They are stored in a long, deep trench known as a clamp and covered with earth, through the ridge of which wisps of straw will form ventholes. Potatoes also will have to be clamped.

In the orchard the late apples and pears will be gathered in, and the trees will now be pruned, and then sprayed to keep down insect pests. Sugar beet is lifted, probably by mechanical means. The tops make good food for sheep and cattle; the beet proper will be taken by lorry or train or both to the factory for processing.

At this time, too, the farmer will probably be sowing wheat for his next harvest. His autumn-sown wheat will probably go where previously he had a root-crop or clover. This changing of the crop for any particular field from year to year is called a rotation and is an important farming principle. Fields, like most of us, welcome a change. If a field were planted to wheat year after year, it would get tired of this particular crop and the yields would begin to fall. The farmer therefore works a rotation.

This is the standard (Norfolk) rotation: in the first year the crop is wheat; in the second, roots ; in the third, barley ; and in the fourth, clover. In the fifth year wheat is sown and the rotation begins again. Recently many farmers have abandoned this four-year rotation in favour of a six-year system which gives them a worthwhile extra cereal crop of barley or wheat.

The wheat seed our farmer is to sow will probably have come from another farm, for a change of seed-type is also good for the land. But our farmer will have seed for someone else, already prepared at harvest time by the combine harvester and dried and stored ready, or now threshed out in his rick yard. As we shall see presently, the combine harvester is a machine that makes threshing machines and certain other implements unnecessary.

Meanwhile, the land is being prepared for sowing, and for this work the farmer will need his plough.

The plough is one of the oldest farming implements. A thousand years ago and more, it was a crude wooden tool that threw up the soil on either side of the sliding block, and it was pulled by the farmer himself—or his wife. To-day, it is a beautifully-made implement of shining metal brightly painted when it is new. It is mounted on, or drawn by, a tractor and can cut one or more furrows, according to its size and design.

The first cut in the soil is made by the coulter, a part in the front of the plough. The share comes behind the coulter to broaden the cut and carry it several inches below the surface. Behind the share is the breast or mouldboard, which takes the slices of soil cut by the share and turns them over in the form of a continuous ridge. The spaces between the ridges are the furrows, and when the ploughing is good they will be straight and of even

depth from one end of the field to the other. Ploughing is perhaps the most important farming operation there is; it opens the soil to air, light and frost, helping to restore its fertility and making it ready for other cultivating implements to work into a seed bed. Ploughing, too, will work farmyard manure or artificial fertilisers into the soil, if these are needed, although this work is often done better by a rotary cultivator.

The Shepherd and His Flock

The sheep are now feeding in the turnip field, where the shepherd sets out, each day, a fresh patch of feeding ground, its limits marked by a movable fence of hurdles. The first feed off the patch is taken by the young sheep that are being fattened for sale. What they leave is eaten by the older ewes, whose baby lambs will be born in January (later, if the farm is in the north). Pigs for fattening and maybe the poultry, too, will get special feeds at this time of the year—barley meal for the fattening pigs, and a warm grain mash for the pullets (young hens), who will be just starting to lay.

Ploughing and sowing continue in November, and even in December if the weather permits. The cattle will find grass becoming scarce and will need feeds of cabbage or hay ; any time now, they will have to be brought into the farm buildings at night. And once the really cold weather sets in, the farmer will have all his cows, cattle and pigs indoors and will keep them there until the worst of the winter is over.

As the December days go by, work starts on the lambing-pen. This is built to protect the baby lambs, soon to be born, from the harsh winter weather. The sides are made of hurdles and packed with straw or bracken so that they are windproof. A shed-like roof of thatch is added, and the floor is carpeted thickly with straw and divided into sections. The size of the pen is

OLD CRAFTS THAT SERVE THE FARMER

Although this is an age of machinery, old crafts and industries still play a part in country life. This Essex saddler, for example, is repairing a horse collar.

This wheelwright is sawing through an oak held firmly by iron dogs over his saw-pit. His apprentice works on the other end of the saw inside the pit.

Photos: John Tarlton.

Larch is the wood used for ladders. The tree is cut in halves, into which oak staves or rungs are fitted 9 inches apart. Irons, top and bottom, hold the finished ladder together.

Finishing a wagon wheel demands great skill. The wheel is shaped with spokeshave and adze, then fitted with an iron tyre shrunk on its outer rim and " boxed " by an axle bearing.

determined, of course, by the number of ewes. A lambing-pen for five hundred ewes may cover as much as two acres.

The shepherd's hut, rather like a shed on four wheels, is brought out to the lambing-pen and here he will stay night and day, looking after the mothers and their baby lambs. Sometimes a mother dies, and then the shepherd takes the baby orphan, gives him a feed of lukewarm cow's milk from a small bottle and tucks him comfortably in a basket beside the stove in his hut. The next day the shepherd will find another ewe to act as mother to the orphan.

There may also be activity at the potato clamps at this time of the year. The clamps will be opened up and the potatoes riddled—that is, sorted into different sizes. The largest will go to market, the middle-sized will be sold as seed, and the small potatoes and any that are damaged in lifting kept as feed for the pigs.

By now the hedger is busy with his slasher, handbill and other tools, trimming the untidy growth and weaving the hedges into a tidy network. Manure carted from the farm is standing in neat rows in the field, ready to be worked in when the weather permits ploughing. The cattle, of course, are still living in the farm buildings, feeding off roots, hay, concentrates and the like. In the barn, the chaff cutting machine will still be hard at work preparing food for these and other livestock.

There is plenty of other work, too, for days when outdoor work is impossible. For instance, the bundles of thatch for roofing hayricks have to be prepared, and some of the farm machinery may require overhaul. These are all jobs for winter months like January and February.

The Arrival of Spring

Our farmer, who has been busy enough all winter, becomes even busier with

John Tarlton.

NIGHT VIGIL IN THE LAMBING-PEN

The lambing-pen protects the baby lambs from the harsh winter weather. The shepherd stays in the pen night and day, looking after the mothers and their babies. His home during this time is a hut on wheels, brought into the pen. Although he may have an electric torch in his pocket, he still likes to have his old lantern as a stand-by.

the arrival of spring. There is still ploughing to be done, and the March winds will soon dry out the top soil of the ploughed land, putting it in the right condition for making a seed bed for the spring sowing. An old country saying declares that the dust raised by the March winds is "worth a guinea a bushel"; what this means, of course, is that the dust shows the land to be ready for the spring sowing.

Oats and barley are the corn crops sown in spring. But before the drills can get to work to sow the seed, the soil must be fined down into a good seed bed. This work may be carried out by a cultivator and tractor, the cultivator having many steel tines, or prongs, that break down the plough clods. Disc harrows also may be used. A typical disc harrow has saucer-shaped discs, about eighteen or twenty inches in diameter, which cut up the clods and level off both the ridges and the furrows. We rake our garden beds and borders to prepare for seed sowing and the farmer harrows with much the same end in view. He may, indeed, have to harrow several times before he is thoroughly satisfied. That is why many farmers to-day are using another implement called a rotavator for preparing their seed beds. This implement is mounted on, or drawn by, the tractor and has revolving hoe-blades which can do the work of discs and harrows often in a single operation. Indeed, with certain types of soil they can do much of the plough's work as well.

Topical.

A LAMB AND ITS NURSE

In this picture, taken on a Northamptonshire farm, a lamb, one of triplets, is being bottle-fed by the shepherd to ensure that the ewe does not lose her offspring.

The actual sowing is done with a machine called a drill, which has a number of coulters or steel fingers that clear a path about three inches deep in the soil. Seed is fed from the seed box of the drill at a rate that can be regulated, dropping into the ground just where it has been scuffled by the coulters. Some large farms will have three kinds of drill: one for corn, another for roots and a third for grass. But the smaller mixed farm will probably have a single drill that can cope with many crops.

What about potatoes? The potato crop, which is particularly important on the farms of Lincolnshire's silt-lands and in the Perthshire and Dunbar districts of Scotland, had once to be planted by hand. But to-day there are several kinds of machine that do this work. The potato planter works behind the tractor, opening furrows just wide enough to take the seed potatoes. The latter are fed automatically into the soil from spouts and then covered. The man supervising this type of fully-automatic planter sits on a raised seat at the back ; with another type of planter two or three men or girls will sit at the back hand-feeding the seed potatoes into the machine for planting.

In March the winter-sown wheat may receive attention also, harrows being drawn across the field to loosen and give air to the soil in which the young crop is beginning to show signs of growth. The grasslands, too, will require cultivating, with a chain harrow or with a rotavator fitted with knife-like blades. Presently the cows will be let out to graze upon the new spring grass. What a welcome sight for them is the lush green of the meadows after their months in the farm buildings !

Hatching the Chicks

This is the poultry breeding season. Carefully-selected eggs are gently placed in an incubator and looked after in a steady temperature for twenty-one days. When the chicks appear, a warmed brooder must be waiting for them because they have no feathered mother to look after them. At this time, too, mangolds and sugar-beet are sown.

How fresh and green the countryside looks in May ! It is no wonder that May is called the merry month. All the animals are out of doors now, romping in the pastures and enjoying the fresh green grass. That land which the sheep cleared so thoroughly must be cultivated and re-sown, and in the sugar-beet and mangold fields the weeds must be cleared from the young crop. Any seedlings that are appearing too thickly must be thinned out. For the farmer May is not only a merry month; it is a busy month, too, one which gives him his first harvest—the wool off the backs of his sheep.

The wool from a sheep is known as a fleece and it is sheared either by hand-

John Topham.

HEAVY WORK ON THE LAND

Two heavy " crawlers " are seen here at work on land which has grown oats in the past season. Now the crawlers are deep ploughing the field in preparation for the sowing of potatoes. Usually the crops follow each other in the order oats, potatoes, wheat, turnips or swedes, barley, hay, though this may be varied according to the location of the farm.

John Topham.

PREPARING FOR SOWING BETWEEN YOUNG TREES

A long-term policy is necessary in the growing of fruit. Here we see a newly-planted orchard of Laxton, Cox and Worcester apples. The ground between the rows of young trees is being cultivated with the aid of a tractor and ridge roll so that it may be used for other crops such as grass or lettuces, or it may be that gooseberry bushes will be planted here.

shears, rather like large scissors, or by shearing machines with clippers like those used by the hairdresser, only larger. The fleeces are taken off in a single piece, then bundled with others to be taken away for sale.

Haymaking heralds the summer proper. The month for this is June, when the ripe grass is cut and converted into hay to provide feed for the stock when grass is both poor in food value and scarce. Many years ago the hay was cut entirely by men wielding scythes ; to-day it is cut by mower and tractor. The mower has a long cutter-bar that stretches out to one side of the tractor. Along this bar are metal fingers across which the knife cuts, leaving in its wake a long neat row of cut grass known as a swath.

If the farmer has a grass drier, or if the grass is to be made into silage, a loader and trailer will work in the field at the same time as the mower to load and carry away the crop as soon as it has been cut. If the grass is to be made into hay it will remain in its swaths for about two days to permit the sun to dry its exposed side. A machine called a side-delivery rake will then be used to turn the grass so that its underside can be dried by the sun. On some farms the grass is gathered into haycocks for drying. These are little heaps through which the wind can blow to dry the stem, a process that requires three or four days. Another method is to pike the grass, that is, build it up in a high mound round a wooden pole or tripod.

Collecting the Hay

Whatever method is used it is important that the hay is not spoilt by over-drying or underdrying. If it is dried too much, its food value will be poor; if it is dried too little, it will get hot in the rick and turn black, or even set fire to the rick.

Collecting the hay can be done with either a hay-loader or a hay sweep. The hay-loader is drawn behind the trailer or truck ; it gathers up the hay as it goes, delivering it to the men on the truck for loading. The hay sweep has large fingers of wood, with steel tips. It is mounted on the tractor and gathers hay, which piles itself against the wooden frame at the back of the sweep. The sweep is then raised and the hay taken to the part of the field where the rick is being made. There are several kinds of hay sweep, some designed for tractors, others for work with horses, and others for fitting to an ordinary car. Another remarkable machine that may be used is the pick-up baler, which gathers the hay, packs it in bales and binds the bales with wire ready for the rick.

The most common implement which helps to make the rick is an elevator. This is worked by a small engine and forms a spiked escalator from ground level to the top of the rick. Such an implement saves a lot of time and human labour in tossing up hay with a long-handled hayfork.

Ricks made in June are usually thatched in July. The thatch is formed of good wheaten straws all lying the same way and packed into bundles, and a start is always made at the bottom so that the second strip or layer can overlap the first, just as do the tiles or slates on a roof. To hold down the straw the thatcher drives in with his mallet spars cut from nut bushes or hazels, connecting them where necessary with lengths of stout twine or strips of straw rope. Some thatchers do not use a mallet to drive in the spars, but have a stout piece of stiff leather fixed over the palm of one hand and use this hammerwise.

When the thatcher reaches the top of the rick he makes a comb of straw to throw off the rain on either side, having first laid dollies or bundles of rough-dried herbage to form the pointed ridge. The comb may be decorated with fanciful ornaments made of straw according to the custom of the county, and exposed corners (where the thatch might break adrift) may be strengthened with heavy cord, chains, or even a baulk of wood.

At the Sheep Fair

While the thatcher is at work on the ricks the shepherd will be getting his lambs and ewes ready for the sheep fairs which take place in July, or later in some parts of the country. Some will be sold for fattening, others for breeding. All that go to the fair will carry a coloured mark to show their age. When they reach the fair they will be sorted into small pens by age and remain there until their

Fox Photos.

LEARNING AN OLD-WORLD ART

There is much to learn before one can thatch a hayrick or cornstack, and above we see an experienced hand explaining the essential parts of the task to some enthusiastic newcomers.

A FARM OF OLD ENGLAND

Here is a typical farm of an English countryside—rolling fields to the uplands, a well-wooded section and then the farm itself with its outbuildings and stackyard. This farmstead is in Buckinghamshire, but similar holdings may be found all over the country, replete with their cattle, sheep, horses and poultry. More than one million men and women earn their living from agriculture in England, Scotland and Wales.

new owner takes them away. The actual business of selling will probably be by auction.

The Grain Harvest

At this time of the year a beautiful change is taking place in the colour of the cornfields. Those fields that have long been green are now turning rapidly to yellow, and still more rapidly to the wonderful golden-brown that proclaims the time for harvesting. August is the month for the harvest, except northwards where harvesting may not take place until September.

A common machine used for cutting the crop is the self-binder, which can be drawn by tractor or horses, or power-driven by the tractor. As it works round the field, it cuts the corn, which then falls on to a slatted platform. From the platform the corn is conveyed by canvases to another part of the machine where it is tightly compressed, automatically tied round the middle with binding twine, and then flung out so that it lies on the ground in the wake of the machine.

The sheaves thus made must not be left lying on the ground; if they were and rain came, the grain in the ears would soon be spoilt. So two or three farmhands will follow the self-binder and build the sheaves into stooks. Four or five pairs of sheaves standing on their butts with the ears uppermost usually form a stook. Arranged like this the sheaves can throw off the rain if it comes, and will also dry out as the wind blows through them. Generally speaking, the sheaves remain in stook from a week to a fortnight, oats invariably taking the longest time to dry. Wagons, carts and tractor-drawn trailers will next be pressed into service to get the sheaves to the stackyard where

Topical Press.

A WILTSHIRE BARLEY HARVEST

These beautiful farmlands are near Fonthill Bishop, in Wiltshire. Their rich harvest of early maturing barley is being gathered by three combine harvesters which, while they are not as picturesque as older harvesting methods, are much more efficient and economical for Britain's larger farms. Such machines make us think of the vast wheatlands of Canada and Australia where they are in much more common use.

THE BUSY TIME OF HARVEST

Mirror Features.

Two or three farmhands following the self-binder have the task of building up the sheaves of ripe corn into stooks. Each stook consists of four or five pairs of sheaves standing on their butts with the ears of corn uppermost. Usually the sheaves will remain in stook from a week to a fortnight.

John Tarlton.

Already the wagon that will take these sheaves of oats to the stackyard is piled high, but there is room for just a few more from the stooks. So up they come, expertly pitched by the farmhands with their long forks. August is the great harvesting month for wheat and oats.

they will be built into stacks that must, after a short time, be thatched.

Later, in October when the farmer's year starts again, the threshing outfit will be brought into use to extract the corn from the ear. The threshing machine and its team of workers will probably be hired by the farmer from a contractor and will come trundling up to the farm one morning, a mysterious train of intricate mechanisms drawn by a steam traction-engine. When it has been set up, sheaves from the stack will be fed into a revolving drum. Here, blasts of air remove the chaff or winnowings, while the grain, after passing through sieves, flows from a spout direct into bags ready to be taken away. The straw that comes from the threshing machine will be handled either by a baler, or by a trusser, and then stacked; or it may be stacked loose, if it is to be used as bedding or feed close at hand.

Combine Harvesting

Many large farms now use a machine called a combine harvester for gathering in their wheat, barley and oats when the crop is dead ripe. The combine harvester can cut the corn, thresh it, lay aside the straw and put the grain into bags right on the field. The straw can afterwards be baled by a pick-up baler, or if it is not required in this form, can be worked back into the soil with a rotavator. Sometimes the straw is burnt; this is a cheap, but rather wasteful method; straw worked back into the soil helps to make it fertile.

Combines are more likely to be seen on large farms where the straw is not needed for bedding and feeds for the livestock. While such a machine reduces the risk of loss from bad weather (because it can harvest the crop so quickly), much of the corn may still require drying after it has been combined, and some form of grain drier will therefore be needed to remove the damp from the grain and make it safe for storage.

The short stumps of corn left after the harvest are called stubble, and pullets and other poultry are often turned on to the stubble fields to eat up any grain that has fallen from the ear. Portable sheds are put out in the fields with the birds so that they have a safe roosting place at night. The birds benefit from the change and exercise they get and are strengthened against the coming of winter.

So we come to September, the last month of the farmer's year. He has

John Topham.

GETTING IN THE HARVEST

In this photograph is seen a remarkable machine known as the Grain Marshall at work on a field of barley which has been badly beaten by heavy rain storms. It is fitted with a special attachment for short-growing straw. The Grain Marshall does much the same work as the combine harvester.

AFTER THE HARVEST

By courtesy of Rotary Hoes Ltd.

The combine harvester has done its work, leaving behind straw and stubble. To chop these up and mix them into the ground, the farmer uses a rotavator. This machine is hitched to his tractor, which also provides the power to operate its hoe-bladed rotor.

already started ploughing again and is concerned also with his potato harvest. Early potatoes will have been lifted in June, but now the maincrop has to be harvested and for this, still more machinery is brought into use. The haulm, that is, the green tops and vines of the potatoes, must be destroyed first to make the actual lifting process easier and more thorough. This will be done either by a machine called a haulm pulveriser, which chops up the haulm and clears the ridges, or by spraying. The potatoes are then lifted either by an elevator digger or by a potato spinner. The latter, which is in very common use, has fingers on the outside of a revolving wheel which turn the tubers out of the ridges, leaving them on the ground all ready to be picked up. Getting the potatoes into sacks is still a job to be done by hand. Men, women and children all take part in this work, but women are considered faster than men at picking up the potatoes, because they stoop more easily.

So the farmer's year comes to its close. The plough is at work once more, and there may be areas of ripe clover to cut and deal with as the hay was dealt with in June.

Life in the Country

The saying " All work and no play makes Jack a dull boy " is as true of farmers as it is of anyone. The farmer and his family have many pleasures, and sometimes he will be able to mix business with pleasure—in the spring or summer, for example, when he may take time off from the farm to spend a day at his county agricultural show, and he will probably go regularly to his local market. There will almost certainly be game of some kind on his farm, and so during certain seasons of the year you may see him going off with his gun and his dog to see what he can bring back for the larder. He may not keep horses for his farm work—sturdy breeds like the Clydesdale, Suffolk Punch, Shire and Percheron, which were once so numerous on our farms—but he may well keep a hunter, and ponies for his children.

The Silent Revolution

Thanks to mechanisation, farm work is now easier and the British farmer more efficient. The great change in farming methods during the past twelve years is little short of a silent revolution. In 1939, many farmers tilled no more than an acre a day with their horse-drawn plough; to-day, one man and a tractor can plough half an acre in an hour. In 1942, there were only just over 101,000 tractors in England and Wales; to-day there are more than 324,000. Even so, we must not imagine that the farmer enjoys a thoroughly carefree and easy life. The fact remains that his work is never done. Nature, like time, waits for no man, and the crops and beasts of the field must receive his constant attention if he is to win a good livelihood from them. Moreover, to a considerable extent his success or failure will depend upon forces beyond his control—the sunshine and the rain, for example. Flood or drought can bring him complete disaster.

Those of us who are merely visitors to the country at week-ends and holiday times may envy the farmers and country-folk their healthy, open-air life amidst the peaceful beauty that Nature provides. But we may remember, too, that these pleasures are paid for in the hard, unceasing work that goes on through all the seasons to bring forth our food from the land.

Harold Burdekin.

WITH THE THRESHING GANG

At threshing time corn stacks are taken down and the sheaves thrown into a revolving drum so that the corn can be removed from the ear and all weed seed and foreign matter left behind. Fine, dry weather is wanted to make threshing successful, and rat-hunts always add excitement to this dusty autumn task.

The Secret
of
Man's
Supremacy

About the
Mental Equipment
of the
Human Being

Copyright.

TRAINING YOUTH FOR MODERN INDUSTRY

Training for commerce and industry is essential, and in this photograph is seen the Drawing Office of the School of Motor Body Engineering at the Regent Street Polytechnic. Here youths are trained in the methods employed for the production of private cars, passenger-carrying, public service and other types of modern vehicles.

HOW THE BRAIN AND THE MIND WORK

THE human brain might be compared with the general headquarters of an army. The general headquarters receives information respecting the whole state of the army and what is happening in the various outposts. The brain is constantly receiving messages and kept informed of the state of the body, that is, of bodily movements, and changes within the body itself, as well as changes taking place outside.

Before, therefore, we consider the nature and work of the brain itself, it will be interesting to consider briefly the kinds of messages it receives.

The Brain Receives Messages

Diagram 1 illustrates these varying types of messages, or stimuli, as the scientists call them, which travel to the brain.

In the first place, there are those messages aroused by events happening in the outside world, giving us sensations of sound, sight, touch, both light and heavy, painful and non-painful, taste and smell. Secondly, there are messages informing us of the position of the body, both when it is at rest and when it is in motion. Some of these messages arise from nerve fibres in the muscles, ligaments, tendons and joints in the various parts of the body. Others are received by the brain from the internal organs of the ear.

You see, the ear is a very complicated organ which not only enables us to hear, but also to know of the equilibrium, or balance of the body. If this part of the ear, called the internal ear, is disturbed or damaged we are sometimes unable to maintain our balance. Thus, when you turn round rapidly many times, you disturb the smooth working of the internal ear and you become " giddy."

Thirdly, there are messages telling us of the changes taking place in the internal organs of the body, including the lungs for breathing, the heart for supply of blood to the body, the digestive system which deals with the food we eat and the eliminative system which gets rid of the waste products of the body.

The Human Telephone

The messages of which we have spoken travel along chains or relays of nerve fibres and nerve cells called neurons. These might be compared with the wires of the telephone system. Now, there are two-way messages, one series of messages from the body to the brain, Diagram 2a, and the other series from the brain to the body, Diagram 2b. In the body there are many millions of these nerve processes and Diagram 2 shows you what they look like. Let us suppose that an animal sees a dangerous object and runs away.

If we compare this sequence of events with the telephone system, then the voice of the caller, the sensory message, which for our animal is the sight of the dangerous object, travels along wires, the sensory nerves, to the exchange, the brain, where it is accepted and interpreted. Then the message is sent from the brain, along a series of wires, the motor nerves, to the receiver of the message, the muscles, which then carry out the appropriate movements of flight.

Just as in the telephone system we have the central exchange including local exchanges which can contact any area, and trunk exchanges which can contact any area over which the telephone wires run, so in the nervous system we have the central nervous system, consisting of the spinal cord and the brain, as well as the nerve processes lying outside the central nervous system. Most of our messages travel to the brain by way of the spinal cord. However, the nerves of the face are connected directly with the brain through small holes in the skull. These nerves carry messages relating to sensations of smell, taste, sight, and hearing and movements of the face and eyes. Moreover, there are certain messages which use only the local exchange, or the spinal cord.

Thus, when you unknowingly touch a hot plate, you immediately and automatically remove your hand. Such a non-willed automatic action is called a reflex action. We have spoken of a reflex action of the spinal cord, but parts of the brain also are responsible for such automatic bodily actions. The tasks which the lower parts of the brain perform are carried out without our consciously willing that they be performed. We will now consider the work of the brain, taking each part in turn.

THE HUMAN BRAIN

The Grey Matter

When we look at a brain, we see a mass of grey and white coloured matter. The grey matter consists of millions of tiny nerve cells, each of which has a fine nerve fibre. It is these fibres which give the brain its white appearance, and they serve either to link up various cells within the brain, or by passing to other parts of the body, to connect the brain with the rest of the body.

Parts of the Brain

The brain is a continuation of the spinal cord, and perhaps it will help us to understand the brain if we make a very rough comparison. Imagine a scout's pole, the top of which is divided into three by notches. The top division of our pole is placed between the cut halves of an orange, and another

TRAINING HAND AND EYE

In this picture we have a view of the School of Motor Body Building, where students are at work in the metal shop, shaping aluminium panels for car bodies. Finished work is hanging from the balcony and in the background are " wheeling machines," used to smooth off and polish the panels. Oxy-acetylene welding, painting, trimming, coach joinery and body assembly also are taught.

smaller orange, also cut in half, is placed against the third division as shown in Diagram 3. In the diagram, the main parts of the brain have been indicated and named.

However, this is a very crude comparison, and we must now consider the various parts of the brain as they really are. Diagrams 4, 5 and 6 are drawings of the brain as it actually appears. Diagram 4 shows how the human brain is situated inside the human skull, and Diagram 5 shows the parts in greater detail. In Diagram 5, the mid-brain and inter-brain are situated in between the two parts of the cerebrum and are not, therefore, seen in the diagram.

Brain Stem and Mid-Brain

The brain stem contains the pathway by means of which the spinal cord is joined to the rest of the brain, and along this pathway impulses or messages travel from the spinal cord to other parts of the brain, and from the brain to appropriate parts of the body. It contains nerve fibres which control our breathing, others which regulate the heart-beat, and therefore the control of blood throughout the body, and still other centres which control processes necessary to eating, swallowing, the secretion of saliva, as when our mouths water at the sight and smell of an appetising meal. The brain stem also controls the work of the digestive system during the assimilation of food.

Now, when you consciously move your eyes, your head automatically moves in the same direction. Similarly, if you consciously move your head, the eyes automatically move in the same direction. In short, they work together; you *will* the movement of the one, the movement of the other is automatic or reflex in character. Again, if you hear a noise, you tend to move the head in that direction, while some animals prick their ears also in response to sound.

These simultaneous movements of the eyes, ears, and head are protective devices which are especially useful to animals, enabling them to be able easily to inspect the events in the outside world so that they may then assess their danger value. The mid-brain contains the cells and fibres which enable the automatic or reflex actions of the eyes to follow a willed movement of the head, and the automatic or reflex action of the head to follow a willed movement of the eyes.

Concerning the Cerebellum

The cerebellum, or lower outgrowth of the brain, is sometimes called the hind-brain because it is situated just above the back of the neck, as you can see from Diagram 4. It is round in shape, but is divided into two hemispheres, which are connected by means of nerve fibres, while other nerve fibres connect the cerebellum with the rest of the brain and also with the joints and muscles of distant parts of the body. The outside of the cerebellum consists of a layer of grey matter which has deep folds, as, for example, has a handkerchief when it is lightly screwed up in the hand.

These folds have a special purpose in that they enable a large amount of grey matter to be tucked away within a very small space. The section of the brain called the pons, as marked in Diagram 5, consists of nerve fibres which connect the two hemispheres. The name " pons," meaning " the bridge," is most appropriate because this part of the brain is a kind of bridge which connects the brain stem with the upper parts of the brain as well as connecting the two hemispheres of the cerebellum. In appearance, you might compare the pons and the cerebellum with a signet ring on a finger, the pons being the ring and the cerebellum a very large signet.

Specially drawn for this work.

AN OPTICAL ILLUSION

Here are two squares of the same size. If you prepare similar squares for yourself and hold them a little apart, the one with the horizontal lines will seem higher than that with the vertical lines.

MESSAGES TO THE BRAIN

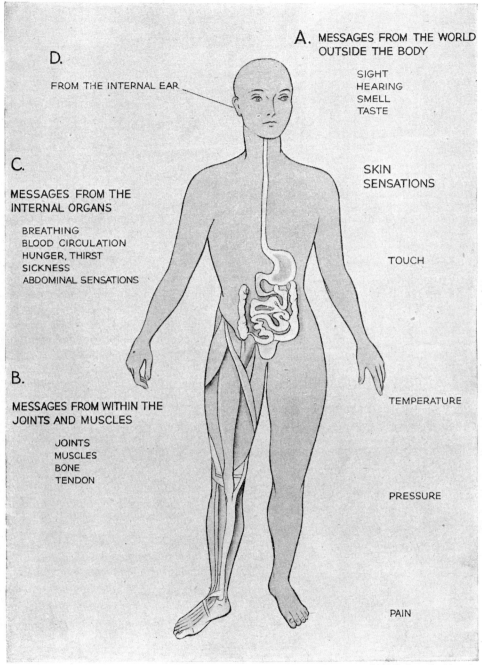

D.

FROM THE INTERNAL EAR

A. MESSAGES FROM THE WORLD
OUTSIDE THE BODY

SIGHT
HEARING
SMELL
TASTE

SKIN
SENSATIONS

C.

MESSAGES FROM THE
INTERNAL ORGANS

BREATHING
BLOOD CIRCULATION
HUNGER, THIRST
SICKNESS
ABDOMINAL SENSATIONS

TOUCH

B.

MESSAGES FROM WITHIN THE
JOINTS AND MUSCLES

JOINTS
MUSCLES
BONE
TENDON

TEMPERATURE

PRESSURE

PAIN

Specially drawn for this work.

Diagram 1. Here we can see the kind of messages received by the brain, and the sensations of
which we are made aware. There are messages informing the brain of what is going on in the
world outside the body (A), and other messages which tell the brain of what is happening inside
the body (B, C, and D).

The Work of the Cerebellum

The chief work of the cerebellum is to co-ordinate the various movements of the body, so that the muscles work harmoniously together. For the tiny child, when he begins to learn, walking is a very difficult process. His movements tend to be jerky, one leg completing its movement before the other leg begins. The movements are carried out consciously, the higher parts of the brain taking part in these early attempts. Soon, however, the process of walking becomes a smooth, harmonious activity, carried out without conscious thought. By this time, the cerebellum has taken over this task, leaving the higher centres of the brain free for other work.

It has been discovered that an animal deprived of its cerebellum does not suffer from paralysis, or inability to move the muscles of the body, but its movements are shaky, jerky, and poorly controlled. In man, disease or injury to the cerebellum causes the same lack of muscular control, and he is unable to carry out the movement of his muscles smoothly and accurately. If, for example, he is asked to touch his nose with his finger, his arm moves jerkily and he fails to hit the mark.

The Inter-Brain

The inter-brain, as we shall call it, is a mass of grey matter lying just above the mid-brain and at the base of the cerebrum. It is the part of the brain which enables us to sense extreme sensations, extreme pain, extreme heat and extreme cold. There are nerve centres which enable the body to adapt itself to these extreme changes. Thus, for example, on a boiling hot day these centres enable the body to lose heat by controlling chemical changes in the body and by increasing the activity of the sweat glands. Further, these centres are concerned with violent reactions —emotions of hate, rage and fear. These violent reactions are usually controlled by the higher centres of the brain.

If, however, these higher centres are removed in an animal, there results a condition of uncontrolled emotional outbursts, such as anger, shown by snarling, clawing and lashing of the tail. Extreme fear is also seen. The heart beats fast, the blood travels at a very quick rate through the body, the pupils of the eyes enlarge and the hair on the body rises in much the same way as in a cat when it is chased by a dog. In man, alcohol tends to inhibit or prevent control being exercised by the higher centres of the brain. It sometimes

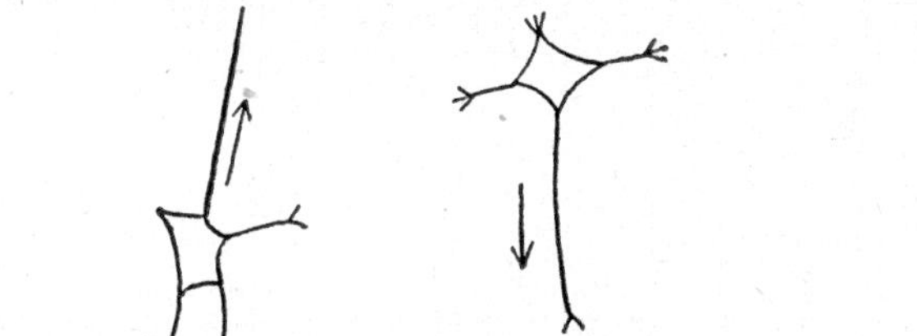

A.   B.   MESSAGES

MESSAGES ALONG THE NEURONS

Diagram 2. In A we see the beginning of the message, which a touch on the skin sends along the sensory neurons on the way to the spinal cord and the brain. In B is seen the final pathway of the message from the brain (or spinal cord) along the motor neurons to the muscle.

happens that a man who is intoxicated displays extreme emotions such as we have described in the animal deprived of the cerebrum.

The Cerebrum and Its Work

The cerebrum is the largest and most important part of the brain in man. In lower creatures, the cerebrum is smaller in proportion to the rest of the brain. As we ascend the evolutionary scale from the fish to man, the cerebrum becomes proportionately greater, until in the dog and monkey it is larger than all the other parts of the brain put together. In man it is so large that all the rest of the brain seems very insignificant.

In so far as it consists of a deeply folded, outer grey crust of nerve cells, and an inner layer of nerve fibres; in so far also as it has two hemispheres joined by nerve fibres, and has nerve fibres connecting it with the rest of the brain and with distant parts of the body, the cerebrum is not unlike the cerebellum in general structure. Diagram 6 shows the right half of the cerebrum. In the diagram, you can see the deep folds of which we have spoken. In appearance, the cerebrum is not unlike the kernel of a walnut which has been extracted from the shell. The cerebrum in human beings, however, is larger in bulk than the cerebellum, and fills most of the skull.

Moreover, the work it has to do is more varied. An interesting difference between the cerebellum and the cerebrum is that in the cerebellum, the right hemisphere controls the joints and muscles on the right side of the body, and the left hemisphere looks after the joints and the muscles on the left side of the body. In the cerebrum, however, this is not so, for here the left hemisphere controls and looks after the opposite or right side of the body; and the right hemisphere controls the left side. You see, the fibres leaving the cerebrum cross each other before they reach the spinal cord. Diagram 7

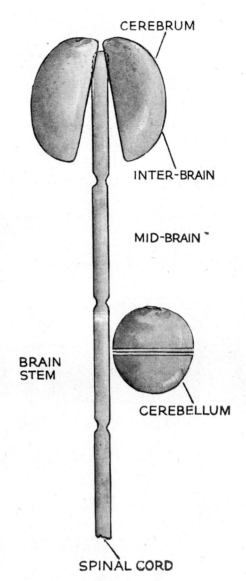

A SIMPLE COMPARISON

Diagram 3. In this drawing the brain is compared with a notched scout's pole, showing the inter-brain, the mid-brain, the brain stem and the spinal cord. The two cut oranges represent the two halves of the cerebrum and the cerebellum.

shows the pathway of nerve fibres from the cerebellum and cerebrum. You can see how the fibres from the cerebrum cross over to the other side of the body when they reach the brain stem.

The Cerebral Cortex

The cerebral cortex is the name given to the grey matter, or nerve cells, which cover the cerebrum. The cerebral cortex is the seat of conscious reactions. It contains centres by means of which we are made consciously aware of our surroundings ; it is the organ of volition or will, for when we will to move some muscle or to perform some task, the nerve cells in the cortex are first stimulated, and messages then sent to various parts of the body.

The cortex is also the centre for higher thought processes, reasoning, memory and speech. In short, this area of the brain firstly makes us conscious of bodily sensations, secondly enables us to use our will or volition, and thirdly, enables us to carry out thought processes.

The Map of the Cortex

Now, it has been found, as a result of experiments on animals, and from the observation of the effect of brain diseases and injuries suffered by man, that certain specific areas of the cortex perform, and are responsible for, certain specific tasks. Scientists have, as a result of their observations and experiments, been able to map out these various areas of the cortex, and Diagram 8 is a sketch of the left half of the cerebral cortex mapped out according to the tasks which the various parts perform. From a study of the diagram you can see that there is :—

1. A motor (or muscle movement) area from which summonses to action are dispatched to the muscles of the body. Each part of the body has its special small area within the motor cortex. When this part of the motor area of the right hemisphere is stimulated by a weak electric current in an animal under anæsthetic, it causes movement of the appropriate muscles on the left side of the body. Disease of, or removal of, the motor area in any one hemisphere produces paralysis of the opposite side of the body. If the motor areas of both the hemispheres are injured, the whole body becomes paralysed.

2. A sensory area which makes us conscious of sensations coming from the muscles and skin. Patients who have had to undergo brain operations using local anæsthetics only, have sometimes permitted the surgeon to stimulate these sensory areas. The patients reported definite sensations of numbness or tingling which they localised in specific parts of the body.

3. An auditory area, which is a special area for hearing, and

4. Another special area for visual per-

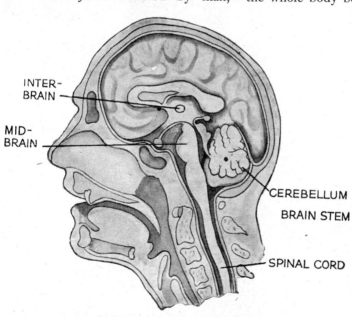

INTER-BRAIN

MID-BRAIN

CEREBELLUM

BRAIN STEM

SPINAL CORD

PROTECTOR OF THE BRAIN

Diagram 4. The skull acts as a protector of the brain. Between the brain and the skull are three layers of fine, supple skin, which protect the brain from the hardness of the inside surface of the skull.

ception, the visual area. In animals it is difficult to say when a sensation appears, but when the auditory area of an animal is stimulated there is a short delay, then a pricking up of the ears ; the stimulation of the visual area is followed by a turning of the head presumably in the direction from which the visual impulse is thought to come.

The rest of the cerebral cortex is sometimes called the " Silent Area " as these parts do not carry out special functions, as do the specific areas considered above. They are also known as " Association areas." To associate means to link one, two or more ideas together. These areas are said to be concerned with learning and memory, thought and reasoning processes; in short, the mental processes which characterise man, and in the exercise of which he is distinguished from the animal.

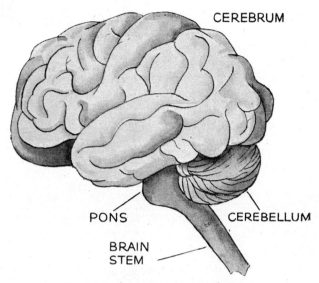

A SIDE VIEW OF THE BRAIN

Diagram 5. Here we see parts of the brain as they are seen on the left side. The mid-brain and the inter-brain are hidden from view.

HOW THE HUMAN MIND WORKS

So far we have been considering the brain, the scientific study of which is carried out by the physiologist. Now, we need to consider man's mind, the student of which is a psychologist. The work of the psychologist, like that of any other scientist, is to observe, to classify the facts which he observes, and then to make scientific laws concerning his observations.

A scientific law says, in effect, " Do so-and-so, and such-and-such will follow," or " If so-and-so happens, such-and-such will follow." Thus is man able to predict or foretell what will happen. It is this power of prediction which gives man control over the world in which he lives.

The psychologist is concerned with

mental events or what happens in the mind. He is concerned, that is, with such facts as sensations, perceptions, emotions, feelings, memory, intelligence and character. Now, for Western man, this study of mental processes is comparatively new. Western man has, especially during the last four hundred years, expended most of his energies in examining objects and events in the world outside him. Thus, he has learned much about the laws which govern their movement and behaviour, and has built up a highly technical civilisation. But the study of the mind has been neglected, and often such a study is regarded by us as strange, if not a little mysterious, and one in which we do not feel quite as much at home as we do when we consider objects in the outside world.

What is Mind ?

Here we ask a question which philosophers have pondered throughout the ages.

Some consider the mind as something which is caused by and is the result of movements and changes in the body, more especially in the brain; as Hobbes, a seventeenth-century philosopher, put it, " The brain secretes thought as the liver secretes bile." However, such an explanation is hardly satisfactory because, as we shall see later, the mind is both active and creative, and it is certainly difficult to explain creativeness and activity in terms of bodily movements and changes. To take an example ; we eat a big supper, and we dream. Now, it may be true that the eating of the big supper causes the digestive system to work overtime and this may stimulate the cells of the brain and so give occasion for dreams. But, in dreaming, we create scenes and events. Some may be more or less repetitions of what we have experienced during our waking hours, others may be new and strange. We might even write a story, book or poem. Coleridge, the poet, created his poem " Kubla Khan " during sleep, and wrote it immediately on waking.

Thus, there is something creative and active, which is influenced by the brain and body but is nevertheless something other than either. The body, as a body, obeys the laws of chemistry and physics, the laws which are obeyed by objects in the outside world. If, for example, a human body falls from a height, it will obey the same laws as did the lead balls which Galileo dropped from the leaning tower of Pisa. A human body can be weighed and measured, but we can hardly measure the inspiration which enabled Beethoven to write his musical works. A brain and body, but not a thought, may be crushed with a hammer.

Relation between Body and Mind

If the mind and body are so different, how can they influence one another ? We accept the fact that one object can be the cause of movement or change of behaviour in another. They are both material objects, consisting of what the scientist calls " matter." But how can a thought cause changes in the body ? Yet, experience tells us that the mind does affect the body.

We decide to do something, that is, we make an act of will, which is a mental event, and the body obeys. Worry and anxiety, mental events again, have been found to cause bodily ills such as indigestion and stomach troubles, heart diseases and asthma, and in certain cases cures have been obtained by treating patients psychologically when the use of drugs has failed. Further, experience tells us that the state of our bodies can affect the state of our minds. We have indigestion and we feel gloomy and depressed. We take drugs and we have visions of ecstasy, or we lose our will power or become obstinate.

Philosophers have given many theories to account for these body-to-mind and mind-to-body influences, but it is perhaps true to say that our commonsense view is as satisfactory as any of the other theories of philosophers. The commonsense view is

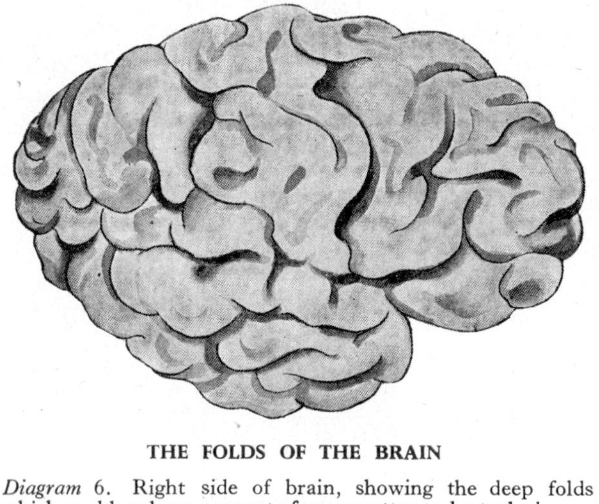

THE FOLDS OF THE BRAIN

Diagram 6. Right side of brain, showing the deep folds which enable a large amount of grey matter to be tucked away in a very small space.

that the body and mind are two separate elements of man, and they obey separate laws. Nevertheless, one can affect the other. How they do this, we do not know, but by observing human behaviour, we must accept the fact that they do so influence each other.

Mental Behaviour is Purposive

The main feature of mental behaviour is that it is purposive. Objects obey mechanical laws and are moved to action by the force of other objects, or else are still. In mental activity, however, there is a goal or purpose and the mind works forward to accomplish its purpose, not blindly, but actively exploring all the time and changing its behaviour according to changing circumstances. Now, a rubber ball running downhill is impelled forward by the force of gravity. If, in its forward movement, it hits an obstacle, say a wall, there its " activity " ends.

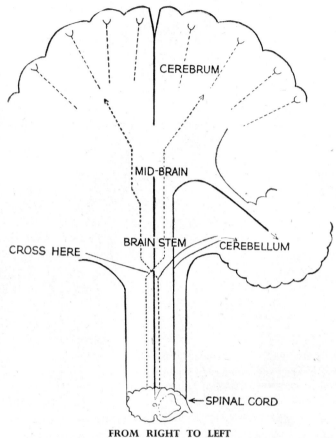

FROM RIGHT TO LEFT

Diagram 7. This shows the nerve fibres from the cerebellum and cerebrum to the spinal cord fibres. Notice how fibres from the cerebrum cross to the other side of the spinal cord. In the cerebrum the left hemisphere looks after the right side and the right after the left side of the body.

Compare the boy who wishes to obtain some apples on the trees on the other side of the wall. He runs down

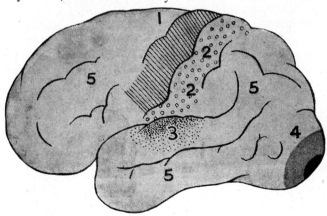

A MAP OF THE BRAIN

Diagram 8. This left view shows the special areas of the brain. 1. The motor area responsible for movements of the muscles. 2. The sensory area where sensations of touch, etc., are perceived. 3. The auditory or hearing area. 4. The visual area, responsible for understanding things seen by the eyes. 5. Association areas, responsible for learning, memory and thought processes.

the hill ; the force of gravity helps him along, but he is urged also by his desires. When he finds the wall too high to climb, he does not stop in his activities but will explore other means of obtaining his goal; nor will he stop, until either the circumstances are greater than he can overcome, or he reaches his goal.

The Mind is Active

The example of the boy and the apples shows us that the mind is constantly active, solving problems and so adapting bodily movements to changing circumstances. Even in the simple process of perceiving, our minds are active. A simple example of this is provided by Diagrams 9 (a, b, c and d). If you look separately at each diagram concentrating your attention all the time, you will see that each drawing can be seen in different ways, but not in more than one way at the same time. Try this little test with each diagram and you will experience these changes from one drawing to the other.

An interesting illustration of the mind's activity in perceiving is given when we look at those puzzle pictures which you find in children's books. For example, there is a forest scene and you are asked to find among the trees, the woodman, his wife and three children. At first you cannot see them, but by searching you find them.

Perceiving is a Form of Thinking

When you discover the woodman and his family, they stand out so obviously that you wonder how it was that you did not see them immediately. But in order to experience this, your mind had to be active. Then we make a judgment, to ourselves, if not in words to someone else, and we say, " There is the woodman." Perceiving is thus a form of thinking and is followed by a judgment of what to us is fact. But there are other processes of thinking which must be distinguished from simple perception as we have so far considered it.

Discovering Relations

When two objects or ideas are given, we also discover that there is some relationship existing between them. When we say that we " see " that two objects are " similar," we do not see " similar " as we see " red " when we say " The pillar box is ' red '." The seeing of " red " is what the psychologist calls a " percept." The " seeing " of " similar " is a concept, that is, it is conceived by or produced by the mind. This mental process of discovering of relations is a very important ability of the mind, for it enables us to see how events and objects in the outside world are connected one with the other. Thus we speak of one event as being " the cause of," or " the result of," just as we speak of one thing being " more beautiful than " or " bigger than " another.

Discovering New Ideas

Suppose you were given the idea " black " and the relation " opposite." From these two you obtain the third and fresh idea " white." You obtain another idea from two ideas given.

Again, suppose you were given two terms, e.g., " coal " and " locomotive." You see there is a relationship between them, for coal enables the locomotive to run. Suppose you were given yet a third term " motor car." You can then find a term, namely " petrol," which stands to motor as coal stands to locomotive, that is, the fuel from which it obtains its energy to move.

We have shown here how the mind is active, first in seeing objects and the qualities they have; secondly, discovering relations between objects, and, thirdly, finding new ideas or objects. These are very simple examples, but the minds of great scientists work in this way to discover new relations between objects and new facts and

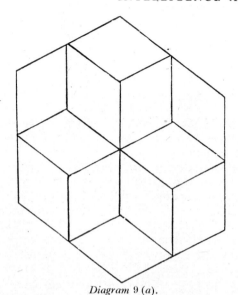

Diagram 9 (a).

laws which have not been discovered before.

Intelligence

Intelligence is the power to perform the types of mental activities we have described. Psychologists have made out special tests to find out how well you can perform these mental tasks. The relationships and new items can be made more and more difficult, and the more difficult the relations you can see, and the more difficult the new terms your mind can discover, the greater your intelligence score.

You must not confuse intelligence with knowledge. A man may gain a lot of knowledge, not only by reading and schooling, but also by travel and life experience. This increases the number of ideas he has in his mind, but not the power of seeing difficult relations and conceiving new ideas. We might compare intelligence with the maximum speed which a car can go; and compare the amount of knowledge a man has obtained, with the number of miles the car has travelled. Now, a car may have travelled 40,000 miles when its maximum speed is only 50 miles an hour. On the other hand, a car may have travelled only 10,000 miles, but have

a maximum speed of 95 miles per hour. In the same way, a man with a smaller intelligence may have greater knowledge than a man with a higher intelligence.

Aptitude

Psychologists call intelligence "general mental ability." In order to become a brilliant mathematician, philosopher and scientist, a great amount of "general mental ability" is needed. However, besides this general ability, we have also special abilities, for example, in music, drawing, painting, craftwork, and motor mechanics. To be good at these we need not necessarily have a high intelligence, or "general" ability, but we do need a "special" ability or special aptitude in the particular subject. Certain tests which psychologists have devised are attempts to predict what tasks you are best able to do. They are called Aptitude Tests.

Learning

There are two main ways of learning. We may learn without realising that we are learning. This we can call "unconscious" learning. A child learns more in the first five years of life than in any other five years of his life, though he may not go to school. Besides learning to walk and talk, he learns skill in handling objects, to know what they are used for. He learns also the kind of behaviour his parents

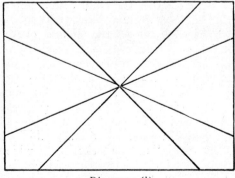

Diagram 9 (b).

expect from him. He learns to like some things, dislike others; he learns to like certain people and to hate and fear others.

In school, much learning is conscious learning. We " pay attention " to the teacher, and he explains facts to us.

In learning, we use our " memory." How we are able to " store up " so many memories, or what exactly " memory " is, is ultimately a mystery. All we can say is that we are able to remember, and that our minds can remember more easily, provided that we understand what we are learning, that is provided we see the relationships between the various items of what we are learning. We can learn merely by rote, or " by heart " (as we put it), without understanding. But this is a very poor way of learning, not only because it is more difficult, but also because things we learn merely " by heart " are easily forgotten. It is always a good rule, therefore, in all your learning to understand, and not merely learn " parrot fashion."

Secondly, learning depends on our feelings about the subject we are learning. Interest and desire to learn are the lubricating oil of the mind. They enable the mind to learn more easily and more quickly. That is why the good teacher is the one who arouses our interests and desires to learn by using pictures, diagrams and stories as aids to learning.

Mental Energy

If we compare the mind with a motor-car engine, we may say that so far we have described the engine of the mind, how the rods and pistons link up one with the other, and what work each does. But what is the source of energy of the mind? What corresponds in the mind to the petrol of the car? Here again, we are faced with an ultimate mystery. Some thinkers speak of " mental energy " which they call by various names including " libido," " élan vital " or " the will to live " by which they mean a general source of energy unseen in itself, but which they conclude must exist from their observations of human behaviour.

Rather than speak of " mental energy " perhaps it is better to speak of " needs " or " instincts." Man has many needs, and in order to satisfy these needs, he is prepared to work the " engine " of his mind.

These needs are, therefore, the petrol which the mind uses. Some of these needs are needs which his body demands. These needs might be called appetites and include the need for food, drink, and physical exercise. Much of our mental energy is carried on in order to satisfy these bodily needs. In most animals these needs are the only needs. If you want an animal to learn, or if you wish to train an animal, the best way is to refuse him food till he is hungry, and then offer him food as a reward for carrying out the task you wish him to do.

Human beings acquire other needs, and these needs vary in strength from one person to another. We need to assert ourselves, and we gain much satisfaction from mastering a task. We like also to please other people and win their affection and esteem so that they will say " What a good boy you are." We may also wish that other people will admire us, and we are urged to activity by this need to impress them so that they recognise how clever we are. Furthermore, we need to join with our fellows and to be able to do the many tasks they do. We would feel " out of it " if others in our little groups could do things which we could not do. It is pleasant to share the work, play and interests of others and to do so we must use our mental energy to learn the skills, the rules of the games which others play. When we are older, our needs may become less self-centred. We have a wife and children and we are urged on by the need to provide for them. Finally, we might feel that our efforts will benefit not only ourselves and our families, but the whole of the human race, and this acts to further our mental efforts.

So, you see, when we are mentally and physically active, we are moved to

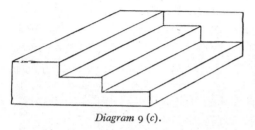

Diagram 9 (*c*).

action by motives or needs. Not all man's needs have been given here. Man has many needs which urge him to mental activity and these needs are sometimes called instincts. To understand why a person attempts to solve particular problems, it is necessary to explain not only how he thinks, but also why he thinks—that is, what real needs does he hope to satisfy by his activity.

The Unconscious Mind

So far we have spoken as if man is aware of all his mental processes. This however, is not generally so. Often we are not fully aware of our desires and needs. We often have feelings of anxiety though we know not why. It is because of these things that psychologists say we have an unconscious mind.

A boy has to take an examination. He has fears about it, but is not aware of them because he refuses to admit them. He "represses" his fears, as the psychologist puts it. So there arises a conflict in his mind. One part says, "I will take the exam.," the other says "You are afraid." Then he becomes ill, and so he does not take the exam., nor does he recognise his fears. In short, his unconscious mind discovered a way out of his fears.

In much the same way, a soldier who is about to perform some dangerous manœuvre against the enemy may "repress" his fears, and develop paralysis of the arm.

Conquering Fears

In both these cases, the fears which they felt were natural, and most people would have similar fears in like situations. But their pride was so great that they were not prepared to admit fear, even to themselves, and because of this, they could not control their fears. The work of the psychologist would be to get them to admit their fears, and to see that such fears are natural to all men. Then they would understand why they had become ill. Having accepted their fears, they would not be overwhelmed by something of which they were unaware. If the treatment were successful, both the illness and the paralysis would disappear, and they would be prepared to carry out the difficult tasks.

Again, a person may "repress" a need for love and say, "I am tough, too tough to want sloppy love." Here

SEEN IN DIFFERENT WAYS

Diagrams 9 (*a*), (*b*), (*c*), (*d*). The mind is very active in perceiving. If you look carefully at each of the drawings on this page and on page 445, you will discover that each can be seen in two different ways.

there is a conflict in the mind between a vain need to be " tough " and a natural need for love and affection. Then suddenly, he begins to steal, and cannot stop himself, or tell why he must steal.

People often " repress " feelings and desires they think they ought not to have. As they repress them and are unaware of them, they experience fears and anxieties, and they cannot account for them. Their fears and anxieties arise because they are afraid these unconscious hatreds and desires will be unloosed. If, however, they can be shown these unconscious factors, they will then be able to control them, and do something about them. Thus, they may " work off " their hatred by " attacking " a mountain and making a tunnel through it, or becoming mountaineers and " overcoming " the mountain. Similarly, other energies may be deflected into socially useful channels by the care of, and service to, others. This the psychologist calls " sublimation," which means the turn-ing of energy, which might but satisfy only an individual need, to work which is socially acceptable and maybe socially useful.

Understanding the Mind

Dreams are expressions of our unconscious desires and our unconscious fears. The psychologist is, therefore, very interested to know of, and to interpret the meaning of his patients' dreams. We generally feel that our dreams are rather silly and muddled and best forgotten. In the Old Testament, dreams are given quite a great deal of prominence. To the psychologist also, they are important and interesting, for they help him to understand the activity of the unconscious mind.

To-day the psychologist is playing an increasingly important part in our lives. The doctor of medicine deals with the ailments of the body; the psychologist is concerned with ailments of the mind and in learning how to test and develop our mental processes.

ANOTHER OPTICAL ILLUSION

Look carefully at the two squares in this picture. The white square has a black centre, and the black square has a white centre. The white central square seems larger than the black central square, although actually they are exactly the same size.